Basic Electrical Principles

Basic Electrical Principles

SECOND EDITION

by *MAURICE GRAYLE SUFFERN*

McGRAW-HILL BOOK COMPANY, INC.

New York   Chicago   San Francisco   Dallas   Toronto   London

ABOUT THE AUTHOR

Maurice Grayle Suffern observed the need for a simple, introductory book on electricity first when he taught in a vocational school and later during World War II when, as a Major, USAR, he organized the Radio and Electronics School at Camp Crowder, Missouri. *Basic Electrical Principles* is his contribution to the fulfillment of that need. Since he had previously graduated from Cornell University with a Bachelor of Science Degree in Electrical Engineering, and afterward did graduate work in education at New York University, his book reflects a sound background not only in educational psychology but also in the natural sciences. The Army recognized the latter when the Ordnance Department subsequently made him Chief of the VT Fuze program, and at the War's conclusion Deputy Director of Electronics.

Actually, he has devoted the better part of his life to the pursuit of knowledge, but unlike some detached scholars, he has also applied it to the solution of pressing human problems. His degrees include an LL.B., an LL.M., and a D.O. respectively from New York University, St. Johns University, and the Chicago College of Osteopathic Medicine and Surgery. He has been licensed in the fields of radio engineering, education, law, and more recently medicine. In 1951 Dr. Suffern decided to engage exclusively in the practice of medicine and surgery, and, as an avocation, to continue his writing program.

TO MY MOTHER
MRS. ELIZABETH C. SUFFERN
who, many years ago, encouraged me to acquire
a knowledge of Basic Electrical Principles

Preface

An author can have no greater satisfaction than the knowledge that his book has been accepted by many people throughout the world. Such satisfaction is deepened even more when he has learned that his book has become a standard of educational guidance in the particular field which he has endeavored to cover. To these people and institutions, the author would like to express his appreciation and, at the same time, his hope that this new edition will also be received as warmly.

This is a textbook designed to aid in the training of electrical-trades students on a vocational-education level. The basic facts of the theory of electricity have been expressed as simply as possible. The Second Edition contains many new photographs of electrical appliances and equipment that show practical applications of electrical theory. Where necessary, portions of the text have been rewritten to bring it up to date. There has been no attempt to approach the higher technical-education level involving an extensive knowledge of mathematics and physics. The author does not believe that vocational training, the purpose of which is to prepare a student for an electrical trade, requires that the student memorize many formulas or be capable of solving abstract and involved mathematical problems. He does believe, however, that a background of knowledge of basic electrical principles is essential before a vocational student can enter a specialized field of training in any of the allied fields of electricity. Hence, it is the purpose of this textbook to prepare the student for further training of a practical nature in the specific electrical trade that he may select.

The author would like to express his sincere gratitude to John

A. Colletti; C. Booth Farkas; and Lawrence A. Lutzke, who drew the illustrations found in the First Edition of this book. He would also like to express his thanks to his associate in the practice of medicine, Jean S. Bower, B.S., D.O., who prepared the new illustrations for the Second Edition, and who gave much advice and counsel concerning its organization. Finally, he would like to thank his wife, Lilli Ann Suffern, B.A., M.A., who tirelessly aided and encouraged him in doing the many thousands of things that must be done in the writing of a book, and who was the bulwark of encouragement toward pursuing the work of the revision.

MAURICE GRAYLE SUFFERN

Contents

Chapter 1. Introduction to Electricity

1. The Electrical World

A flash of lightning during a storm, the spark that occurs when one walks across a carpeted room and touches a door-

Fig. 1. The electrical world.

knob, the bright light that appears when an electric light is turned on, the voice heard on the telephone—all these things and countless others occur because of the phenomenon we know as *electricity* (Fig. 1).

The modern world can rightly be called an *electrical world* because electricity is the basis of much of what produces a modern civilization. Yet, electricity, or more accurately, its effects, have been known from the earliest times. Primitive man

1

feared the effect of lightning and thought of it as a weapon of the gods. Even in modern times there is a tendency to relegate to the supernatural that which cannot be fully explained. This attitude, fortunately, is gradually disappearing as more and more people receive the advantages of education.

When scientists attempt an explanation of some phenomenon, they first of all evolve a *hypothesis*, which is simply a brief outline of what they believe the explanation to be. When they have conducted a number of tests and feel that they have a firm foundation for the explanation, the statement of what they believe to be an accurate description of this phenomenon is called a *theory*. When this theory has been thoroughly confirmed by innumerable tests conducted by many qualified persons, it becomes known as a *law*. A scientific law states facts that never change and are known to be completely accurate.

To explain the phenomenon of electricity, we must resort to the *Electron Theory*. At the present time, this theory offers the best explanation of electricity that is known to science. It is a fairly new theory, too, and one cannot yet say whether it will develop into a law. In other words, science accepts the theory as such, but our minds must not be closed to a possible new theory that may come before us in the future. We always keep trying to discover the absolute truth, and when we are convinced beyond a reasonable doubt that the absolute truth has been found, then, and only then, will it be called a *law*.

2. The Electron Theory

We are living on one of the planets of the solar system. Our planet is called *earth*, and we know that there are eight other planets in the solar system. These planets vary in size one from the other but they all have one main characteristic, that is, they all revolve around the sun in fixed paths, called *orbits*. The sun is the heart or center of the entire solar system (Fig. 2).

Our solar system is just one of many such systems which comprise the universe. Our sun is a star, that is, a body that gives off heat and light. Other stars in exactly the same fashion are the centers of systems of their own. Thus, in distinguishing between the solar system and other star systems, we could say that the former has nine planets revolving around it while Star *X* system has but five.

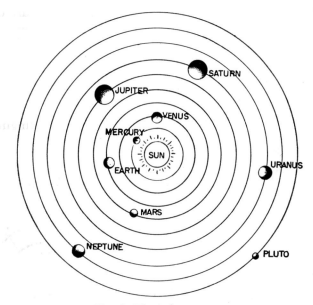

Fig. 2. The solar system.

Now, if we had a microscope powerful enough to let us see exactly how every material on the earth is actually constructed, we would find that every such material is made up of miniature "solar systems." These extremely minute systems are known as *atoms*, and all *matter* (matter being a term used to designate all substances such as gases, liquids, or solids in one lump sum) is actually composed of atoms.

The atomic "solar system" has a nucleus (which corresponds to the sun) and one or more *electrons* (which correspond to the planets) revolving around the nucleus in fixed orbits at a high rate of speed.

Atoms differ one from the other only in the structure of their individual systems. Just as the solar system has nine planets, one type of atomic system may have nine electrons revolving around its nucleus. Others have many more; some have a few less. Thus, an atom of hydrogen has only one electron revolving around its nucleus whereas an atom of carbon has six (Fig. 3).

There are actually 101 different kinds of atoms distinguishable by their atomic structure. When a substance is made up of only one kind of atom, it is called an *element*. If it is made up of two

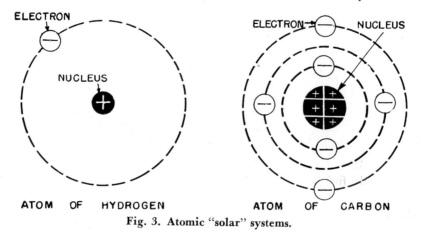

Fig. 3. Atomic "solar" systems.

or more kinds, it is called a *compound*. Everything about us is either an element or a compound, and all the physical or chemical properties of these substances are dependent solely upon the way their component atoms are constructed and joined together to form that substance.

The nucleus and the electrons that compose an atom are really electrical *charges*. The word "charge" means a potential force, or what may be termed a possible source of energy that is held in readiness to perform some kind of work. When any kind of work is done, energy is expended. Before energy can be expended, a potential force must exist to serve as the source of energy. In our study, we are thinking in terms of electrical energy whose source is the electric charge.

The nucleus of an atom is composed of *neutrons*, which are electrically neutral, that is, bear no charge, and *protons*, which bear a *positive* charge to exactly the same degree that an *electron* bears a *negative* charge. The proton gives the nucleus its predominantly positive characteristic; the neutron simply gives it added mass or weight. The protons and neutrons are firmly bound together, and do not tend to leave their proper place.

On the other hand, some of the electrons traveling around

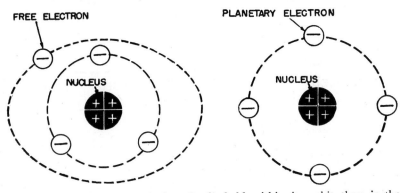

FREE ELECTRON   PLANETARY ELECTRON

NUCLEUS   NUCLEUS

Fig. 4. The free electron is less firmly held within its orbit than is the planetary electron.

the nucleus are less firmly bound to their orbits, and given an opportunity, will rush away. This type of electron is called a *free* electron. An electron that tends to circulate in its orbit and cannot be readily removed is known as a *planetary* electron (Fig. 4).

Since the atom normally has a number of protons exactly equal to the number of electrons, it is electrically *neutral*, that is, the positive charges on the nucleus balance out the negative charges of the electrons (Fig. 5).

However, when one or more of these negatively charged free electrons leave their orbits, the balance is upset and the atom is no longer neutral. Since it has lost a negatively charged electron, the atom now acts as a *positively* charged body (Fig. 6).

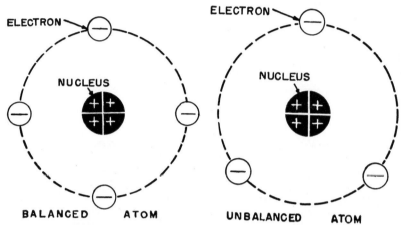

Fig. 5. The neutral atom. The negative charges of the electrons balance the positive charges on the nucleus.

Fig. 6. The atom has lost an electron. It now bears a positive charge.

Any object that bears a *positive* charge will attract any *negatively* charged bodies in its vicinity. Contrariwise, bodies bearing *like* charges will repel each other. This fact has given rise to the rule that *like charges repel, unlike charges attract.* Hence, an atom that has been unbalanced and is in a condition of bearing a

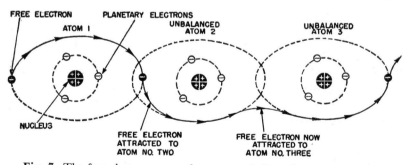

Fig. 7. The free electron moves from one unbalanced atom to another.

positive charge rather than being neutral will attract any free electrons that wander near it (Fig. 7).

It is only the electrons that actually move, however, and it is this movement of electrons from one atom to another that gives rise to the "electric current," or flow of electricity.

Hence, according to the electron theory, the electric current is simply a movement of free electrons from one unbalanced

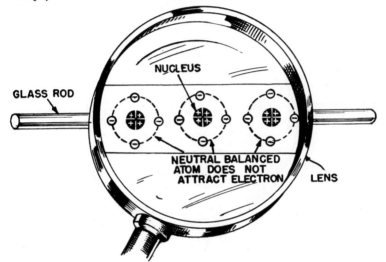

Fig. 8. An insulator lacks free electrons. The atoms are balanced.

atom to another, and that is why an electric current in the modern concept is considered to flow from a point of negative potential to a point of positive potential.

3. Conductors and Insulators

Since all matter can be thought of as being composed of atoms, and since atoms are made up of electrical charges, it must follow that all matter is basically electrical in nature. This is entirely correct. Some substances, however, retain their electrons much more firmly than others. These materials, therefore, do not permit an electron movement as readily as those materials that have a lesser hold on their electrons. Since we have learned that electricity is really a *movement* of electrons from one atom to another, it follows that substances that resist this movement can act as insulators or nonconductors. Such substances are considered to have few free electrons. On the other hand, if we consider a substance that does not retain its

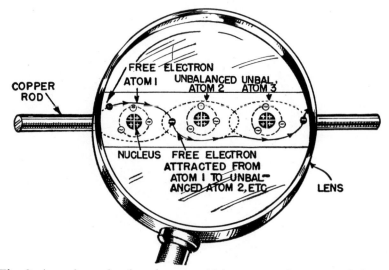

Fig. 9. A conductor has free electrons which can move from one unbalanced atom to another.

electrons readily, and thus aids the movement of electrons, we speak of it as a *conductor*. Hence a conductor is a substance with a large number of free electrons (Figs. 8 and 9).

Materials such as copper and silver are excellent conductors, whereas glass and mica, for example, are excellent insulators. No substance is a perfect conductor or a perfect insulator, but for practical purposes, the terms *conductor* and *insulator* are used. Thus, if we want to aid the flow of electrons, we use a conductor; if we want to prevent the flow of electrons, we use an insulator.

An electrical circuit is simply a path through which electrons can move freely. In establishing such a circuit, conductors such as metal wire must be used. At points of the circuit where it is necessary to avoid loss of electrons, or to shut off their flow entirely, insulators would be used. A circuit is said to be *closed* when it is electrically complete, allowing the electrons to flow

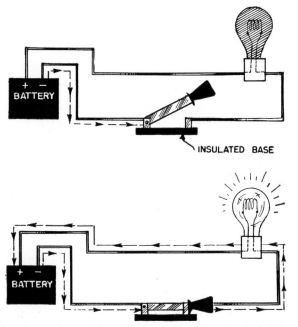

Fig. 10. The electron's path is called a circuit. The circuit is "closed" when the electrons can move freely from a starting point and return there. It is "open" when the path is incomplete.

through it and to return to their original source. A circuit is *open* or *broken* when the path is no longer complete (Fig. 10).

4. Resistance and Conductance

The degree that electron movement in any substance is hampered is called its *resistance*. Even the very best conductors known possess some degree of resistance. The unit of resistance measurement is called the *ohm*. In a given substance, resistance is proportional to the length and inversely proportional to the cross-sectional area. This simply means that the resistance of a length of wire will double in value if it is made twice as long, but will be cut in half if its cross-sectional *area* is made twice as great with its length remaining unchanged. As an example, suppose a 1-ft. length of wire with a cross-sectional area of 1 sq. in. had a resistance of 4 ohms. If an additional foot of wire were added, the resistance of this double length would be

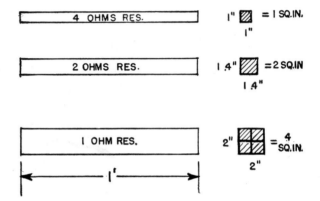

Fig. 11. The resistance of a conductor is determined by its cross-sectional area as well as its length.

2 × 4, or 8 ohms. Similarly, if still another foot of wire were added, the total resistance would now be 3 × 4, or 12 ohms. In all these illustrations, the cross-sectional area remained the same. Now, let us assume that the original 1-ft. length of wire had its cross-sectional *area* increased to 2 sq. in. The resistance would now be inversely proportional to the cross-sectional area. Since the area is *twice* as great, to obtain an inverse (opposite) proportion, we must invert (turn upside down) the number 2. Thus, the resistance would be $\frac{1}{2}$ × 4, or 2 ohms. Inverting the whole number 2 (which could be written $\frac{2}{1}$ instead of just "2" were it not less convenient) gives the figure $\frac{1}{2}$. If the cross-sectional *area* had been made *four* times as great, the resultant resistance would have been $\frac{1}{4}$ × 4, or 1 ohm (Fig. 11).

Conductance is a term whose meaning is directly opposite to that of resistance. It is that property of a substance which determines its ability to aid the flow of electrons. Copper has greater conductance than iron, whereas iron has far greater conductance than glass. The greater the value of conductance, the more valuable is the substance as a conductor of electrons; the greater the value of resistance, the more valuable is the substance as an insulator. The unit of conductance is the *mho*, which, as can be seen, is a word formed by reversing the spelling of ohm. In most practical applications, resistance alone is the factor considered and, in a later chapter, it will be seen how it is computed.

5. Sources of Electromotive Force (e.m.f.)

We now know that electricity is really a movement of electrons. Hence, to produce electrical activity in any of its many forms, we must cause electrons to move. To achieve this end, a source of *electromotive force* must be found and, in fact, a number of means are at our disposal. Such means may be

a. Friction.		*d.* Piezoelectric.
b. Heat.		*e.* Chemical.
c. Light.		*f.* Mechanical.

a. *Frictional Electricity.* A person walking across a carpeted floor will often acquire an electric charge as a result of friction between the carpet and the shoes he is wearing. What has literally happened is that free electrons have been rubbed off the carpet and have accumulated on the body of the person. He thus has acquired an excess of negative electrons and can be said to be *negatively charged*. When this person now touches a doorknob or some other object, the excess electrons tend to rush off, giving rise to the spark and slight shock that he experiences. This is one example of an electric charge produced by friction.

Another common example of frictional electricity can be demonstrated with an ordinary fountain pen or rubber pocket comb. If either of these articles is briskly rubbed against one's coat sleeve (Fig. 12), it will be found to have become electrically charged in exactly the same way and for the same reason the person in the previous illustration became charged. If the charged pen, for example, is touched to a small piece of paper, the paper will adhere to it. The paper was originally neutral,

Fig. 12. Charging a pen by friction.

but when the negatively charged pen touched the paper, electrons were repelled from that side of the paper closest to it. This left that side of the paper positively charged. Obeying the law "Unlike charges attract," the paper now adhered to the pen (Fig. 13).

Some materials, like rubber, always assume a negative charge since they *gain* electrons when friction with another material takes place. Other materials, like glass, become positively charged because they *lose* electrons.

This can be shown by using a pith (fiber) ball suspended on a silk thread. If a *negatively* charged rubber rod is brought into

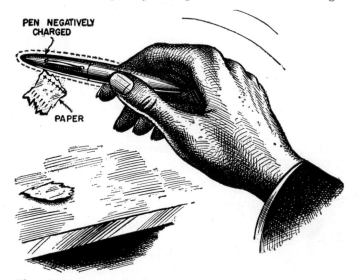

PEN NEGATIVELY CHARGED

PAPER

Fig. 13. The negatively charged pen will attract another object.

contact with the ball, the ball will assume a negative charge as well, since some of the electrons will escape to it (Fig. 14).

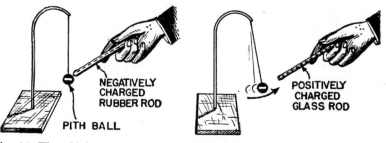

NEGATIVELY CHARGED RUBBER ROD

PITH BALL

POSITIVELY CHARGED GLASS ROD

Fig. 14. The pith ball assumes a negative charge when brought into contact with the negatively charged rod.

Fig. 15. The positively charged glass rod attracts the negatively charged pith ball.

Now, if a charged glass rod is brought near the ball, the ball will be attracted toward the rod (Fig. 15). Thus it can be seen that the glass rod must bear a positive charge; otherwise, the law of attraction between oppositely charged bodies would not have been demonstrated. Two suspended pith balls bearing

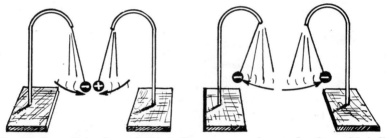

Fig. 16. Oppositely charged pith balls are attracted to each other; pith balls with like charges repel each other.

opposite charges will be drawn together; two balls bearing like charges will be forced apart, illustrating this law still further (Fig. 16).

Fig. 17. The electroscope.

The presence of frictional electricity can also be demonstrated on an *electroscope*, which is constructed by hanging a piece of foil across a wire (Fig. 17). A charged rubber rod brought into contact with the terminal of the electroscope will cause the foil leaves to spread apart (Fig. 18). The electrons have escaped to the leaves, and since like charges repel each other, the now negatively charged leaves act in the manner described. If the electroscope is now *grounded* (connected to the earth by a wire), the leaves will fall into their original position because the electrons can now escape to the earth (Fig. 19). Exactly the same events would occur if a positively charged object had been used for the experiment.

The area surrounding a charged object can also be shown to be under the influence of the electric charge, and this charged area is known as the *electric field*. This can be demonstrated on the electroscope. If a charged object is brought towards the electroscope terminal without touching it, the leaves will begin to spread (Fig. 20). The closer the rod is brought to the terminal, the more pronounced is the action, indicating that the effect of the field is strongest when the distance is least. The electric field is assumed to be composed of invisible *lines of force*, which appear around a charged body. Such lines of force play an important part in the field of electricity.

Frictional electricity is one form of *electrostatic* or *static* electricity, so called because the electrical energy in charged objects is at rest, and no movement of electrons from atom to atom is normally taking place even though the electrons are traveling

Fig. 18. The leaves of the electroscope spread apart as they receive like charges.

Fig. 19. Grounding the electroscope allows the electric charges to escape and the leaves collapse.

around their respective nuclei at all times. The field around a charged object is known as an *electrostatic field*.

It should be noted that an *insulator* (rubber or glass) was used to show the effects of electrostatic electricity. Use of a conductor such as copper or silver would not have been successful. In a conductor, the electric charges can escape readily (Figs. 21 and 22).

Because of this fact, the term *dielectric field* is often used instead of *electrostatic field*, and this is the preferred term. *Dielectric* is just another name for an insulator or nonconductor of electricity.

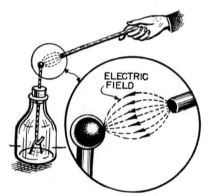

In studying the action of a capacitor, a device that stores electricity, we shall hear more about dielectrics and dielectric fields.

b. *Heat Electricity.* When two dissimilar metals are joined together and heat is applied to the point of junction, electrons are driven from one metal to the other if an electrical circuit is established. This is the basis of the *thermocouple*, an instrument

Fig. 20. An electric field always exists around a charged object. The leaves of the electroscope can be charged without direct contact between the charged rod and the electroscope terminal.

by which variations in heat are measured by an electrical meter or recording device (Fig. 23). As a general rule, it may be said that heating increases electronic movement. In fact, the movement may become so intense that the electrons tend to fly off into space. Use is made of this fact in the operation of vacuum tubes such as are found in radio equipment.

c. *Light Electricity.* Certain chemicals have *photoelectric* qualities, that is, they tend to produce electrical activity when subjected to a beam of light (Fig. 24). Advantage of this action is taken in photoelectric tubes, which usually consist of two basic elements or parts. One element is coated with the light-sensitive material; the other element is uncoated, but both form part of a complete electrical circuit. When light strikes the coated element, electrons

ELECTRONS ACCUMULATE
ON END OF ROD

RUBBER ROD

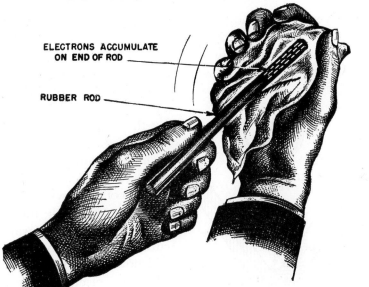

Fig. 21. The electrons that accumulate on the rubber rod cannot escape to the ground. Rubber is a good insulator.

" A "

COPPER ROD

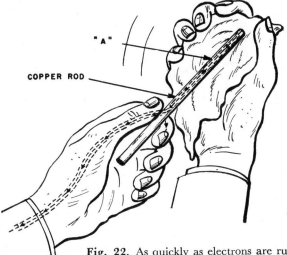

Fig. 22. As quickly as electrons are rubbed onto the metal rod, they are conducted to the ground. Metals are good conductors of electricity.

are driven off, and most of them reach the other element, returning to their original starting point through the conducting circuit. The amount of current produced is small, but the use of suitable amplifiers (enlargers) allows useful work to be done.

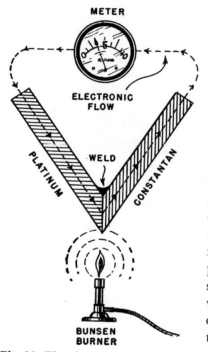

Fig 23. The thermocouple. Heat applied to the junction of two dissimilar metals produces a movement of electrons.

It should be noted that here again, as in electricity produced by the action of heat, we are actually speaking of electricity in motion. This is called a *current* because scientists originally thought of the flow of electricity as acting in much the same manner as the flow of water. A current of electricity, however, will flow only when there is a complete electrical path or circuit that will allow the electrons leaving from one point to return again to that very same point. We shall find later that such a current will flow only when the circuit is electrically complete, and when, in addition, a difference of potential or charge created by some form of electromotive force exists between the points of the circuit. It is this electromotive force (e.m.f.) which urges the electrons on their journey.

The photoelectric cell is popularly used as an exposure meter in photography (Fig. 24a). Generally, an amplifier is not required, and, therefore, the amount of electrical energy is read directly on a suitable meter calibrated for the specific purpose.

A more complicated use is seen in automatic light-dimming devices found in some modern automobiles (Fig. 24b). Here the

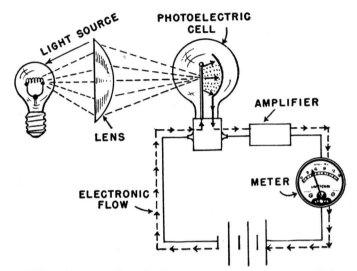

Fig. 24. The photoelectric cell. Electron movement occurs as light strikes the light-sensitive element.

Fig. 24a. A photoelectric-cell type of exposure meter used in photography. (*Courtesy of G-M Laboratories, Inc.*)

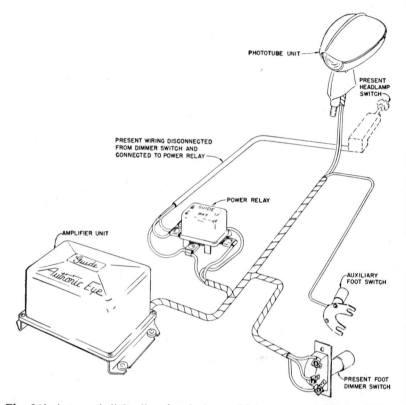

Fig. 24b. Automatic light-dimming device used in some automobile headlights. (*Courtesy of Guide Lamp Div. of General Motors Corp.*)

phototube is so connected in an electric circuit that the headlights of the car are switched from their upper beam to their lower beam upon the approach of another automobile.

d. *Piezoelectricity.* A number of crystalline substances will produce an electric current if subjected to mechanical pressure. In such crystals, the atoms are so arranged that pressure upon the crystal surfaces causes the electrons to move more readily in one direction than in the other (Fig. 25). This causes a positive charge to appear on one surface and a negative charge on the

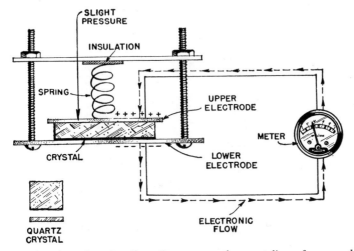

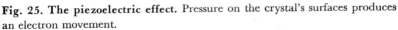

Fig. 25. The piezoelectric effect. Pressure on the crystal's surfaces produces an electron movement.

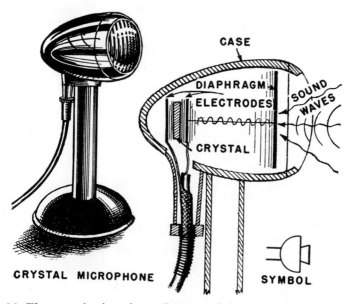

Fig. 26. The crystal microphone. Pressure of the sound waves on the diaphragm varies the pressure on the crystal.

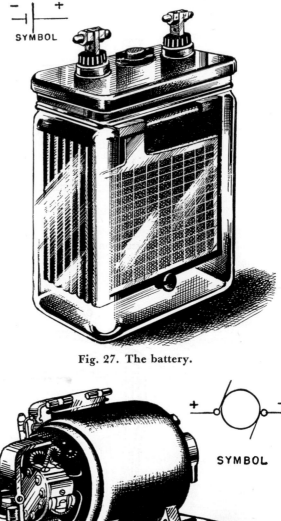

Fig. 27. The battery.

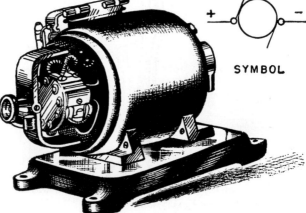

Fig. 28. The generator.

other. This action is known as the *piezoelectric effect*, and advantage is taken of it in specialized devices such as crystal *oscillators* (vibrators) and crystal microphones (Fig. 26).

e. *Chemical Electricity.* When certain metals are immersed in a chemical solution, called an *electrolyte*, electrical activity will take place if a complete circuit exists. The two metals (often termed the *electrodes*) and the electrolyte comprise the single unit known as a *cell.* A battery may be made up of a single cell or a group of cells, the latter being joined both physically and electrically (Fig. 27).

f. *Mechanical Electricity.* Where large sources of electrical power are required, the most economical means of obtaining such energy is from generators (Fig. 28). Generators are mechanical units driven by electric motors, steam turbines, or even by water power. Their principle of operation depends upon the fact that electrical activity can be produced in a conductor (usually a coil of wire) when it is forced to move through a magnetic field. The action of batteries and generators will be studied in detail later.

SUMMARY

1. Electrical activity may be explained in terms of the Electron Theory, which states that all matter is composed of atoms, and the atoms, in turn, are composed of a positively charged nucleus around which negatively charged electrons travel in fixed orbits. Electrical activity occurs when the electrons tend to move from their fixed paths.

2. Electrical charges are either positive or negative. Like charges repel each other; unlike charges attract each other.

3. A *conductor* is a substance that releases electrons readily and, therefore, allows a movement of electrons (usually called a *current* of electricity) to occur.

4. An *insulator* is a substance that retains electrons firmly and does not readily allow a movement of electrons.

5. An electric *circuit* is a path made up of conductors through which the electronic movement from atom to atom (flow of current) takes place. A circuit is said to be *closed* when it is electrically complete, allowing the electrons to flow through it and return to their original source. A circuit is *open* or *broken* when the conducting path is no longer complete.

6. Electrical activity may be produced by means of friction, heat, light, and piezoelectrical, chemical, and mechanical action.

Quiz: Introduction to Electricity

Directions: This quiz will help you review the material just studied. Each question consists of a statement completed in four possible ways. Read each question carefully and decide which one of the four forms of the statement is the correct one. Indicate your decision on a separate sheet of paper, in accordance with the following example:

1. Water in its ordinary state is that type of substance classified as a: *a.* solid; *b.* liquid; *c.* gas; *d.* gaseous solid.

The correct answer is "liquid." Therefore, on your answer sheet write down 1*b*. This indicates that the statement comprising question 1 is correct as completed in *b*.

1. A substance made up of only one kind of atom is called: *a.* an electron; *b.* a nucleus; *c.* an element; *d.* a compound.

2. A balanced atom is one in which there is an: *a.* excess of protons; *b.* excess of neutrons; *c.* unequal number of electrons and protons; *d.* equal number of electrons balancing the positive charges on the nucleus.

3. A statement of scientific facts proved beyond doubt is known as a: *a.* supposition; *b.* law; *c.* theory; *d.* hypothesis.

4. According to the Electron Theory, all matter is basically: *a.* physical; *b.* gaseous; *c.* destructible; *d.* electrical.

5. The neutron within the nucleus of an atom gives it: *a.* a positive charge; *b.* a negative charge; *c.* mass and weight; *d.* a negative effect.

6. An atom is composed of: *a.* protons and neutrons; *b.* electrons only; *c.* electrons, protons, and neutrons; *d.* neutrons and electrons only.

7. The basic *negative* electric charge is known as: *a.* neutron; *b.* nucleus; *c.* proton; *d.* electron.

8. The basic *positive* electric charge is known as: *a.* neutron; *b.* nucleus; *c.* electron; *d.* proton.

9. An excellent conductor is: *a.* wood; *b.* silver; *c.* mica; *d.* glass.

10. An excellent insulator is: *a.* mica; *b.* silver; *c.* copper; *d.* platinum.

11. A free electron: *a.* cannot readily escape from its orbit at any time; *b.* cannot escape unless accompanied by a neutron; *c.* can readily escape when being repelled by a proton; *d.* can readily escape when under attraction of an unbalanced atom.

12. The word *charge* means: *a.* ability of an electron to move out of its orbit; *b.* ability of a proton to move out of its orbit; *c.* potential force; *d.* potential resistance to any force.

13. An electric current is a movement of: *a.* protons; *b.* electrons; *c.* neutrons; *d.* both electrons and neutrons.

14. The unit of resistance is: *a.* a volt; *b.* a watt; *c.* a mho; *d.* an ohm.

15. A planetary electron: *a.* can readily leave its orbit; *b.* cannot readily leave its orbit; *c.* can leave its orbit when it bears a positive charge; *d.* cannot leave its orbit because it is neutral.

16. The unit of conductance is: *a.* a mho; *b.* an ohm; *c.* a watt; *d.* a volt.

17. *Conductance* is a term whose meaning is: *a.* the equivalent of resistance; *b.* directly opposite to that of resistance; *c.* equivalent to electromotive force; *d.* directly opposite to electromotive force.

18. The area surrounding a charged object is said to be under the influence of: *a.* an electric field; *b.* an electric discharge; *c.* a dielectric current; *d.* a dielectric discharge.

19. The rule applying to the action of electric charges is: *a.* Unlike charges repel; like charges attract. *b.* Like charges can neither repel nor attract. *c.* Like charges repel; unlike charges attract. *d.* Unlike charges can neither repel nor attract, whereas like charges can both repel and attract.

20. A circuit is said to be closed when it is: *a.* electrically incomplete; *b.* electrically neutral; *c.* electrically complete; *d.* electrically charged.

21. To prevent the flow of electrons, it is necessary to use: *a.* conductors; *b.* electric lamps; *c.* electroscopes; *d.* insulators.

22. The modern concept of electricity considers a flow of current to exist from a point of negative potential to one of positive potential. This statement is true because: *a.* Only electrons can move. *b.* Only protons can move. *c.* Only unattached protons can move. *d.* Only neutrons can move.

23. A circuit is said to be "open" when it is: *a.* electrically charged; *b.* electrically neutral; *c.* electrically incomplete; *d.* electrically complete.

24. A substance is considered a conductor when it: *a.* possesses only balanced atoms; *b.* does not retain electrons easily; *c.* retains electrons firmly; *d.* possesses extremely high resistance.

25. An electric switch in a circuit is used: *a.* to drain excess electrons; *b.* to prevent shocks; *c.* to allow the addition of insulators; *d.* to open and close the circuit.

26. An insulator is a substance lacking: *a.* free electrons; *b.* balanced atoms; *c.* free protons; *d.* free neutrons.

27. An electric circuit may be defined as: *a.* a group of insulators through which electrons can move freely; *b.* a group of insulators through which protons can move freely; *c.* a path through which electrons can move freely; *d.* a path through which protons can move freely.

28. The two metals used in a battery cell are called: *a.* diodes; *b.* triodes; *c.* electrodes; *d.* pentodes.

29. If a pith ball is charged negatively: *a.* It will move toward a negatively charged rod. *b.* It will move away from a negatively charged rod. *c.* It will move to and fro from a negatively charged rod. *d.* It will stand absolutely still as a negatively charged rod is brought near.

30. In a given substance, resistance is: *a.* proportional to the length and is unaffected by the cross-sectional area; *b.* inversely proportional to the length and proportional to the cross-sectional area; *c.* inversely proportional to both the length and cross-sectional area; *d.* proportional to the length and inversely proportional to the cross-sectional area.

31. A source of electromotive force (e.m.f.) is required in order to: *a.* prevent the escape of electrons; *b.* change the property of conductance into resistance; *c.* get electrons into motion; *d.* insulate the electrons from the unbalanced atoms.

32. A 100-ft. length of wire that is used in a circuit has a resistance of 5 ohms. It is found necessary to add wire of exactly the same type in order to make the resistance of the circuit 20 ohms. How much wire will be needed? *a.* 300 ft.; *b.* 100 ft.; *c.* 50 ft.; *d.* 4 ft.

33. An electric field is composed of: *a.* invisible free electrons; *b.* invisible units of conductance; *c.* invisible units of resistance; *d.* invisible lines of force.

34. A length of wire used in a circuit has a resistance of 10 ohms. If this wire were replaced by another wire of the same material and the same length, but with a cross-sectional area only one-half as great, the resistance would be: *a.* 20 ohms; *b.* 15 ohms; *c.* 10 ohms; *d.* 5 ohms.

35. In order to produce electricity by chemical means, certain metals must be immersed in: *a.* distilled water; *b.* mineral oil; *c.* an electrolyte; *d.* methyl alcohol.

36. A device used to produce an e.m.f. through the action of *heat* is called a: *a*. battery; *b*. thermocouple; *c*. piezoelectric crystal; *d*. photoelectric cell.

37. A device used to produce an e.m.f. through the action of a chemical is called a: *a*. battery; *b*. thermocouple; *c*. piezoelectric crystal; *d*. photoelectric cell.

38. A device used to produce an e.m.f. through the action of light is called a: *a*. battery; *b*. thermocouple; *c*. piezoelectric crystal; *d*. photoelectric cell.

39. A device used to produce an e.m.f. by the action of pressure on the surface of a substance is called a: *a*. battery; *b*. thermocouple; *c*. piezoelectric crystal; *d*. photoelectric cell.

40. A photoelectric cell operates by virtue of the fact that: *a*. Protons are driven from the coated element in the dark. *b*. Electrons are driven from the coated element in the dark. *c*. Protons are driven from the coated element in a beam of light. *d*. Electrons are driven from the coated element in a beam of light.

Chapter 2. Batteries

1. The Battery as a Source of Direct-current E.M.F.

An electrical *circuit* must have at least three basic components:

a. A path of suitable conductors.
b. A load.
c. A source of e.m.f.

A conducting path for the electron flow is usually made up of suitable copper wire, which is used to connect the source of e.m.f. to the load.

The word *load* is used to represent any electrical device in which the electrical energy is dissipated and usually made to perform useful work.

The sources of e.m.f. for most practical purposes, other than in special applications, are the battery and the generator. For our purpose, before the characteristics of a complete circuit are studied, the battery as a source of direct-current (DC) e.m.f. will be considered. *The electron movement in a direct current is always in one direction.* Another form of electricity in motion, alternating current (AC), in which the direction of flow is reversed periodically, will be studied later.

2. The Primary and Secondary Cells

Batteries are divided into two main types, the *primary cell* and the *secondary cell.* The primary cell, once it has exhausted its activity, is of no further value. A secondary cell can be restored to activity by passing a current through it in reverse direction. This process is known as *charging.* Since secondary cells can be discharged and then recharged, they are referred to as *storage batteries.* It must be remembered, however, that no battery actually stores electricity—it is simply a chemical unit that under certain conditions produces an e.m.f.

The symbols used in diagrams of electrical circuits to indicate a battery are shown in Fig. 29. Symbol *A* indicates a single-cell battery; symbol *B* a multi-cell battery, that is, a battery made up of more than two cells. It is common practice to indicate the longer line of the symbol as the positive terminal, and the shorter line as the negative terminal. Identical symbols are used for both primary and secondary cells.

3. The Primary Cell

If two different metals are placed within a chemical solution, called an *electrolyte*, electrical activity will result when the metal electrodes (called *plates*) are joined through an electric circuit. The e.m.f. (pressure or *voltage*) created will depend solely upon two factors: (1) the material from which the plates are made and (2) the type of electrolyte used.

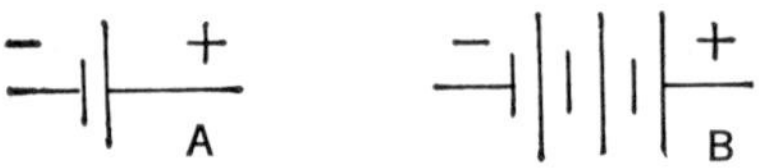

Fig. 29. Battery symbols.

The *size* of the plates or the distance separating them has no effect upon the *voltage* generated in the particular cell. The *capacity*, or amount of energy that the cell will deliver, however, is dependent upon the *area* of the plates exposed to the electrolyte.

Primary cells may be of either the *wet* or *dry* types. In a wet cell the electrolyte is in completely liquid form. In a dry cell, an absorbent material is saturated with the electrolyte and is then placed in contact with the plates. The advantage of the dry cell thus is apparent. The electrolyte will not spill out of its container. Note, however, that a dry cell is in no sense actually *dry*. If all the electrolyte were to evaporate from the originally saturated absorbent, no chemical activity could be observed. The result would be failure of the battery to generate an electric voltage.

4. Action of the Wet Primary Cell

The fundamental action of both primary and secondary cells is the same. Since the construction of the wet primary cell is quite simple, however, it can be readily used to explain the electro-chemical action that takes place (Fig. 30).

If an electrode of copper (Cu) and one of zinc (Zn) are inserted in a solution of dilute sulfuric acid (a mixture of the acid and

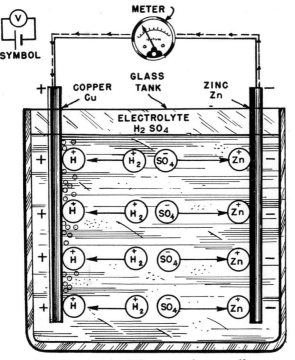

Fig. 30. Action of the wet primary cell.

water), and an electrical circuit completed between the electrodes, the electrolyte *ionizes*, that is, breaks up into its component atoms. Some atoms bear an excess of positive charges and are known as *positive ions*. Some bear an excess of negative charges and are called *negative ions*. In the ionization of sulfuric acid, the hydrogen atoms bear the positive charges, and the oxygen and sulphur atoms bear the negative charges.

At the same time that the electrolyte is being ionized, the same chemical solution is causing the neutral atoms of the zinc plate to lose some of their electrons, leaving them positively charged. These *positive ions* leave the zinc and enter the solution, *thus leaving the zinc itself negatively charged.*

The positive zinc ions strongly repel the positive hydrogen ions, driving them toward the copper plate. The positive hydrogen ions attract electrons from the copper *leaving it positively charged.*

Now see what we have: A zinc plate overflowing with *negative* electrons, a copper plate robbed of its normal supply, and thus bearing a positive charge. Since the negative (Zn) plate is connected to the positive (Cu) plate by an external electric conductor, the electrons are under a powerful attraction or pressure to rush forward. It is this *movement* of electrons, then, that produces the *current*, but it is the *pressure* just spoken of that causes the movement. This pressure is called the *electromotive force* (e.m.f.) or *voltage* and must always be present if an electric current is to flow in a circuit.

5. Polarization and Local Action.

In a primary cell, the negative plate is gradually decomposed and must be replaced if further electrical activity is desired. The zinc is eaten away by the action of the electrolyte.

Under certain conditions, so many hydrogen atoms will collect around the positive plate that electrons cannot escape freely. When this occurs, the battery is said to be *polarized*, and *polarization* results in decreased voltage and current. It also increases the cell's *internal resistance*, which prevents a free flow of current.

The battery cell is part of an electric circuit, and like all conductors of electricity it also possesses a degree of resistance to the flow of current. The term *internal resistance* is used to distinguish this resistance from that of the external circuit. The internal resistance will depend upon the condition of the cell. A new cell will have less resistance than an older unit.

Polarization may be prevented to a great extent by so constructing the cell as to allow the excess hydrogen to escape, or by the use of a *depolarizing agent*. The latter is a chemical that combines readily with the hydrogen to form water. Manganese dioxide (MnO_2) is particularly good for this purpose.

The term *local action* refers to a condition in which impurities within the zinc plate form "cells" of their own when combining with the pure part of the zinc itself. This action causes the zinc to deteriorate faster than is desirable and produces no useful energy. Local action may be overcome by the use of very pure zinc or by *amalgamating* (coating) it with mercury, which, in effect, acts as a shield around the impurities but allows free action of the zinc itself.

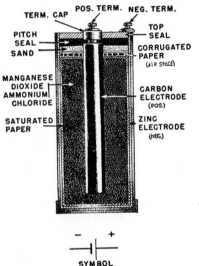

Fig. 31. The dry cell.

6. The Dry Cell

For practical purposes, the dry cell is preferable to the wet cell. It is readily portable and may be used in any position since there is no liquid to spill.

The ordinary dry cell (Fig. 31) consists of a zinc case or container (acting as the negative plate of the battery), a carbon rod, placed within it but not contacting the zinc at any point, acting as the positive plate. The electrolyte is a solution of ammonium chloride (NH_4Cl), which saturates an absorbent that fills the container. Powdered manganese dioxide is also included for depolarization purposes. Between the zinc and the saturated absorbent material is a cardboard layer that acts as an insulator, separating the zinc from the other elements but allowing chemical action to occur since it also becomes saturated with the electrolytic solution.

On the top of the cell, a layer of pitch is placed to act as a seal for the contents. Connections to the cell are made by the use of screw binding posts or clips, which are fastened to the carbon and zinc electrodes.

When the terminals of a dry cell are connected to an electric circuit (Fig. 32), the ammonium chloride electrolyte ionizes to form ions of ammonia (NH_4) and chlorine (Cl), the former bear-

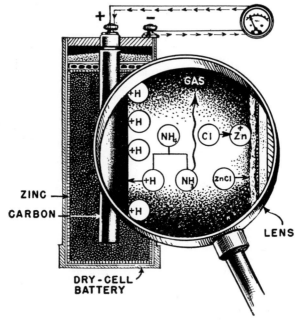

Fig. 32. Action of the dry cell.

ing a positive charge, and the latter a negative charge. Positive zinc ions escaping from the zinc plate leave the zinc bearing an excess of electrons. This leaves the zinc plate negatively charged. Some of the positive zinc ions combine with the negative chlorine ions to form zinc chloride ($ZnCl$), which is deposited on the zinc plate.

At the same time, the positive zinc ions are repelling the ammonia ions, which are also positively charged, and under this influence, the NH_4 ion breaks up into hydrogen ions (bearing a positive charge) and ammonia gas (NH_3). The ammonia gas tends to escape, but the hydrogen is further repelled toward the carbon plate, giving it a positive charge. Since a conducting path exists between the negatively charged zinc plate and the positively charged carbon plate, the negative electrons on the zinc plate are attracted by the positive charge on the carbon. This results in a current flow from the negative terminal through the electric circuit to the positive terminal of the cell (Fig. 32).

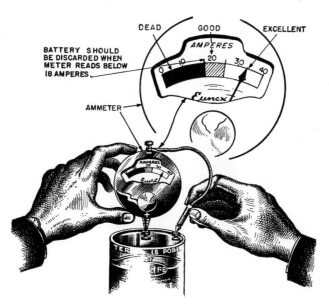

Fig. 33. Testing a dry cell.

A dry cell delivers an e.m.f. of 1.5 volts when it is in good condition. The voltage, it will be recalled, does not depend upon the size of the cell, but the amount of current it can supply is directly dependent on the size. Thus, dry cells, such as are used in flashlight batteries, are quite small, whereas those used for heavier current drains are larger.

Since the voltage is fairly constant during the life of the cell, measurement of the available voltage by use of a voltmeter is not the best procedure. Dry cells are usually best tested by determining the amount of current they can deliver under a stipulated load (Fig. 33). A good cell of the large 6-in. type will show a maximum discharge rate of 25 to 30 amperes (the ampere being an electrical unit of current flow, abbreviated "amp.") when the battery is new. A battery of this type should be discarded when a reading of less than 18 amp. is obtained. *

Every battery has a discharge rate that must not be exceeded over long periods of time if efficient service is to be expected. A dry cell of the type mentioned has a permissible continuous discharge rate of approximately $\frac{1}{4}$ amp. For brief, intermittent

Fig. 33a. Mallory mercury cells. (*Courtesy of P. R. Mallory and Co.*)

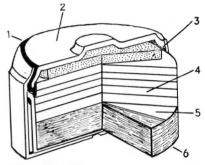

Fig. 33b. Flat-type mercury cell: (1) gasket; (2) steel casing; (3) amalgamated zinc anode; (4) potassium hydroxide electrolyte in absorbent material; (5) barrier; (6) mercuric oxide depolarizing cathode.

service this rate may be exceeded. Actually, no dry cell serves best under conditions of prolonged continuous service, as excessive polarization occurs. This increases the internal resistance of the cell rapidly, and, in turn, lowers its capacity and efficiency.

Dry cells deteriorate even when not in use, owing to evaporation of the electrolyte and decomposition of the zinc electrode. Smaller cells deteriorate more quickly than do the larger units.

The Mercury Cell

In order to overcome some of the disadvantages of the ordinary dry cell and to obtain a high ratio of energy availability com-

* Readings as low as 5 amp. are permissible on some types of special-service batteries.

pared to the weight and volume of that type of cell, the *mercury cell* was developed (Figs. 33*a* and *b*).

The positive plate (*anode*) may be in one of two forms: (1) a pellet (small ball) of pure, amalgamated zinc (Zn) or (2) a winding of thin, corrugated (folded) zinc strip. The form used depends upon the size of the cell and the purpose for which the particular cell is designed. The negative plate (*cathode*) is mercuric oxide (HgO), and the electrolyte is potassium hydroxide (KOH).

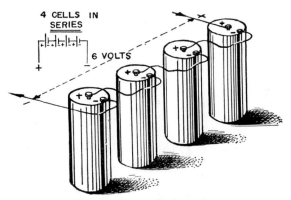

Fig. 34. Dry cells in series.

The e.m.f. produced by this type of cell is 1.345 volts. Because of the highly stable chemical components used, no internal cell reaction normally occurs. Thus, more efficient performance is provided over a greater period of time than is the case with the ordinary dry cell.

Mercury cells are usually housed in a strong metal container that is corrosion-resistant and that permits their functioning under various extremes of temperature and strain without seriously affecting the internal components.

7. Cells in Series and Parallel

Though it has been indicated that the individual dry cell (single-cell battery) delivers an e.m.f. of approximately 1.5 volts, under actual load the voltage is somewhat lower. One and a half volts is said to represent the *no-load*, *open-circuit*, or *internal* voltage, whereas the voltage *under load* or on a *closed circuit* is called the *terminal voltage.*

Since it is often necessary to have higher voltages available, individual cells are connected in *series.* A series connection consists of two or more cells so connected that the negative terminal of one cell is joined to the positive terminal of the subsequent unit, the number of cells in the series circuit being determined by the voltage desired (Fig. 34).

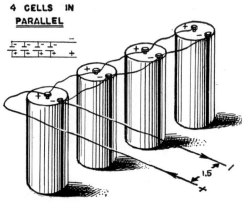

4 CELLS IN PARALLEL

Fig. 35. Dry cells in parallel.

Two 1.5-volt cells connected in series will deliver 3 volts. Three in series will deliver 4.5 volts; four will deliver 6 volts. Hence, to compute the total available voltage from a group of cells connected in series, the unit voltage (1.5) is multiplied by the actual number of cells.

All the cells connected in series can then be considered as a *battery,* the entire device acting as a single electrical unit. Note that one positive terminal (of the first cell) and one negative terminal (of the last cell) are free. It is these two terminals that become the positive and negative terminals of the battery.

When cells are connected in series, the available voltage has been increased, but the current *capacity* remains the same as for a single cell. If increased capacity is required, cells may be connected in parallel (Fig. 35).

If two cells are placed in parallel, the positive terminal of one unit is connected to the positive terminal of the other. Similarly, the negative terminals are joined together. The positive and negative terminals so joined remain the positive and negative terminals of the battery as a unit.

Two 1.5-volt cells capable of delivering 30 amp. each will still deliver 1.5 volts in a parallel connection, but the total available

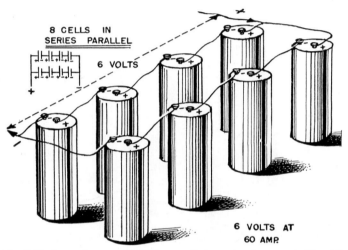

8 CELLS IN SERIES PARALLEL

6 VOLTS

6 VOLTS AT 60 AMP.

Fig. 36. **Cells in series parallel.** Four cells in series form each "bank"; two banks are in parallel delivering 6 volts with a capacity of 60 amp.-hr.

current capacity of parallel cells can be determined by multiplying the *capacity* of each cell by the total number of cells.

Where it is necessary to increase both the available voltage and current capacity, the series-parallel connection is used (Figs. 36 and 37). Note that the number of cells in each *bank* (group of cells) comprising those in series must be the same as in each other bank. If this is not done, the higher voltage bank will discharge into the lower one. In other words, the smaller bank will act as a load to the larger bank rather than as a parallel device. This also explains why it is inadvisable to put a bank of new cells in parallel to one of old cells even if the number of cells is the same. The new cells will have a higher voltage than the old unit and tend to discharge across them.

8. The Lead-acid "Storage" Battery

The *storage* or *secondary* cell has a number of advantages over the primary cell, the most outstanding of which are

    a. It can be recharged.
    b. It can be built to provide heavier current capacities.
    c. It is more economical in the long run.

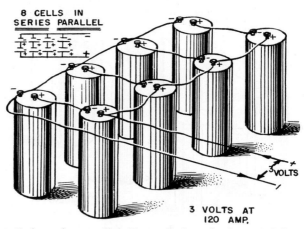

Fig. 37. Cells in series parallel. Two cells in series form each "bank"; four banks are in parallel delivering 3 volts with a capacity of 120 amp.-hr.

Since the storage battery is more economical to operate, it is used predominantly in automobiles, airplanes, telephone exchanges, and other places where direct current must be supplied.

The most common storage battery is the *lead-acid* type, the name being derived from the fact that the plates are of lead, and the electrolyte is sulfuric acid (Fig. 38).

The negative plate is made up of pure sponge lead (Pb), the term *sponge* referring to the softness of the material. The positive plate is composed of lead peroxide* (PbO_2), which gives it its characteristic reddish color in contrast to the dull gray of the

* Also called *lead dioxide.*

negative plate. In order to obtain higher current capabilities, each cell is usually fitted with a number of positive and negative plates, each group of positive and negative plates being strapped together to form a positive or negative group. This allows a greater amount of surface to contact the electrolyte. Thus a lead-

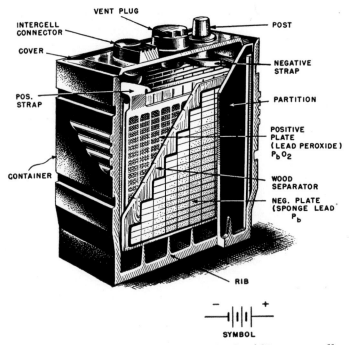

Fig. 38. Internal construction of the "lead-acid" storage cell.

acid battery is often called a 15-plate or 21-plate battery, meaning that each cell contains that particular number of plates. Of course, the size of the plates is very important. A 15-plate battery whose plates measure 12 in. square would be far "heavier" (in capacity) than a 21-plate whose plates measure only 5 in. square.

Note that the number of plates is an odd number—15, 21, etc. This is due to the fact that the negative group has one more plate than the positive group so that when mounted together to form an element, negative plates are on the outer side. The individual plates are kept apart by a *separator*, an insulating plate of Fiberglas or wood. This prevents short-circuiting (allowing the individual plates to touch each other). The completed element, upon which suitable *lugs* (terminal posts) are mounted, is housed in a rubber or glass case with a suitable insulating cover. The electrolyte is also placed within this case through a vent, or opening, sealed by a removable plug.

Lead-acid storage batteries are frequently supplied without the electrolyte. The electrolyte is added

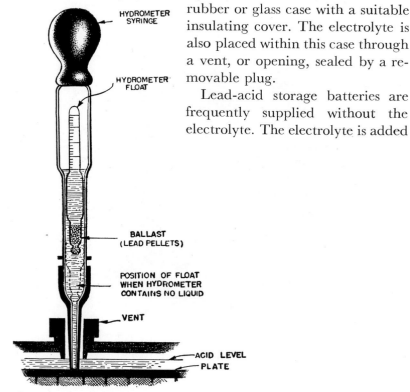

HYDROMETER SYRINGE

HYDROMETER FLOAT

BALLAST (LEAD PELLETS)

POSITION OF FLOAT WHEN HYDROMETER CONTAINS NO LIQUID

VENT

ACID LEVEL

PLATE

Fig. 39. The hydrometer is used to determine the specific gravity of an electrolyte.

only when the battery is placed in service. This is intended to lengthen the "shelf- life" (storage wear and tear) of the device.

Specific gravity of the electrolyte is about 1.300* in a fully charged, new battery. *Specific gravity* of a substance is its comparative weight with respect to the weight of an equal volume of

* Specific gravity is often written as 1300 rather than 1.300, etc.

water. Water has a specific gravity of 1.000. This fact is important, as the condition of a storage cell is checked by a hydrometer, an instrument that determines the specific gravity of the electrolyte (Fig. 39).

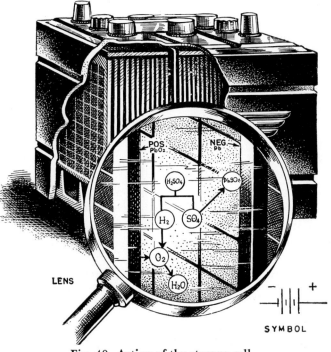

Fig. 40. Action of the storage cell.

9. Action of the Lead-acid Cell

Like that in the primary cell, the action of the lead-acid cell is chemical in nature (Fig. 40). When the terminals are connected through a suitable conductor, the electrolyte is ionized. The sulfuric acid breaks down into positively charged hydrogen ions (H_2) and negatively charged sulfate ions (SO_4). The hydrogen ions move toward the positive plate, and in combining with the oxygen (O) of the lead peroxide (PbO_2) form water (H_2O). *It is this water that tends to dilute the electrolyte and thus reduce its specific gravity*. (This explains why the hydrometer is useful in testing a storage battery).

The positively charged hydrogen ions have, in effect, removed negatively charged oxygen ions from the lead peroxide plate, leaving it positively charged. That is why the lead peroxide plate acts as the *positive* plate of the battery.

At the same time, some of the sulfate (SO_4) ions combine with the lead (Pb) part of the lead peroxide (PbO_2), forming lead sulfate ($PbSO_4$). Other negatively charged sulfate ions move toward the sponge-lead plate where, combining with positive ions of lead, they leave the plate negatively charged and form a layer of lead sulfate on its surface. As this takes place, the negative electrons that have accumulated on the negative lead plate are being attracted to the positive plate through the outside conductor. Thus, here again, as in the primary cell, we see an attraction or pressure being set up by the positive electrode, creating a condition that forces the electrons on the negative electrode into movement. This pressure, as we know, is called the *voltage* or e.m.f. of the cell.

10. Charge and Discharge of the Lead-acid Cell

At this point, we should note again that both the positive and negative plates are being converted to lead sulfate during the process of *discharge*, that is, producing an e.m.f. As soon as both plates are covered with a layer of this substance, the battery can no longer act as a source of e.m.f. because there must be two *different* materials immersed in an electrolyte to fulfill the conditions required. Now, only one material, lead sulfate, is in contact with the electrolyte. Further, during the process of discharge, more and more water has been formed, thus diluting the acid to a very large degree.

A storage cell is said to be *fully discharged* when the specific gravity of the electrolyte drops to approximately 1.120 from its original reading of 1.300. In order to restore a storage cell to renewed activity, the chemical process must be reversed, and this is done by *charging* the battery. A current is allowed to flow through the battery in reverse direction from an *external* source of e.m.f. The current ionizes the water in the discharged cell, causing the hydrogen (H^+) to unite with the sulfate ($SO_4^=$) of the lead sulfate ($PbSO_4$) to form sulfuric acid (H_2SO_4). This removes the sulfate deposit from both plates. The negatively charged oxygen ions (O^{++}) move toward the positive plate and form lead peroxide (PbO_2) again.

Thus, we have the plates restored to their original conditions, and the electrolyte is again composed of sulfuric acid with a specific gravity of about 1.300.

$$Pb + PbO_2 + 2H_2SO_4 \underset{\text{Charge}}{\overset{\text{Discharge}}{\rightleftarrows}} 2PbSO_4 + 2H_2O*$$

| Negative plate | Positive plate | Sulfuric acid | Negative and positive plates | Water |

11. Maintenance of Lead-acid Batteries

The common lead-acid battery is usually composed of a number of cells joined together in series and housed within a single container. Commonly used units are the three- and six-cell types, the latter being standard equipment in most automobiles. Ordinarily, no more than six cells are used in one container because of the tremendous weight of such batteries. Each fully charged cell of this type of battery can actually deliver a no-load voltage of approximately 2.2 volts. The total no-load voltage for a six-cell battery is around 13.2 volts. However, a no-load test is not an accurate indication of the condition of the battery. In practice, there are two methods in use: (1) the *hydrometer* test and (2) the *load* test.

1. The Hydrometer Test. The hydrometer (Fig. 39) consists of a glass float housed in a glass tube. On top of the tube is a rubber bulb and at the bottom is a rubber nozzle. The glass float is graduated by lines indicating different specific gravities from about 1.100 to 1.300. To test a battery cell, the plug is removed

---

* This formula is given for reference only. It need not be memorized.

from the vent on top of the cell, and the nozzle is dipped into the electrolyte. The rubber bulb is then squeezed gently and released gradually. This causes some of the electrolyte to be drawn up into the glass tube. Enough electrolyte should be drawn up to

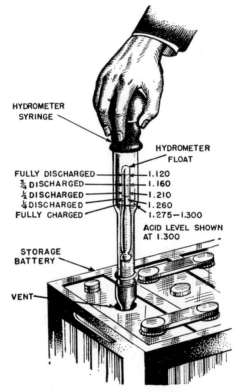

HYDROMETER
SYRINGE

HYDROMETER
FLOAT

FULLY DISCHARGED — 1.120
¾ DISCHARGED — 1.160
½ DISCHARGED — 1.210
¼ DISCHARGED — 1.260
FULLY CHARGED — 1.275—1.300

ACID LEVEL SHOWN
AT 1.300

STORAGE
BATTERY

VENT

Fig. 41. Testing a storage battery with a hydrometer.

cause the float to float freely (Fig. 41). A glance at the level of the liquid against the marking on the float at that level will indicate the state of charge. Good storage cells when fully charged will read between 1.280 and 1.300. Fully discharged cells will read as low as 1.120. Each cell of a battery should be tested. Testing one cell is no indication of what others may read, though when batteries are new, it is common practice to test but one cell of a bank (called a *pilot cell*) on the supposition that no serious defect in other cells would normally exist.

2. *The Load Test.* Even a poor battery may give a normal voltage reading when not under a load. Therefore, in some

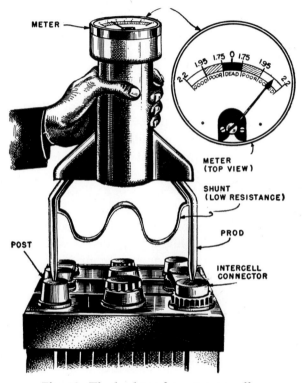

Fig. 42. The load test for a storage cell.

instances, it is advisable to test the cells of a battery under a very heavy load. For this purpose, a special instrument is available consisting of a two-pronged piece of heavy metal mounted on an insulating handle. Across the prongs, a voltmeter is also mounted along with a heavy wire of very low resistance, which acts as a load. When the prongs of the test device are placed across the terminals of the cell (Fig. 42), a very large current will flow due to the low resistance of the load. The reading on the voltmeter will then indicate the load voltage, which should not be less than 1.95 volts for a cell in good condition.

Since this type of test subjects the battery to a great strain, the test should be conducted rather quickly. Due to the low internal resistance of a storage cell, it is capable of delivering from 200 to 500 amp., depending upon the size and number of the plates. Such amounts of current, however, must not be drawn over great lengths of time as the heat created may buckle (bend) the plates and cause a rapid evaporation of the water in the electrolyte.

3. *Adding Water or Acid.* Unless acid is lost by spilling, none should be added to the cell at any time. It does not evaporate; the water alone does. Pure distilled water (water from which impurities have been removed) should be added whenever the level of the electrolyte is less than $\frac{1}{2}$ in. above the top of the plates. The water may be added by means of a clean rubber syringe, or the hydrometer can be used for this purpose.

In cases where an electrolyte must be mixed owing to loss by spilling, the sulfuric acid should be added in small quantities to the distilled water in a separate glass container until a specific gravity of 1.300 is reached. The pure acid is much heavier; hence the need for dilution. Never add water to the pure acid—a violent reaction will occur that may cause injury.

12. Battery Charging

Recharging a battery requires a source of direct current (DC), that is, current flowing in one direction such as is furnished by batteries, DC generators, and suitable rectifiers.* Operation of these devices will be studied later. At present, one rule should be learned: *In connecting any type of battery charger, the positive terminal of the charger must be attached to the positive terminal of the battery; the negative terminal of the charger to the negative terminal of the battery* (Fig. 43).

* A *rectifier* is an electrical device that converts alternating current to direct current.

Before removing a battery from the charging circuit, the charger should be disconnected from the line. This prevents sparking at the terminals. Such sparking may ignite the hydrogen gas given off from the batteries and cause an explosion.

Batteries are designed to operate at a predetermined charge and discharge rate to prevent overheating. Such ratings should

THE POSITIVE (+) LEAD FROM CHARGER IS CONNECTED TO POSITIVE (+) TERMINAL OF THE BATTERY; THE NEGATIVE (−) TO THE NEGATIVE (−) TERMINAL.

BATTERY CHARGER

Fig. 43. Charging a battery.

not ordinarily be exceeded. A battery is also rated in ampere-hours (amp.-hr.); this rating gives an indication of how much current can be supplied over a period of time. A battery rated at 100 amp.-hr. will deliver 10 amp. for 10 hours (10 hr.) since 10 × 10 = 100, or 1 amp. for 100 hr. (1 × 100 = 100). Such ratings, however, are approximate and depend greatly upon the condition of the battery and the type of service in which it is placed. An excessive rate of charge or discharge tends to overheat the battery, causing rapid evaporation of the water in the electrolyte. In addition, the plates may buckle due to the heating and thus create an internal short.

The material forming the plates may also peel off; this will rapidly decrease the effective capacity of the battery. A battery left discharged over long periods of time will become "sulfated," that is, remain in a discharged condition regardless of the

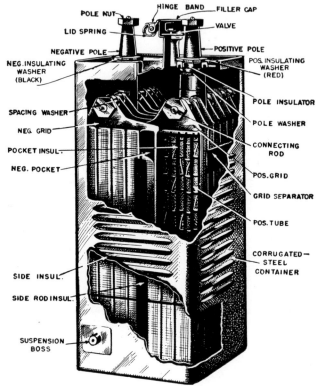

Fig. 44. Internal construction of the Edison cell.

amount of charging. This is due to the fact that the lead sulfate formed on the plates during discharge adheres very firmly and cannot be removed after being left in this state over a lengthy period.

13. The Edison Cell

The Edison cell (Fig. 44) is not as common as the lead-acid cell. Its main advantage lies in the fact that it is practically indestructible, being housed in a strong steel case. Further, unlike the lead-acid cell, which must always be kept in a charged condition to avoid chemical destruction due to sulfation, it may be discharged and left in such condition without injuring the plates. It is also a lighter weight battery. These advantages are counterbalanced by high initial cost and the fact that the battery's internal resistance is very high. This high internal

GREASING BATTERY POST TERMINAL

Fig. 45. A light layer of grease on the battery posts prevents corrosion.

resistance prevents large amounts of current from flowing when such may be required. In starting an automobile, for instance, the sudden drain may be 200 amp. or more. An Edison cell cannot effectively furnish this large amount of current.

Construction of the Edison Cell. The Edison cell is often called a *nickel-iron-alkaline* battery. The positive element is made up of a number of perforated nickel-plated steel tubes in which alternate layers of pure nickel (Ni) and nickel hydroxide

[Ni(OH)$_2$] are placed. The negative element is made up of a gridlike structure into which pockets of granulated iron oxide (FeO) are placed. The electrolyte is an alkali (nonacid) consisting of a 21 per cent solution of potassium hydroxide (KOH), also called *caustic potash*, and a small amount of lithium hydroxide. The latter chemical acts as a *catalyst*, which means that it aids the chemical reaction without taking part directly.

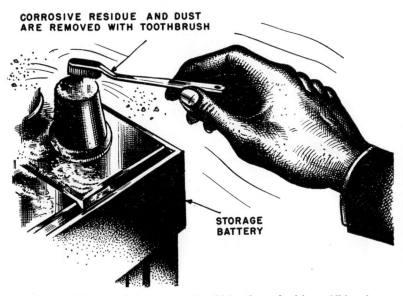

CORROSIVE RESIDUE AND DUST
ARE REMOVED WITH TOOTHBRUSH

STORAGE
BATTERY

Fig. 46. The top of the battery should be cleaned with a stiff brush.

The specific gravity of the electrolyte is 1.200 and drops but little during discharge. For this reason, a hydrometer is of no value in checking the condition of charge in a battery of this type. A voltmeter should be used while the battery is under load. A fully charged cell under load will read 1.2 volts, dropping to approximately 0.9 volt as the point of complete discharge is reached. If it should be necessary to use a hydrometer to check an Edison cell, or to replace evaporated water, care must be taken to see that it is clean. If it has been used on a lead-acid cell, the sulfuric acid that may remain in the tube will react with the alkaline electrolyte, affecting its chemical activity.

14. Battery Maintenance

A storage battery should be kept in a clean condition in a well-ventilated spot. Good ventilation assures the proper escape

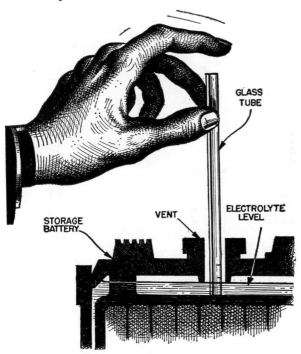

Fig. 47. Determining the level of the electrolyte.

of corrosive fumes and prevents overheating of the cells in either charging or discharging.

To prevent corrosion, a light layer of vaseline or other grease should be used to cover the terminals (Fig. 45). A stiff brush (a toothbrush will do) should be used to clean the top of the battery frequently, clearing away dust and corrosive residues that tend to accumulate (Fig. 46).

Before connecting the cable clamp onto the battery terminal, the battery terminal should be thoroughly cleaned. Then after the clamp is firmly attached to the terminal, a light layer of grease should be applied to both the clamp and the terminal in order to prevent corrosion.

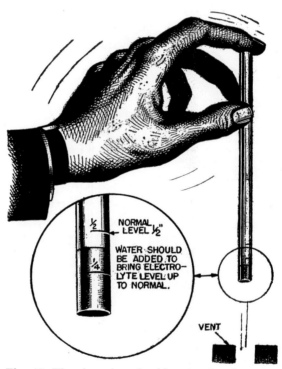

Fig. 48. The electrolyte should cover the plates to a depth of $\frac{1}{2}$ in.

The water level should be carefully maintained, and distilled water used whenever possible to replenish that lost by evaporation. Since it is often difficult to see whether the electrolyte level is at least $\frac{1}{2}$ in. above the surface of the plates by simple inspection, a handy device to use in a glass tube marked off at different levels with a file. By inserting the tube within the cell vent so that it contacts the top of the plates, and then holding one's finger on top of the tube to retain the electrolyte within it, it is possible to measure the level quite accurately (Figs. 47 and 48).

Proper use and maintenance will assure long life for a lead-acid battery. Under normal operating conditions, a battery of this type may last for 5 or more years.

SUMMARY

1. Batteries are divided into two main categories—the primary-cell and the secondary-cell types.

2. The primary cell, once discharged, cannot be recharged.

3. The secondary, or storage, cell can be recharged by sending a current through it in the reverse direction.

4. All cells operate on the same principle though the plates and electrolyte may differ. When the battery terminals are joined together by a conductor, the electrolyte ionizes, and the ions are attracted to, or repelled by, the plates. The plate *losing* electrons becomes the positive plate; the plate *gaining* electrons becomes the negative plate. The accumulated electrons on the negative plate are under the pressure of the attraction exerted by the positive plate and tend to move toward it through the conducting path. This pressure is called the *electromotive force* (e.m.f.) or *voltage*.

5. Polarization is due to an accumulation of hydrogen on the positive plate, which results in increased internal resistance and, therefore, lower battery voltage and capacity. The use of a depolarizing agent (manganese dioxide) tends to prevent this.

6. *Local action* refers to countervoltages set up in a plate due to chemical impurities. It is prevented, in the dry cell, by amalgamating the zinc with mercury.

7. A particular cell has a given voltage dependent upon the material of which the plates are made and the electrolyte used.

The size and number of plates affects the capacity alone, not the voltage.

8. Cells are connected in series to increase the total voltage available; in parallel to increase the capacity; in series-parallel

Comparison of Lead-acid and Edison Cells

Items	Lead-acid cell	Edison cell
Positive plate............	Lead peroxide	Nickel hydroxide
Negative plate..........	Sponge lead	Iron oxide
Electrolyte.............	Sulfuric acid and water	21 per cent solution of potassium hydroxide and water with small amount of lithium hydroxide
Voltage—no load:		
Fully charged........	2.4 volts	1.37 volts
Discharged...........	2.00 volts	1.25 volts
Voltage—under load:		
Fully charged........	1.95 volts	1.2 volts
Discharged...........	1.75 volts	0.9 volts
Specific gravity:		
Fully charged........	1.280	1.200
Discharged...........	1.120	1.150
Advantages............	Low cost Heavy current capacity	Light weight Practically indestructible
Disadvantages.........	Heavy weight Destructive acid and fumes Plates can be damaged by overheating	High initial cost Inability to stand sudden heavy loads Lower current capacity

(with an equal number of cells in each bank) to increase both voltage and capacity.

9. Lead-acid storage batteries are usually available as three- or six-cell units, the cells being connected in series.

10. A hydrometer is used to determine the specific gravity of lead-acid cells, but suitable meters reading under load serve best to indicate the condition of dry cells and Edison cells.

Quiz: Batteries

This quiz will help you review the material just studied. See the quiz directions on page 24 before answering the questions below.

1. Batteries are classified as: *a.* primary cells only; *b.* secondary cells only; *c.* primary and secondary cells only; *d.* primary and tertiary cells only.

2. In a battery, the positive plate: *a.* gains electrons; *b.* gains protons; *c.* loses protons; *d.* loses electrons.

3. A storage battery is a form of: *a.* primary cell; *b.* secondary cell; *c.* tertiary cell; *d.* tertiary cell with some primary-cell features.

4. An electric circuit must have at least the following components: *a.* a path of suitable insulators, a load, and a source of e.m.f.; *b.* a source of complete atoms, a load, and a path of suitable conductors; *c.* a path of suitable conductors, a switch, and a source of e.m.f.; *d.* a path of suitable conductors, a load, and a source of e.m.f.

5. One essential difference between primary and secondary cells lies in the fact that: *a.* A primary cell is always larger. *b.* A primary cell can be recharged. *c.* A secondary cell can be recharged. *d.* A secondary cell is less expensive.

6. In a dry cell battery, the function of the manganese dioxide is to act as a: *a.* depolarizing agent; b. polarizing agent; *c.* positive electrode; *d.* negative electrode.

7. The *basic* battery cell consists essentially of an: *a.* electrolyte and two like electrodes; *b.* electrolyte and two like insulators; *c.* electrolyte and two unlike electrodes; *d.* electrolyte and two unlike insulators.

8. The ampere is the electrical unit of: *a.* e.m.f.; *b.* current flow; *c.* circuit resistance; *d.* load value.

9. In a dry cell, local action rapidly destroys the: *a.* zinc electrode; *b.* carbon electrode; *c.* manganese dioxide; *d.* ammonium chloride.

10. When a dry cell is operated without a load, a voltmeter will measure the: *a.* terminal voltage; *b.* closed voltage; *c.* internal voltage; *d.* charging voltage.

11. The amount of e.m.f. generated by a cell will depend solely upon the: *a.* size of the plates and the type of electrolyte used; *b.* type of electrolyte and the material from which the plates are made; *c.* material from which the plates are made and the size of the plates; *d.* quantity of electrolyte and the size of the plates.

12. The *negative* plate of a fully charged lead-acid storage cell is composed of: *a.* lead peroxide; *b.* lead sulfate; *c.* lead chlorate; *d.* sponge lead.

13. The electrolyte used in a lead-acid storage cell is: *a.* acetic acid with a specific gravity of 1.115; *b.* hydrochloric acid with a specific gravity of 1.215; *c.* sulfuric acid with a specific gravity of 1.300; *d.* picric acid with a specific gravity of 1.515.

14. The specific gravity of a substance is its comparative weight with respect to the weight of an equal volume of: *a.* alcohol; *b.* oil; *c.* Prestone; *d.* water.

15. A hydrometer that is being used to test a cell of a lead-acid storage battery shows a reading of 1.120. The cell is: *a.* fully charged; *b.* fully discharged; *c.* half charged; *d.* one-quarter discharged.

16. Compared with the battery that it is charging, a battery charger must deliver a: *a.* higher DC voltage; *b.* lower DC voltage; *c.* higher AC voltage; *d.* lower AC voltage.

17. In connecting a charger to a storage battery, connections from the charger to the battery must be made as follows: *a.* positive to positive-negative to ground; *b.* positive to positive, negative to negative; *c.* positive to negative, negative to positive. *d.* positive to ground, negative to negative.

18. When a load is applied to a storage battery, the terminal voltage will: *a.* vary cyclically; *b.* be greater than the no-load voltage; *c.* be equal to the no-load voltage; *d.* be less than the no-load voltage.

19. The electrolyte in an Edison cell is: *a.* sulfuric acid; *b.* potassium sulfate; *c.* sulfur dioxide; *d.* potassium hydroxide.

20. Local action is due to the use of: *a.* amalgamated zinc for the negative electrode; *b.* poor carbon for the positive electrode; *c.* very pure zinc for the negative electrode; *d.* zinc containing impurities and not amalgamated.

21. If the level of the electrolyte *above the tops of the plates* in a typical lead-acid storage cell drops to $\frac{1}{8}$ in., the proper procedure is to add: *a.* distilled water to raise the level to about $\frac{1}{2}$ in.; *b.* dilute sulfuric acid with a specific gravity of 1.300 to raise the level to $\frac{1}{2}$ in.; *c.* distilled water to raise the level to at least 2 in.; *d.* sulfuric acid with a specific gravity of 1.000 to raise the level to $\frac{1}{2}$ in.

22. A storage battery is being tested with a hydrometer. The reading obtained, if the battery is fully charged, will be approximately between: *a.* 1.100 to 1.150; *b.* 1.150 to 1.200; *c.* 1.200 to 1.250; *d.* 1.250 to 1.300.

23. Polarization is due to an: *a.* excess of electrons around the negative electrode; *b.* excess of hydrogen atoms around the positive electrode; *c.* excess of electrons around the positive electrode; *d.* excess of chlorine atoms around the negative electrode, producing too much ammonia gas.

24. Four new dry cells are connected in series. Four more dry cells, similarly connected, are placed in parallel to the first bank. The resultant output voltage will be: *a.* 4 volts; *b.* 6 volts; *c.* 8 volts; *d.* 10 volts.

25. The lead-acid cell produces, under fully charged conditions, a: *a.* higher voltage than the Edison cell; *b.* lower voltage than the Edison cell; *c.* voltage equal to the Edison cell; *d.* voltage twice the maximum obtained from the Edison cell.

26. A large dry cell has a capacity rating of 30 amp. To have 6 volts available, it is necessary to arrange a group of the cells. The desired result may be obtained by connecting: *a.* four cells in series; *b.* four cells in parallel; *c.* four cells in series-parallel with two cells in each bank; *d.* six cells in series.

27. Before removing a battery from the charging circuit, the charger should be: *a.* short-circuited; *b.* connected to ground; *c.* disconnected from line; *d.* discharged into protective load.

28. In order to charge a dead 6-volt 100-amp.-hr. battery from a 10-volt charging source in about 5 hr., the charging rate must be at least: *a.* 5 amp.; *b.* 10 amp.; *c.* 15 amp.; *d.* 20 amp.

29. In testing a standard large 6-in. dry cell with a special ammeter, the cell should be discarded if the meter reads less than: *a.* 2 amp.; *b.* 18 amp.; *c.* 25 amp.; *d.* 30 amp.

30. The capacity of a cell is dependent upon the: *a.* quantity of electrolyte used; *b.* material of which the plates are made; *c.* type of electrolyte used; *d.* area of the plates exposed to the electrolyte.

31. The *positive* plate of a fully charged lead-acid storage cell is composed of: *a.* lead peroxide; *b.* lead sulfate; *c.* lead chlorate; *d,* sponge lead.

32. As ionization occurs, an electric current will flow through the conducting path between the electrodes because of the: *a.* accumulation of positive charges on both plates; *b.* accumulation of electrons on both plates; *c.* pressure or attraction exerted on the electrons accumulated on the negative plate by the positive charges on the positive plate; *d.* breakdown of the insulating separators between the plates.

33. A load test indicates the condition of a battery most accurately because it shows: *a.* the available voltage on an open circuit; *b.* most closely the voltage available under load conditions; *c.* the available current on an open circuit; *d.* the degree of polarization within the cell.

34. A dry cell is a form of: *a.* primary cell; *b.* secondary cell; *c.* tertiary cell; *d.* secondary cell with some primary-cell features.

35. In a storage battery, acid should be added to the electrolyte when: *a.* the original acid has evaporated; *b.* the original acid has spilled out; *c.* too much water has been formed on discharge; *d.* too much water has evaporated.

36. As a storage battery is discharged, the electrolyte is: *a.* diluted; *b.* strengthened; *c.* concentrated; *d.* evaporated.

37. A dry cell is so called because it: *a.* can be dried out completely and still work; *b.* is the only type of cell that will work in dry, humidity-free areas; *c.* contains material that absorbs moisture from the air and thus keeps itself dry; *d.* contains an absorbent saturated with the electrolyte and thus has no liquid electrolyte to spill out.

38. A lead-acid cell differs from an Edison cell in that the lead-acid cell can withstand: *a.* sudden, very heavy drains; *b.* heat and cold; *c.* excessive mechanical pressures; *d.* variations in charging voltage.

39. When a conductor is connected across the terminals of a cell, the electrolyte ionizes. *Ionization* is a term that most nearly means the: *a.* breaking up of the electrolyte into its component atoms; *b.* rapid evaporation of the electrolyte; *c.* slow disintegration of the electrodes; *d.* rapid disintegration of the electrodes.

40. Two new dry cells are connected in series, and three additional pairs of cells are similarly connected. When the four pairs are placed in parallel, the output voltage will be: *a.* 0.5 volts; *b.* 1.5 volts; *c.* 3.0 volts; *d.* 4.5 volts.

Chapter 3. The Electric Circuit

1. The Electron Path

Before useful work can be performed using the potential electrical force available in a source of e.m.f., the electrons must

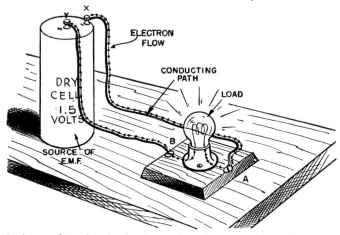

Fig. 49. A complete electric circuit consists of a source of e.m.f., a conducting path, and a "load." The circuit is said to be "closed" when the current can flow from the source of e.m.f., through the load, and return to the source.

have a path, or *circuit*, over which they may travel. An electric circuit must always be complete, that is, it must start at the source of e.m.f., go through the load or loads it is energizing, and then return to its starting point by a separate path. This is illustrated in Fig. 49, which shows a battery as a source of e.m.f. feeding a load represented by the electric lamp. The electron movement is from X to point A, then through the lamp to point B and back again to the battery at point Y. This is the first rule of any electrical circuit, that is, the electron path must be complete to and from the source of e.m.f. in order for an electric current to flow. Suppose, as in Fig. 50, a switch* (which would close or open the circuit) were inserted in the circuit. If the switch were open, that is, having the blade making no contact with the jaw, electrons could not pass through the open switch and the circuit would be open or incomplete. To close

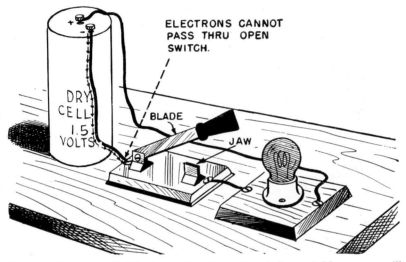

Fig. 50. The circuit is "broken" when the switch is "open." No current will flow through an open circuit.

the circuit and complete the path, the blade must contact the jaw. This will then allow electrons to flow past the switch, then through the load, and finally return to the battery.

2. Series and Parallel Circuits

Just as cells of a battery may be connected in series, in parallel, or in series-parallel arrangements, electric circuits may consist of more than a single path through which the current may flow.

* The switch shown is known as a *single-pole single-throw* (s.p.s.t.) *knife switch.* *Single-pole* refers to the fact that it has only one make and break contact (where the knife blade contacts the jaw), and *single-throw* to the fact that the switch blade can be thrown (shifted) so as to open or close only a single circuit.

The circuit in Fig. 51 is called a *series* circuit because the electrons will flow through the first lamp and then through the second prior to returning to the battery.

Electric lamps as well as other devices are designed to operate on specific voltages. Thus, a lamp may be designed to operate

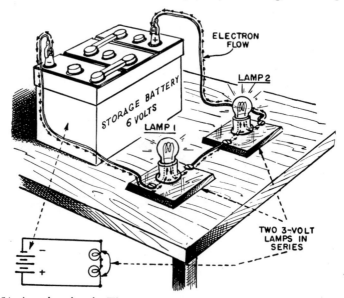

Fig. 51. A series circuit. The current flows from the source of e.m.f. through the first lamp, then through the second, before returning to the source. Both lamps together form the *load*. Removing one lamp opens the circuit causing the other lamp to "go out."

on 3, 6, 32, or 110 volts. Such devices are connected in series only when the sum of their individual voltage ratings equals the available supply voltage. Two 3-volt lamps connected in series act as a 6-volt lamp, just as two 3-volt batteries in series act as a single 6-volt battery. Hence the supply voltage must be 6 volts if the lamps are to operate at full incandescence (brilliance). Devices connected in series must also be designed to draw the same amount of current, as the *current* in a *series* circuit is of the same value at any point in the circuit.

In a parallel circuit, there is more than one path through which the electrons may flow. Thus, in Fig. 52, the electrons divide between lamps 1 and 2 at point X, some going through lamp 1, and others through lamp 2.

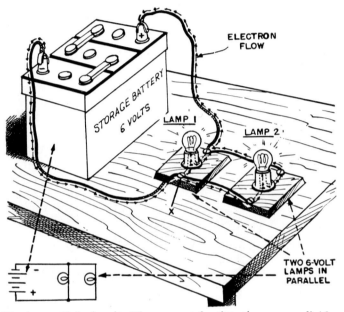

Fig. 52. A parallel circuit. The current leaving the source divides, part going through one lamp and part through the other. Each lamp is a *branch* of the parallel circuit. Removing one lamp does *not* cause the other to go out since in a parallel-circuit opening one branch does not prevent the current flow through the other.

Electric wiring in buildings is of the parallel-circuit type. When electric lamps or appliances are being used, they are connected in parallel. This allows the use of each single electrical device as required. In a series circuit, disconnecting one unit opens the entire circuit. Thus, if one electric lamp were to burn out, *all* the lights would go out; whereas in a parallel circuit, the burning out of one lamp will not affect the operation of the others.

In a parallel circuit, each device must be designed to operate at the same voltage, that which the power supply delivers. Individually, they may draw different values of current. The ordinary house *main* (electric power supply) supplies 110 volts approximately. (The figure often used for computations is 117 volts since it most nearly represents the *average* voltage available because of variations from the source.) Hence all appliances connected in parallel across the main must be of the 110-volt type

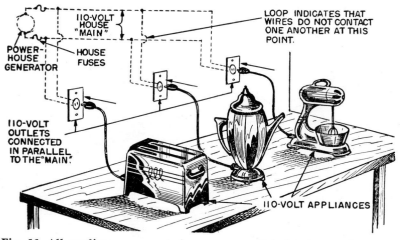

Fig. 53. All appliances connected across a parallel circuit must have the same voltage rating.

(Fig. 53). The use of lower voltage units, for example, 32-volt devices, would cause such units to burn out.

In a series-parallel circuit, as the name implies, there are both series and parallel paths. In Fig. 54, lamps 1 and 2 are in *series* with each other, while lamp 3 is in *parallel* to the series combination.

In Fig. 55 the single lamp in parallel to the series combination (lamp 3) is replaced by two lamps in series. This second series circuit is then connected in parallel to the first series circuit. We now have two series circuits in parallel with one another.

The circuits illustrated are comparatively simple, but it is possible to have extremely complicated circuits, which, however, can always be broken down into one of the three types mentioned.

In a parallel or series-parallel circuit, *each complete parallel section* is called a *branch*. Thus, in Fig. 52, lamp 1 and lamp 2

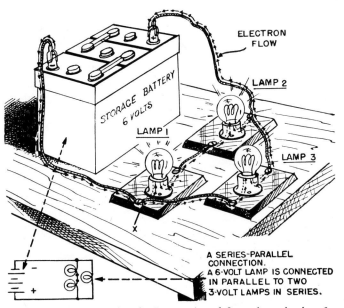

Fig. 54. A series-parallel circuit. Lamps 1 and 2 are in series but form one branch of the parallel circuit. Lamp 3 is the second branch.

are each branches of the complete circuit. In Fig. 54, lamp 1 and lamp 2 compose a branch even though they are in series with each other. *Together*, they form one branch of the parallel circuit with lamp 3 as the other branch.

3. Ohm's Law

We have already learned that there is no such device as a *perfect* conductor. Hence, every conductor possesses some degree of resistance. Resistance, we know, is the opposition offered to the movement of electrons from one unbalanced atom to another. Since all circuits and load devices are composed of conductors in one form or other, it follows that resistance will be found in all electric circuits in a varying degree, dependent upon the length, cross-sectional area, and material of the wire

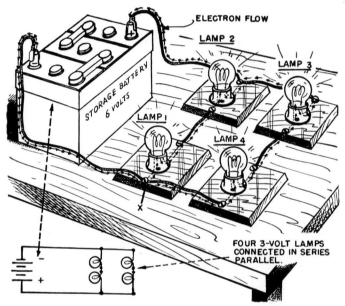

Fig. 55. Each branch of the parallel circuit contains two lamps in series.

used, as well as upon the particular characteristics ("constants") of the load devices themselves.

Resistance, then, is an important factor to be considered in any circuit analysis. In addition, there are two other factors that must always be considered:

    (*a*) The voltage or e.m.f.
    (*b*) The current or flow of electrons.

Resistance (*R*), voltage (*E*), and current (*I*) bear a relationship to each other that has been formulated into a law, called *Ohm's Law*. This law may be illustrated in three formulas, two being derived from the other.

$$E = IR$$

$$R = \frac{E}{I}$$

$$I = \frac{E}{R}$$

Hence, Ohm's Law states three main facts that must be understood.

1) Voltage (E) in a given circuit may be determined by multiplying the current (I) in amperes by the resistance in ohms.

Example: A current of 5 amperes is flowing in a circuit having a resistance of 2 ohms. What is the voltage?

Step 1.	$E = IR$	*This is the formula. E must be determined since that is the unknown value.*
Step 2.	$E = 5 \times 2$	*Here we substitute the actual values of current ($I = 5$) and resistance ($R = 2$), which are the known constants.*
Step 3.	$E = 10$	*Here, having multiplied $I \times R$, we have the answer in volts.*

Answer: Since E (representing the e.m.f.) is measured in volts, a volt being the unit of electromotive force, $E = 10$ volts.

2) Resistance (R) in a given circuit may be determined by dividing the electromotive force (E) in volts by the current (I) in amperes.

Example: What is the resistance of a circuit in which the voltage measures 10 volts and the current is 5 amp.?

Step 1.	$R = \dfrac{E}{I}$	*This is the formula since R is the unknown that must be determined.*
Step 2.	$R = \dfrac{10}{5}$	*Here we substitute the actual values of voltage ($E = 10$) and current ($I = 5$), which are the known constants.*

Step 3. $R = 2$ *Here, having divided E by I, we have the answer in ohms.*

Answer: Since R (representing the resistance) is measured in ohms, an ohm being the unit of electrical resistance, $R = 2$ ohms.

3) Current (I) in a given circuit may be determined by dividing the voltage (E) by the resistance (R).

Example: If an e.m.f. of 10 volts is applied to a circuit having a resistance of 2 ohms, what current will flow?

Step 1. $I = \dfrac{E}{R}$ *This is the formula since I is the unknown that must be determined.*

Step 2. $I = \dfrac{10}{2}$ *Here we substitute the actual values of voltage $(E = 10)$ and resistance $(R = 2)$, which are the known constants.*

Step 3. $I = 5$ *Here, having divided E by R, we have the answer in amperes.*

Answer: Since I (representing the current) is measured in amperes, an ampere being the unit of electrical current flow, $I = 5$ amp.

A simple way to remember Ohm's Law is by the use of the diagram in Fig. 56. To determine the value of the unknown quantity, cover the symbol representing it, and the remaining symbols will indicate whether the values are to be multiplied or divided to obtain the answer.

Example: What is the voltage in a circuit when the current measures 4 amp. and the resistance is 4 ohms?

Step 1. Voltage is represented by the symbol E. Therefore, cover the E in the figure. This leaves I and R below the horizontal line (Fig. 57).

Step 2. When the known symbols are below the horizontal line, their actual values are multiplied. Since I = 4 amp. and R = 4 ohms, the answer is 4 × 4, or 16 volts.

Example: What is the current in a circuit measuring 4 ohms and having an e.m.f. of 16 volts?

Step 1. Current is represented by the symbol I. Therefore, cover the I in the figure. This leaves E above, the R below, the horizontal line (Fig. 58).

Step 2. When one known symbol is above, and the other below the horizontal line, the upper value is divided by the lower one. Since E = 16 volts and R = 4 ohms, the answer is $\frac{16}{4}$ or 4 amp.

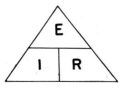

Fig. 56. Ohm's Law in diagram form.

Fig. 57. To find *E* where *I* and *R* are known, cover the *E* with a finger. Where the known symbols are below the horizontal line, multiply the actual values they represent. $E = I \times R$.

Fig. 58. To find *I* where *E* and *R* are known, cover the *I*. When one symbol is above and the other below the horizontal line, the upper value is divided by the lower one. $I = \frac{E}{R}$.

4. Voltage Drop

When current is flowing in a circuit, voltage measurements at different points in the circuit will indicate different values. The values become lower as more resistance is found between the source of e.m.f. and the point at which the measurement is made.

In Fig. 59*a*, the battery acting as a source of e.m.f. is connected directly across the load represented by the electric light. Figure 59*b* shows a wiring diagram of the circuit.

If the connecting wires between *A* and *C*, and *B* and *D*, had *no resistance whatsoever*, the e.m.f. across points *CD* would be exactly the same as that appearing across the battery terminals

AB. However, circuit resistance is bound to exist, and if the voltage across *CD* were measured, it would be found to be less than that across the battery. This loss in voltage is called the *voltage drop* or *IR loss*, because the loss is due to the *current flowing through the circuit resistance.* The diagram symbol used to indicate resistance is ⌐√√√√ .

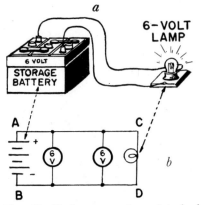

Fig. 59. If the connecting wires had no resistance, the voltage at the load would equal the voltage at the source.

The circuit can, therefore, be drawn as in Fig. 60, the symbol *R* representing the resistance of the circuit. The voltage drop across *R* can be determined by Ohm's Law ($E = IR$). Assume that the resistance (R) of the circuit is 1 ohm and the current flowing in the circuit is 2 amp. The voltage drop across *R* will be 2 volts ($I \times R = 2 \times 1 = 2$ volts). Hence if the voltage across *AB* (the battery e.m.f.) were 6 volts, the *actual* voltage appearing across the lamp at points *CD* would be 6 — 2, or 4 volts (Fig. 61).

The resistance that causes the voltage drop may be the resistance of the connecting wire (as illustrated in the example given) or even the internal resistance of the battery. The resistance of the load itself must also be considered. For this reason, circuits are often drawn showing a resistance as the load (Fig. 62).

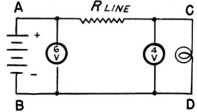

Fig. 60. *R* represents the resistance of the "line" (conducting path). Some degree of resistance always exists.

In order to minimize the voltage drop in the wiring of a circuit, the wire used must be large enough to carry the required current. Wire that is too small will not only increase the voltage drop owing to its higher resistance, but will overheat and even burn out entirely.

Wire is available in different *gauges* or degrees of measurement,

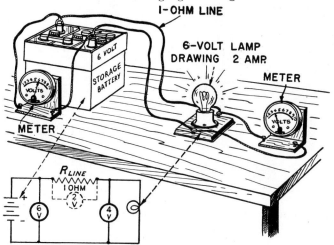

Fig. 61. The voltage drop in the line represented by "*R* line" can be found by using Ohm's Law. The 2 amp. drawn by the load will cause a 2-volt drop in the 1-ohm line. $E = I \times R = 2 \times 1 = 2$ volts.

such as No. 10 or No. 14. In the gauge system used, the smaller the number, the "heavier" the wire. Thus No. 10 wire is heavier than No. 14, and No. 0 is much heavier than No. 10. Heavier wire is wire of a greater cross-sectional area.

The heating effect of different kinds of wire through which a current is flowing must also be considered. In an electric toaster, iron, or heater, the primary purpose is to produce heat. Therefore, these instruments are

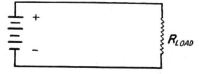

Fig. 62. Since all loads offer a degree of resistance to the line, they are often represented by the resistance symbol in electric-circuit diagrams.

wound with a wire of comparatively high resistance, capable of dissipating large amounts of heat. Nichrome steel wire is often used for such purposes, but for the electric wiring itself, such

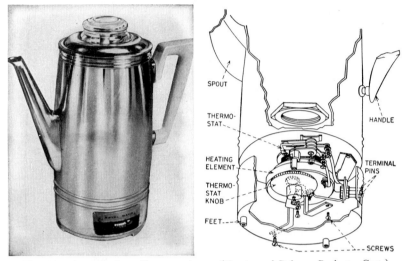

Fig. 62a. Automatic coffee percolator. (*Courtesy of Robeson Rochester Corp.*)

Fig. 62b. Built-in electric room heater. (*Courtesy of Thermador Electrical Manufacturing Co.*)

Fig. 62c. Electric steam iron. Note cast-in rod-type element.

Fig. 62*d*. Parts of a soldering iron: (1) tip; (2) front nut and set screw; (3) hexagonal case; (4) handle nut; (5) terminal contact screws; (6) ground-wire contact screw; (7) element; (8) heat deflector; (9) element lead wires; (10) cord-strain hole. (*Courtesy of Hexacon Electric Co.*)

Fig. 62*e*. Electric stove showing position of heating elements. (*Courtesy of Thermador Electrical Manufacturing Co.*)

Fig. 62*f*. The wire of the heating element of the electric stove may be enclosed in a metallic sheath formed from a special alloy.

high-resistance wire would be detrimental. For such purposes, copper wire is used exclusively.

Good examples of wire intended for heating purposes are found in the automatic percolator, the electric room heater, the electric steam iron, the soldering iron, and the electric stove. In the latter device particularly, one finds the wire enclosed within

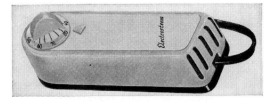

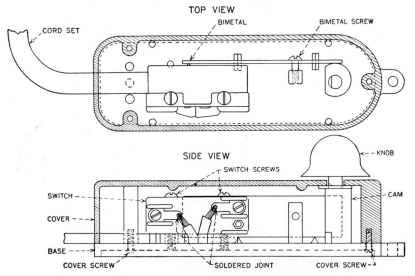

Fig. 62g. Wall thermostat used with electric heaters to maintain a given temperature. The assembly drawing shows the construction of this straight bimetal thermostat unit. (*Courtesy of Electric Steam Radiator Corp.*)

a metallic sheath that is formed from a special alloy (Fig. 62*f*). To insulate the wire from the sheath, magnesium oxide powder is compressed within the sheath, thus separating the inner electrical *conducting* component from the outer, rigid, nonconducting coil. This outer coiled sheath absorbs the heat produced by the enclosed wire and, in turn, heats the object placed upon it.

Many electrical devices of modern design use a *thermostat* to maintain a given temperature under the operating conditions. A thermostat (Fig. 62*g*) consists of a metallic element that changes its relative position as it is affected by temperature variations.

Its changing position causes it to open (break) or close (make) a complete electric circuit.

In order to safeguard circuits when an excess current flows, a *fuse* is commonly used. A fuse (Fig. 63) is simply a piece of metal

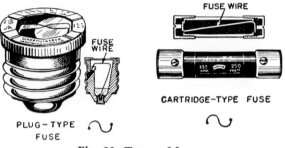

FUSE WIRE

CARTRIDGE-TYPE FUSE

PLUG-TYPE
FUSE

Fig. 63. Types of fuses.

that melts very quickly when heated beyond a normal amount. Placed in *series* with a load, it allows normal values of current to be drawn, but overheats, melts, and breaks the circuit if an

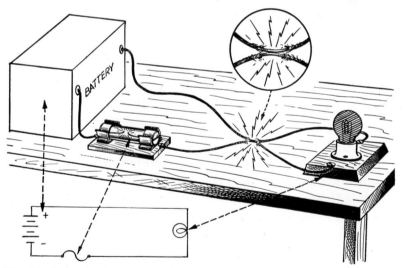

Fig. 64. A fuse is always connected in series with the line and the load. An excessive current such as may be caused by a short circuit melts the fuse and opens the circuit.

excessive current appears (Fig. 64). An excessive current will flow, for instance, when a short circuit occurs. The term *short circuit* means a connection, usually accidental, between points where ordinarily no connection is intended. A short circuit will usually place a very heavy load on the line. It also prevents

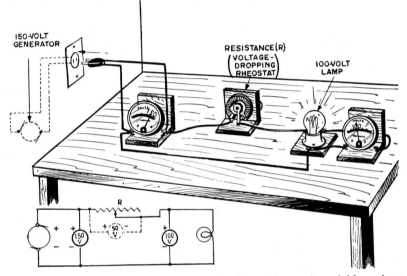

Fig. 65. Resistance R is used to drop the line voltage. A variable resistor (rheostat) is shown but a fixed (nonvariable) resistor can be used as well.

normal circuit operation. Fuses are supplied in various current ratings and are selected on the basis of circuit requirements.

It is often necessary to introduce resistance into a circuit to produce a voltage drop. This is generally the case where the e.m.f. is higher than is required for the load. In Fig. 65, the line e.m.f. is 150 volts, and the lamp load is intended to operate on 100 volts. Since 150 volts will cause an excessive current to flow, resistance R must be added to produce a voltage drop. The value of this resistance will depend on two factors:

   a. The voltage drop required.
   b. The current the lamp will draw.

If we assume that the lamp draws 2 amp., the problem is solved as follows:

Step 1. E.m.f. (across line) − e.m.f. (across lamp)
= voltage drop required across *R*.

Step 2. Voltage drop = 150 − 100 = 50 volts.

Step 3. *We now must determine the resistance necessary to produce a 50-volt loss when 2 amp. are flowing through the circuit. To do this, we use Ohm's Law.*

R (unknown resistance required)

$$= \frac{E \text{ (known voltage drop required)}}{I \text{ (known current)}}$$

Step 4. $R = \dfrac{50}{2} = 25 \text{ ohms}$ *Ans.*

When it is necessary to introduce resistance into a circuit, *resistors* (Fig. 66) are used. Resistors are made of wire, carbon, graphite, and certain molded compositions, depending upon the use to which they are put. Variable resistors are called *rheostats* and *potentiometers*. A potentiometer is simply a rheostat having three connections, and is usually of higher resistance (Fig. 67).

A rheostat is always connected in *series* with a load to limit the amount of current in the circuit by causing a greater or lesser voltage drop across its resistance. Thus, in the example shown in Fig. 65, where it was required to operate a 100-volt lamp on a 150-volt line, a rheostat would have to be of such a value that at one point it would measure 25 ohms. Twenty-five ohms produced a voltage drop of 50 volts and allowed the proper value (2 amp.) of current to flow. Where a minimum resistance of 25 ohms is required in a circuit, safe practice would call for a rheostat of somewhat higher value. In this case, 30 to 50 ohms would probably be used. By the proper setting of the moving-

arm contact the correct value can be used as required, and lesser
or greater values of resistance obtained if the e.m.f. source
rises above or drops below the original value of 150 volts.

A potentiometer may be used as a rheostat, if it is of the correct
resistance and current-carrying capacity, by connecting it within

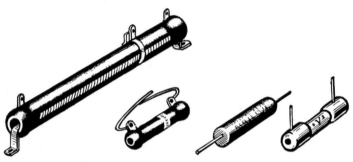

Fig. 66. **Wire-wound and composition types of resistors.**

a circuit in exactly the same manner as a rheostat. Ordinarily,
however, potentiometers are used as illustrated in Fig. 68.

In Fig. 68*A*, the potentiometer is connected in parallel to a
source of e.m.f. and only a portion of the voltage drop across
the entire unit is utilized. In Fig. 68*B*, the entire resistance of

RHEOSTAT   **POTENTIOMETER**

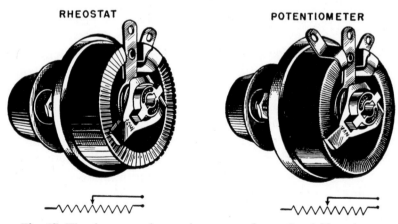

Fig. 67. The rheostat and potentiometer are forms of variable resistors.

the potentiometer is in series with the main load, and the full unit is acting as a voltage-dropping resistor for this load. A portion of this voltage drop across X is being used as a source of e.m.f. for a secondary load.

5. Electric Power

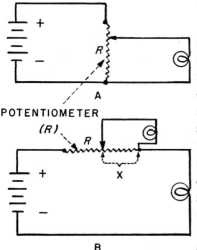

POTENTIOMETER
(R)

B

Fig. 68. **Use of the potentiometer in electrical circuits.**

When any kind of work is done, energy is expended. The man who lifts a heavy weight up a flight of stairs expends energy. The soldier on a long march does the same. When a source of e.m.f. forces a current through a circuit, energy is also expended. Energy is the *capacity* to do work, and the *rate* at which it is done is called the *power.*

For measuring electrical power, the unit used is the *watt* (represented by the symbols W or P). The watt denotes the power used when 1 volt forces 1 ampere of current to flow. It is the product obtained by multiplying the voltage (E) by the current (I). The basic formula, therefore, is

$$W = EI$$

Example: An electric lamp operating on 100 volts draws 2 amp. What is the power consumed?

Step 1.	$W = EI$	*This is the formula in which voltage and current are the known factors.*
Step 2.	$W = 100 \times 2$	*Here we substitute the actual values of voltage $(E = 100)$ and current $(I = 2)$.*
Step 3.	$W = 200$	*Here, having multiplied $E \times I$, we have the answer in watts.*

Since the basic formula for power is $W = EI$, we can see that it is made up of two of the same components that are found in Ohm's Law, that is, voltage (E) and current (I). In some problems, we may first have to determine the values of E and I before we can compute the power.

Example: What is the power in an electric circuit where 2 amp. is flowing through a resistance of 5 ohms? (Note that we do not yet know the voltage E, but since Ohm's Law, $E = IR$, can be used, we can find the voltage.)

Step 1.	$E = IR$	*This is the formula that will allow us to determine the voltage, when we know the current and resistance.*
Step 2.	$E = 2 \times 5$	*Here we substitute the actual values of current and resistance.*
Step 3.	$E = 10$ volts	*Now we have the voltage.*
Step 4.	$W = EI$	*Here is the formula for power when voltage and current are known.*
Step 5.	$W = 10 \times 2$	*Here we substitute the values of voltage, just found by Ohm's Law, and the known current.*
Step 6.	$W = 20$	*Here we have the answer in watts.*

What we have actually done by this method is to substitute in the original equation for power $(W = EI)$, the Ohm's Law equation for the unknown voltage $(E = IR)$.

Step 1.	$W = EI$	*Here is the power equation.*
Step 2.	$W = (IR) \times I$	*Here we substitute the Ohm's Law equation for the unknown E since $E = IR$.*

Step 3. $W = I^2R$ *Here we have the resultant equation, which allows us to compute power when we know current and resistance values.*

With this formula, a considerable amount of mathematics can be eliminated. Instead of having six steps to go through, we can now use four in solving the same problem.

Example: What is the power in an electric circuit where 2 amp. is flowing through a resistance of 5 ohms?

Step 1. $W = I^2R$ *Here is the power equation where current I and resistance R are known.*

Step 2. $W = 2^2 \times 5$ *Here are the actual values of current and resistance.*

Step 3. $W = 2 \times 2 \times 5$ *Here the equation is solved. Since 2 must be squared, it is the equivalent of multiplying it by itself; then its product is multiplied by 5.*

Step 4. $W = 20$ *Ans.*

In similar fashion, another form of the power equation in relation to Ohm's Law may be formulated. Thus, when voltage and resistance are known, the formula is

$$W = \frac{E^2}{R}$$

This gives us, in all, three formulas for electrical power just as we have three for Ohm's Law.

Electrical Power	Ohm's Law
$W = EI$	$E = IR$
$W = I^2R$	$I = \dfrac{E}{R}$
$W = \dfrac{E^2}{R}$	$R = \dfrac{E}{I}$

The resultant answer is the same as if we used Ohm's Law first to determine voltage or current as required before substituting in the basic $W = EI$ formula.

We have already noted that electrical devices are marked according to the voltages on which they may be used, such as a 110-volt electric light. Such devices are also rated in watts, indicating the amount of electric power they consume. Thus, a lamp may be marked "110 V.: 100 W," which means that it is designed to operate on a 110-volt circuit and will dissipate 100 watts of power.

Since electrical devices are usually marked with their wattage and voltage ratings, it is often desirable to be able to compute their resistance values or the amounts of current in amperes that will be drawn from the line. In some cases, the voltage must be computed when the wattage and current are known. Such problems may be solved with the following formulas:

$$R = \frac{W}{I^2}$$

$$I = \frac{W}{E}$$

$$E = \frac{W}{I}$$

Example: What is the resistance of a 200-watt lamp drawing 2 amp. from the line?

Step 1. $R = \dfrac{W}{I^2}$

Step 2. $R = \dfrac{200}{2^2} = \dfrac{200}{4} = 50$ ohms   *Ans.*

It is sometimes necessary in a problem to determine first what current is being drawn before the resistance can be found.

Example: A 200-watt lamp is connected to a 100-volt circuit. What is its resistance?

Note: Knowing the *wattage* and *voltage,* we must first find the *current* being drawn.

Step 1. $I = \dfrac{W}{E}$ *This is the formula to compute the current when wattage and voltage are known.*

Step 2. $I = \dfrac{200}{100} = 2$ amp.   *This is the current in amperes, which can now be used in the formula in Step 3.*

Step 3. $R = \dfrac{W}{I^2}$ *This is the formula for resistance when wattage and current are known.*

Step 4. $R = \dfrac{200}{2^2} = \dfrac{200}{4} = 50$ ohms   *Ans.*

6. Terms and Symbols

It is often convenient to use very large or very small values in speaking of watts, volts, current, and resistance. Thus, when using a value of 1,000 watts, it is simpler to say *1 kilowatt, kilo* meaning 1,000. If only $\frac{1}{1000}$ watt were being used, the term *1 milliwatt* would apply. *Milli* means one-thousandth $\left(\frac{1}{1000}\right)$. A *microwatt* would be one-millionth of a watt, and these prefixes are also used with the word *volt* as follows:

$$\text{Kilovolt} = 1{,}000 \text{ volts}$$
$$\text{Millivolt} = \frac{1}{1{,}000} \text{ volt}$$
$$\text{Microvolt} = \frac{1}{1{,}000{,}000} \text{ volt}$$

Small values of current may be measured in terms of *milliamperes* and *microamperes.*

$$\text{Milliampere} = \frac{1}{1{,}000} \text{ amp.}$$
$$\text{Microampere} = \frac{1}{1{,}000{,}000} \text{ amp.}$$

Larger values of resistance may be measured in terms of *megohms,* while small values may be measured in terms of *microhms.*

$$\text{Megohm} = 1,000,000 \text{ ohms}$$

$$\text{Microhm} = \frac{1}{1,000,000} \text{ ohm}$$

These commonly used prefixes have identifying symbols:

Prefix	Meaning	Symbol
Micro................	$\dfrac{1}{1,000,000}$	μ
Milli................	$\dfrac{1}{1,000}$	m
Kilo................	1,000	k
Mega................	1,000,000	M

The electrical units also have identifying symbols:

Unit	Symbol
Ampere...................	a
Volt.....................	v
Watt....................	w
Ohm....................	Ω

Examples:

10 kilovolts.........	10 kv.
5 megohms........	5 MΩ
100 milliamperes.....	100 ma

7. Series and Parallel Resistance

When resistors are connected in series, the total resistance offered to the current is the *sum* of their individual values. In Fig. 69, resistors R_1 and R_2 each measure 10 ohms. The total resistance is, therefore, 20 ohms ($R_1 + R_2 = R_{\text{total}}$).

We should note that resistors may be in series even if there are additional devices between them. Thus, in Fig. 70, the lamp (R_3) is connected between R_1 and R_2, and is thus part of the series circuit. If the resistance of the lamp were 50 ohms, the total circuit resistance would be $R_1 + R_2 + R_3$, or 70 ohms.

When resistors are in parallel, the current divides. In Fig. 71, R_1 and R_2 are in parallel. Some of the current will pass through R_1 and some through R_2.

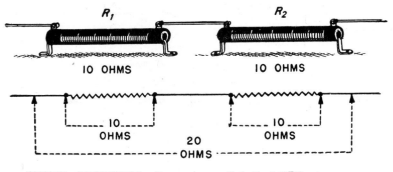

Fig. 69. When resistors are connected in series, the total resistance is the *sum* of the individual values

The voltage across parallel resistors is the same, but the amount of current passing through each branch will depend upon its resistance. Hence, in a circuit containing parallel resistances, the *total* resistance must be known before the current can be determined.

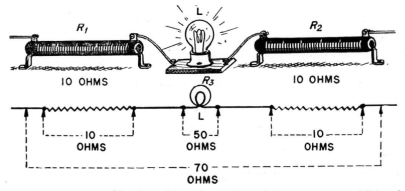

Fig. 70. The lamp in series with resistors R_1 and R_2 acts as an additional series resistor.

Since the current can flow through more than one path in a parallel circuit, it follows that the total opposition to the current flow must be less. This is exactly the case. *The total resistance of a bank of parallel resistors is always less than the resistance of any individual resistor.*

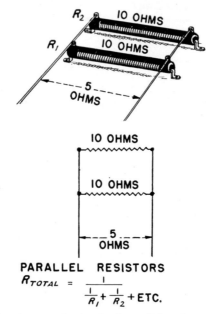

PARALLEL RESISTORS

$$R_{TOTAL} = \cfrac{1}{\frac{1}{R_1} + \frac{1}{R_2} + \text{ETC.}}$$

Fig. 71. The total resistance of a bank of parallel resistors is always less than the resistance of any individual resistor.

The formula used to determine the total effective resistance of parallel resistors is

$$R = \cfrac{1}{\dfrac{1}{R_1} + \dfrac{1}{R_2} + \text{etc.}}$$

This is termed *obtaining the reciprocal of the sum of the reciprocals. Reciprocal* is a mathematical term that means "the quotient obtained by dividing unity (1) by a number."

Example: One 10-ohm resistor and one 20-ohm resistor are connected in parallel. What is the total effective resistance?

Step 1. $R = \dfrac{1}{\dfrac{1}{R_1} + \dfrac{1}{R_2}}$ *This is the formula for parallel resistors.*

Step 2. $R = \dfrac{1}{\dfrac{1}{10} + \dfrac{1}{20}}$ *Here we have substituted actual values of R_1 and R_2.*

Step 3. $R = \dfrac{1}{\dfrac{1}{10} + \dfrac{1}{20} \diagdown \!\!20}$ *Here we have found the least common denominator 20 to solve the fractions. 10, the denominator in one fraction, and 20, that in the other, will divide into 20, the least common denominator.*

Step 4. $R = \dfrac{1}{\dfrac{2+1}{20}} = \dfrac{1}{\dfrac{3}{20}}$ *Here we mark down the fact that the denominator of one fraction (20) goes into 20 once, and the other denominator (10) goes into 20 twice. Adding them up we have 3.*

Step 5. $R = \dfrac{20}{3}$

$= 6.66$ ohms (*Ans.*)   *Here we solved the fraction below the main dividing line by inverting it. This is the reciprocal.*

Example: Two electric lamps having a resistance of 50 and 150 ohms, respectively, are connected across a 100-volt line. What is the *total* resistance across the line?

Step 1. $R_{total} = \dfrac{1}{\dfrac{1}{R_1} + \dfrac{1}{R_2}}$

Step 2. $R_{total} = \dfrac{1}{\dfrac{1}{50} + \dfrac{1}{150}}$

Step 3. $$R_{\text{total}} = \frac{1}{\dfrac{3+1}{150}} = \frac{1}{\dfrac{4}{150}}$$

Step 4. $$R_{\text{total}} = \frac{150}{4} = 37.5 \text{ ohms } Ans.$$

When all resistors in a parallel circuit are of the same value, the total effective value may be found by dividing the resistance of one unit by the number of units.

Example: Five 100-ohm resistors are connected in parallel. What is the total resistance?

$$\frac{100 \text{ (ohms value of one resistor)}}{5 \text{ (number of resistors in parallel)}} = 20 \text{ ohms}$$

Proof: By usual formula.

$$R = \frac{1}{\dfrac{1}{R_1} + \dfrac{1}{R_2} + \dfrac{1}{R_3} + \dfrac{1}{R_4} + \dfrac{1}{R_5}}$$

$$R = \frac{1}{\dfrac{1}{100} + \dfrac{1}{100} + \dfrac{1}{100} + \dfrac{1}{100} + \dfrac{1}{100}} \bigg\rangle 100$$

$$R = \frac{1}{\dfrac{5}{100}} = \frac{100}{5}$$

$$R = 20 \text{ ohms} \qquad\qquad Ans.$$

8. Power Dissipation and Efficiency

When current passes through a resistance, some of the electrical energy is dissipated in the form of heat. The amount of power expended can be found by using the formula $W = I^2R$.

Example: If a 100-ohm resistor has 2 amp. flowing through it, what power is being dissipated?

$$W = I^2R$$
$$W = 2 \times 2 \times 100$$
$$W = 400$$

Answer: 400 watts.

Resistors are rated in watts as well as in their ohmic value. A 100-ohm resistor rated at 10 watts will burn out quickly if required to dissipate 50 watts. It is, therefore, necessary to select a resistor for a given purpose bearing these two factors in mind:

  a. Ohmic resistance.
  b. Rating in watts.

When resistors are connected in a circuit, the total wattage is the *sum* of the individual wattage ratings. If three 100-watt resistors are used, for example, the total wattage would be 300 watts ($W_{total} = W_1 + W_2 + W_3$). In practice, circumstances may arise in which an exact duplicate resistor cannot be found for insertion within a circuit. In such cases, it is common practice to assemble a group of resistors connected in series or parallel as may be necessary to furnish a unit that is *electrically* the equivalent of the original device. Suppose a 100-watt 100-ohm resistor had to be duplicated. Two 200-ohm 50-watt resistors in parallel would serve as the electrical equivalent.

Proof:

$$\text{Total } W = W_1 + W_2 = 50 + 50 = 100 \text{ watts}$$
$$\text{Total } R = \frac{R \text{ (single unit)}}{N \text{ (number of resistors)}} = \frac{200}{2} = 100 \text{ ohms}$$

When resistors are connected in series, care must be taken that the amount of current flowing in the circuit does not exceed the rated value of the smallest unit, that is, smallest in current-carrying capacity. If a resistor is designed to pass 1 amp. and is used in series with a resistor that can pass 2 amp., the current in the circuit should not exceed 1 amp. This can be illustrated by considering two 100-ohm resistors, one designed to pass 1 amp. (therefore rated at 100 watts) and the other able to carry 2 amp. (therefore rated at 400 watts). If 1 amp. is flowing, both units will be required to dissipate only 100 watts each. If 2 amp. were to flow through the circuit, the 100-watt resistor would be dissipating four times its normal allowable value ($W = 2 \times 2 \times 100 = 400$) and would burn out. Safe practice requires the use of somewhat larger wattage units than mathematically required.

By comparing the actual wattage output of a circuit with the input value, it is possible to determine circuit efficiency.

$$\text{Efficiency} = \frac{\text{watts output}}{\text{watts input}}$$

It is never possible to obtain 100 per cent efficiency since some of the energy is always wasted, usually in the form of heat.

Example: A battery delivers 100 watts to a long line circuit terminated on an electric lamp rated at 75 watts. What is the efficiency?

$$\text{Efficiency} = \frac{\text{output}}{\text{input}} = \frac{75}{100} = 75\%$$

SUMMARY

1. A complete electric circuit in which an electric current will flow consists of a path of conductors to and from the source of e.m.f.

2. A series circuit is one in which the current does not divide into separate paths.

3. A parallel circuit is one in which the current divides into different paths.

4. A series-parallel circuit is a combination of series and parallel paths.

5. Ohm's Law may be stated in three ways:

$$E = IR \qquad\qquad R = \frac{E}{I} \qquad\qquad I = \frac{E}{R}$$

6. Voltage drop or *IR* drop is caused by current flowing through resistance and may be determined by Ohm's Law ($E_{drop} = IR$). The watt is the unit of electric power and may be stated as follows:

$$W = EI \qquad W = I^2R \qquad W = \frac{E^2}{R}$$

7. The value of resistors in series may be found by adding their individual values together.

$$R_{total} \text{ (in series)} = R_1 + R_2 + R_3 + \text{etc.}$$

8. The value of resistors in parallel is obtained by finding the reciprocal of the sum of the reciprocals of the individual resistances.

$$R_{total} \text{ (in parallel)} = \frac{1}{\dfrac{1}{R_1} + \dfrac{1}{R_2} + \dfrac{1}{R_3} + \text{etc.}}$$

9. Resistors must be selected for use with regard to both their wattage and ohmic resistance ratings.

Quiz: The Electric Circuit

This quiz will help you review the material just studied. See the quiz directions on page 24 before answering the questions below.

1. Ohm's Law may be stated as follows: *a.* $I = \dfrac{E}{R}$

b. $R = R_1 + R_2$ *c.* $W = I^2R$ *d.* $E = \dfrac{W}{I}$

2. A 100-ohm 100-watt resistor is connected in *series* with a 100-ohm 400-watt resistor. As a safety factor, the current through the circuit should not exceed: *a.* 4 amp.; *b.* 2 amp.; *c.* 1 amp.; *d.* $\frac{1}{2}$ amp.

3. A current of 5 amp. is flowing through a 50-ohm resistance. The power dissipation is: *a.* 1,250 watts; *b.* 250 watts; *c.* 125 watts; *d.* 25 watts.

4. When resistors are connected in series, the *total* resistance is: *a.* the equivalent of the smallest resistance value; *b.* the sum of the individual resistance values; *c.* the equivalent of the largest resistance value; *d.* less than the value of the smallest resistance.

5. Two 3-volt lamps are available for use in a specific circuit that has as its source of e.m.f. a 6-volt storage battery. Without additional equipment best operation would be obtained by connecting the two lamps in: *a.* parallel directly across the battery; *b.* parallel across one section of the battery; *c.* series-parallel with each other and in series with the battery; *d.* series with each other and the battery.

6. When three resistors are connected in parallel, the correct formula to use is:

a. $R_{\text{total}} = \dfrac{E}{I}$

b. $R_{\text{total}} = R_1 + R_2 + R_3$

c. $R_{\text{total}} = \dfrac{1}{\dfrac{1}{R_1} + \dfrac{1}{R_2} + \dfrac{1}{R_3}}$

d. $R_{\text{total}} = \dfrac{\dfrac{1}{R_1} + \dfrac{1}{R_2} + \dfrac{1}{R_3}}{1}$

7. In the construction of an electric heater, it is best to use: *a.* copper wire; *b.* platinum wire; *c.* carbon steel wire; *d.* nichrome steel wire.

8. In order to minimize the voltage drop in a circuit, it is necessary to use: *a.* proper gauge of heavy copper wire; *b.* very small-gauge nichrome steel wire; *c.* very small-gauge copper wire; *d.* medium-gauge nichrome steel wire.

9. A fuse is always connected in: *a.* parallel with load; *b.* series with load; *c.* series-parallel with load; *d.* either series or parallel, depending upon circuit constants.

10. Appliances that are connected to an electric outlet must be rated at the same: *a.* ampere-hours; *b.* wattage; *c.* voltage; *d.* amperage.

11. In an emergency, three 32-volt 100-watt electric lamps are being considered for use on a 100-volt circuit. The lamps should: *a.* not be used at all; *b.* be connected in parallel; *c.* be connected in series-parallel; *d.* be connected in series.

12. In the selection of a rheostat to regulate safely the amount of current in the circuit, the ohmic resistance of the rheostat should always be: *a.* less than the resistance required; *b.* more than the resistance required; *c.* exactly equal to the resistance required; *d.* 10 per cent less than the resistance required.

13. A 200-watt lamp intended to draw 2 amp. on a 100-volt circuit must be connected across a 200-volt source. The voltage-dropping resistor should measure: *a.* 5 ohms; *b.* 50 ohms; *c.* 100 ohms; *d.* 500 ohms.

14. Electric wiring in a house has parallel connections for all electrical devices. This is done to: *a.* allow the use of any individual device as required, without having all the other devices used simultaneously; *b.* economize on the power consumed; *c.* allow the use of smaller wire; *d.* prevent injury when the current is turned on.

15. A *milliampere* is the equivalent of: *a.* 1/10 amp.; *b.* 1/100 amp.; *c.* 1/1,000 amp.; *d.* 1/1,000,000 amp.

16. A thousand *milliwatts* is the equivalent of: *a.* 1 watt; *b.* 1 kilowatt (kw.); *c.* 1/1,000 watt; *d.* 100 watts.

17. One *megohm* is the equivalent of: *a.* 100 ohms; *b.* 1,000 ohms; *c.* 100,000 ohms; *d.* 1,000,000 ohms.

18. Two resistors measuring 100 and 200 ohms, respectively, are connected in series across a 100-volt source. If the voltage drop across the 200-ohm resistor is measured, it will be: *a.* equal to the drop across the 100-ohm resistor; *b.* less than the drop across the 100-ohm resistor; *c.* exactly twice the drop across the 100-ohm resistor; *d.* exactly one-half the drop across the 100-ohm resistor.

19. Two resistors measuring 100 and 200 ohms, respectively, are connected in *parallel* across a 100-volt source. If the voltage across the 200-ohm resistor is measured, it will be: *a.* higher than the voltage across the 100-ohm resistor; *b.* less than the voltage across the 100-ohm resistor; *c.* exactly twice the voltage across the 100-ohm resistor; *d.* equal to the voltage across the 100-ohm resistor.

20. A 100-volt electric outlet is protected by a 10-amp. fuse. Three devices rated at 500 watts, 200 watts, and 100 watts are connected in parallel across the line. The fuse will: *a.* burn out immediately; *b.* not burn out; *c.* burn out after a short period of time; *d.* burn out and restore the circuit automatically.

21. A battery delivers 200 watts to a line terminated by a lamp drawing only 100 watts. The *efficiency* of the circuit is: *a.* 25 per cent; *b.* 50 per cent; *c.* 75 per cent; *d.* 100 per cent.

22. If a circuit had *no* resistance whatsoever, the e.m.f. measured at the load would: *a.* exactly equal the e.m.f. at the source; *b.* be more than the e.m.f. at the source; *c.* be less than the e.m.f. at the source; *d.* automatically equal the voltage required by the load.

23. An electric switch is used to: *a.* increase the operating value of a fuse; *b.* decrease the operating value of a fuse; *c.* eliminate the need for a fuse; *d.* open and close an electric circuit as required.

24. The term *short circuit* means most nearly a: *a.* connection between two points where ordinarily no connection is intended; *b.* length of wire that has been cut too short; *c.* load connected to a circuit for only short intervals; *d.* light load connected to a circuit.

25. If, in error, a 200-volt electric stove and a 100-volt electric heater were connected in parallel across a 100-volt circuit, the voltage appearing across the electric stove would be: *a.* 100 volts; *b.* 150 volts; *c.* 200 volts; *d.* 300 volts.

Chapter 4. Electromagnetism

1. The Dielectric Field

By using an electroscope, it can be shown that the area surrounding a charged object is under the influence of the charge. To explain this phenomenon, it is assumed that unseen lines of force radiate from the charged object in all directions, and the area occupied by such lines is called a *field* (Fig. 72).

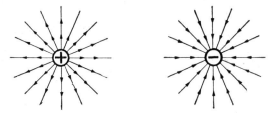

Fig. 72. Lines of force radiating from a charged object form the dielectric field.

The field around a charged object is termed an *electrostatic* or *dielectric* field. If two oppositely charged objects are brought into relationship with one another, the fields tend to meet. Some of

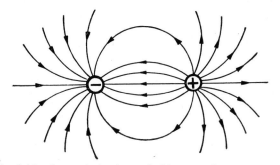

Fig. 73. The fields of oppositely charged objects tend to attract when brought toward one another.

the lines of force emanating from one object enter the other (Fig. 73). If objects bearing similar charges are brought towards each other, their fields tend to move away in accordance with the rule that like charges repel, unlike charges attract (Fig. 74).

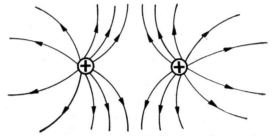

Fig. 74. The fields of similarly charged objects tend to repel one another.

Electrical energy may be said to be *stored* in the dielectric field as well as in the charge itself, because work can be accomplished by the use of the field alone. Thus, the leaves of the electroscope will change their position when subjected to the effect of the field.

2. The Electromagnetic Field

Since an electric current is actually a flow of electrons from one unbalanced atom to another, it would seem that a field should exist around the electrons themselves and also around the circuit through which they are passing. If a piece of wire is connected across a battery, and the wire held close to a pile of iron filings, the filings will cling to the wire as long as the current is flowing. When the current ceases, the iron filings drop away (Fig. 75).

The field around a wire carrying a current can be further demonstrated by sprinkling the filings on a cardboard through which the wire passes vertically (Fig. 76). The filings will arrange themselves in a circular pattern around the wire, showing a more dense concentration close to the wire and decreasing in density the farther away. This *circular* field around a conductor through which an electric current is flowing is known as the *electromagnetic field*, because the field produced by the current possesses magnetic ability, that is, the power to attract iron. It

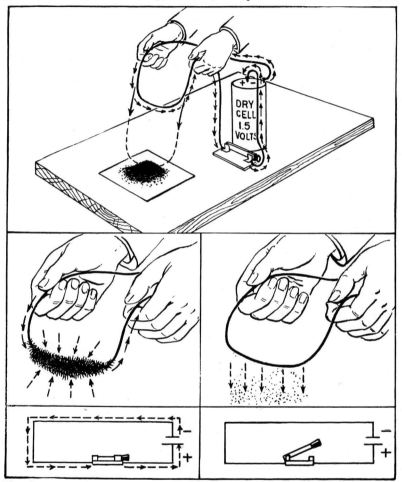

Fig. 75. A wire in which a current is flowing acts like a magnet and will attract iron filings.

should be noted that a *dielectric* field is associated with *nonconductors* (hence, the term *dielectric*), whereas a *magnetic* field is always associated with *conductors*.

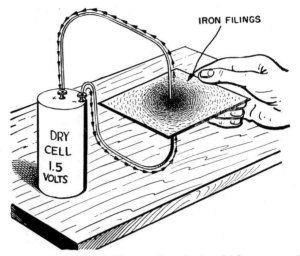

Fig. 76. The electromagnetic field around a wire in which a current is flowing forms a circular pattern.

However, it must also be understood that a magnetic field is capable of penetrating a dielectric (nonconductor) substance. This can be shown by using a horseshoe magnet (Figs. 76a and b). In Fig. 76a, the iron filings on *top* of the glass plate are in complete disarray. The magnet, some distance away from the filings, is not exerting any magnetic influence on them. When the magnet is placed *under* the glass (Fig. 76b), the iron filings *on top* of the glass arrange themselves in a typical pattern. Thus, the lines of force emanating from the poles of the magnet are acting in exactly the same fashion as occurs when a wire conducting electricity produces the electromagnetic field shown in Fig. 76. It can thus be seen that the magnetic field can penetrate a dielectric, in this case, the glass plate. If a metallic plate were substituted for the glass plate, such action would not occur. This would indicate that a magnetic field cannot easily penetrate a conductor. Advantage of this fact is taken in many electrical devices by using a *shield* to prevent a magnetic field from operating. The shield (discussed in Chap. 6) is a piece of metal cut in suitable form to surround the device producing the field.

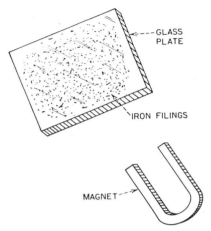

GLASS PLATE

IRON FILINGS

MAGNET

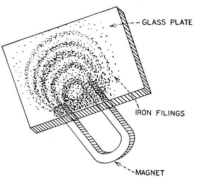

GLASS PLATE

IRON FILINGS

MAGNET

Fig. 76a. Iron filings on top of glass plate are in complete disarray when magnet is some distance away.

Fig. 76b. When horseshoe magnet is placed *under* the glass, its field penetrates through the glass, and the iron filings arrange themselves in a distinctive pattern under the influence of the field.

LOADSTONE

IRON FILINGS

Fig. 77. Loadstone is a natural magnet.

3. Magnetism

The property of attracting iron, known as *magnetism*, is possessed by a number of substances found in a natural state. Manufactured devices are known as *magnets*, the latter being called *electromagnets* when their operation depends upon a flow of current, and *artificial* or *permanent* magnets when their operation is self-inherent.

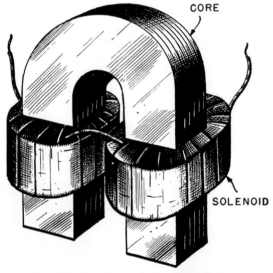

Fig. 78. One form of electromagnet.

A typical natural magnet is the *loadstone* (Fig. 77), known since ancient times. This material is actually an iron ore, and its magnetic properties were ascribed to supernatural causes by the men of long ago who first noted its singular action in attracting iron.

Artificial magnets can be made by stroking a loadstone or an artificial magnet with a piece of iron or steel. The most effective method, however, is to insert the iron within a coil of wire through which a current is flowing.

Electromagnets, in fact, are simply coils (called *solenoids*) with an iron or steel core (Fig. 78). When the core is removed, it can be used as a magnet by itself, as it retains its magnetic properties. This is known as *residual magnetism*—magnetism that remains in the iron after it is removed from a magnetic field. The terms *bar*, *horseshoe*, and *ring* are often used to describe the physical shape of a magnet. A bar magnet, as its name implies, is a straight piece of iron, while a horseshoe magnet (Fig. 79) is

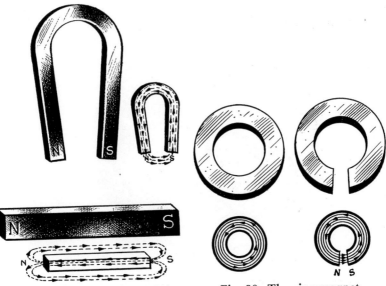

Fig. 79. The horseshoe and bar magnets.

Fig. 80. The ring magnet.

curved in the shape of an exaggerated horseshoe. The latter type of magnet is used where it is desirable to concentrate the magnetic field existing between the two ends, called the *poles*. Where it is necessary to concentrate the magnetic field still further, a ring magnet is used (Fig. 80). In this type of magnet, there is no external field as the lines of force are completely concentrated within the core itself. If, however, the ring is broken at any point so that an air gap is formed, an external field will be found to exist between the two newly created poles.

4. Magnetic Poles

If a bar magnet is suspended by a string and allowed to come to rest, it will be found that one of the two ends will always point in the direction of the earth's North Pole; this end of the magnet is known as the *north pole*; the other as the *south pole*.

The earth itself is a huge magnet, but it should be noted that the North Pole of the earth is really its south pole, considering it from the point of view of its acting as a magnet. That is why

Fig. 81. The compass is a bar magnet. Its north pole will point to the earth's North Pole. The North Pole of the earth is, in reality, a south pole considering it from the point of view of its acting as a magnet.

the *north* pole of a compass (which is simply a bar magnet mounted on a pivot) points toward it (Fig. 81).

If two bar magnets are suspended close together, it will be found that the north pole of one magnet will be attracted to the south pole of the other. If a bar magnet is held close to the suspended magnet, it will either move toward, or be repelled from, that magnet depending upon the polarity of the poles (Fig. 82). *Like poles repel; unlike poles attract.* In other words, exactly the same laws of electrical attraction and repulsion exist for magnetic poles as for electric charges. That is why the positive sign (+) is often used to indicate the north pole and the negative sign (−) the south pole of a magnet.

The magnetic field surrounding a magnet is assumed to leave by way of the north pole, and to return via the south.

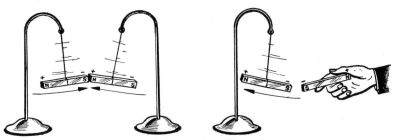

Fig. 82. Like poles repel; unlike poles attract.

5. Magnetic Induction

If a magnet (Fig. 83) is placed on a table near a piece of iron, it will be found that the iron has become a magnet as well. The field leaving the north pole of the original magnet enters the piece of iron, creating a south pole at that point. Leaving

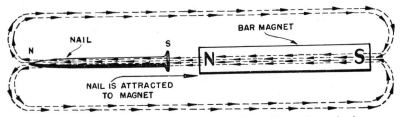

Fig. 83. Magnetic induction. The magnetic lines of force from the bar magnet cause the nail to become magnetized with the north pole of the nail facing the south pole of the magnet. This causes the nail to be attracted to the magnet.

the other end of the piece, it forms a north pole there and then reenters the south pole of the original magnet. Inducing a magnet to be formed in this manner by placing the object within a magnetic field is called *magnetic induction*. It is because of magnetic induction that iron is attracted to a magnet. The originally unmagnetized iron actually becomes a magnet itself with an *unlike* pole closest to the pole of the original magnet. Following the rule that unlike poles attract, the newly formed magnet tends to move toward, and attach itself to, the original magnet. It will be shown later that magnetic induction plays an important part in the transfer of energy between closed circuits, and many practical applications of electricity are the direct result of this phenomenon.

6. Electron Theory of Magnetism

As has been shown, a circular magnetic field is formed around a wire through which a current is flowing (Fig. 84). It is this

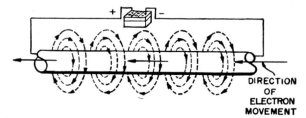

Fig. 84. A circular magnetic field is formed around a wire through which a current is flowing.

magnetic field, and *not* the copper wire itself (copper being a nonmagnetic substance), that causes iron filings to attach themselves to the wire.

In a sense, we can think of the field as acting like a group of bar magnets surrounding the wire in a fan-shaped arrangement somewhat like the spokes of a wheel, as shown in Fig. 85.

Now, if the straight length of wire is wound into a loop, the magnetic effect becomes even greater. It is just as if the individual bar magnets shown in Fig. 85 were all mounted together, and the resultant effect is just as if a single, more powerful, bar magnet were passed right through the center of the loop perpendicularly to its plane (Fig. 86).

In other words, a current through a conductor arranged as a coil or loop creates a magnetic effect exactly similar to the effect created by a bar magnet. The lines of force pass through the center of the coil in perpendicular (straight up-and-down) fashion. These lines of force, just as did the bar magnet to which we have compared it, produce the effect of a north pole and a south pole.

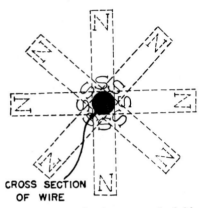

CROSS SECTION OF WIRE

Fig. 85. The circular magnetic field around a conductor can be imagined as a series of bar magnets arranged in spokelike fashion.

Since an electric current is a *movement of electrons*, it should follow that the magnetic action we have observed is a direct result of such electronic movement. Each electron revolving around its nucleus in its particular orbit is completing, in effect, an electric circuit or loop, just as did the total electron flow (current) in the loop of wire. Since we have seen that the loop of wire under such circumstances creates the effect of a bar magnet, it is logical to assume that *a similar magnetic field appears around the electron orbit*, and that it, too, creates the effect of an infinitesimally small bar magnet itself (Fig. 87). It is this assumption that gives rise to the *Electron Theory of Magnetism*.

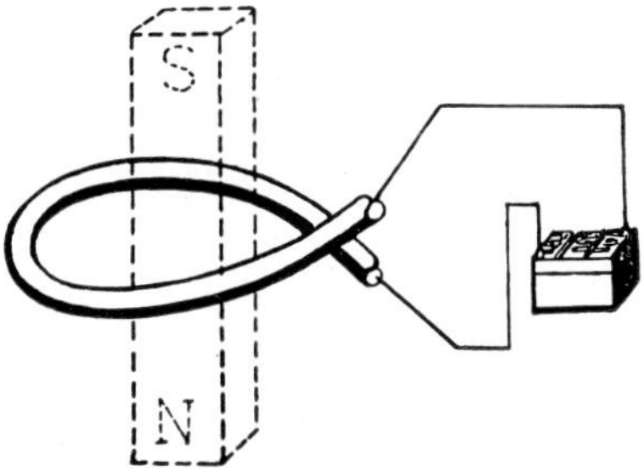

Since all matter is composed of atoms which, in turn, include electrons as component structural units, it would seem that all substances should possess magnetic properties. We know this is not the case, however. In terms of this theory, only those substances can be magnetized whose electron orbits can be lined

Fig. 86. A conducting loop through which a current is flowing has a magnetic effect similar to that of a bar magnet.

up so that their individual fields aid each other, instead of opposing and neutralizing each other (Fig. 88).

Thus, when a piece of iron is inserted within a magnetic field set up by a current flowing through a solenoid, the electron orbits of the iron atoms tend to arrange themselves so that each individual electron's magnetic field acts in the same direction. This action gives an effect of a magnetic field that seems to emanate from the iron itself.

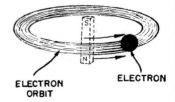

ELECTRON ORBIT   ELECTRON

Fig. 87. The electron orbit, just as does a loop of wire, acts like a bar magnet.

Some materials have atoms whose electron orbits refuse to arrange themselves readily to produce a magnetic effect. Such materials are called *nonmagnetic*. Materials like iron, steel, and certain other alloys of iron readily accept magnetization.

An apparent proof of the Electron Theory of Magnetism is found in the fact that heating or jarring a permanent magnet will cause weakening or loss of its magnetic properties. The heating or jarring disarranges the axes of the electron orbits so that the fields no longer aid each other.

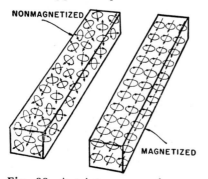

NONMAGNETIZED

MAGNETIZED

Fig. 88. A substance may become magnetized only when the individual electron orbits can be lined up so that their magnetic fields aid each other.

7. Electromagnets

The simplest electromagnet is a wire through which a current is flowing. If the wire is now wound into a coil or solenoid, the strength of the magnetic field is increased to a very large degree. This increased strength is due to the fact that the field around each turn of the coil adds its effect to the fields of all the other turns, just as would occur if a number of permanent magnets were tied together. The resultant magnetic field is the sum total of *all* the individual fields (Fig. 89).

The comparison shown in Fig. 90 may aid in understanding this action. We have already seen how a coil or loop of wire in which a current is flowing acts like a bar magnet. If two bar magnets are joined together, the magnetic effect will be doubled.

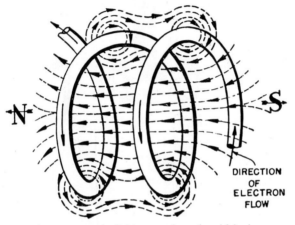

Fig. 89. The resultant magnetic field around a solenoid is the sum total of all the individual fields around the conductor.

If three magnets are so joined, the effect is still greater, as shown by their ability to lift a heavier weight. In similar fashion, coiling the wire increases the total magnetic strength of the "electromagnet" that is formed.

The strength of an electromagnetic field is determined by

a. The number of turns of wire forming the solenoid
b. The strength of the current in amperes flowing through the solenoid
c. The material of which the core is made (if any)
d. The size of the core (if used)

The effect of the core, usually made of iron or steel, on the strength of the field can be easily shown by an experiment. If a solenoid is held near a suspended bar magnet, and a current passed through the winding, the magnet will be attracted to, or repelled from, the solenoid depending upon the respective polarities of the magnet and the coil (Fig. 91). If an iron bar is

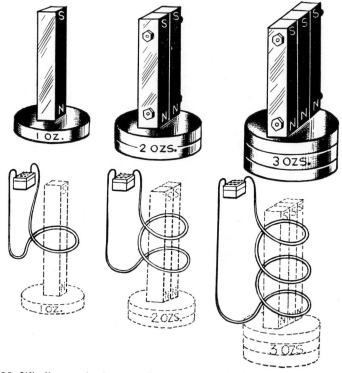

Fig. 90. Winding a wire into a coil concentrates the lines of force. The spiraling acts to produce the same effect as if a number of bar magnets were fastened together, increasing the over-all magnetic force.

now inserted within the coil, the degree of attraction or repulsion will be greatly intensified (Fig. 92).

The reason a core increases the magnetic strength is that the lines of force forming the magnetic field can be concentrated and thus intensified (Fig. 93). Magnetic lines of force, just like an electric current, will flow more readily through a good con-

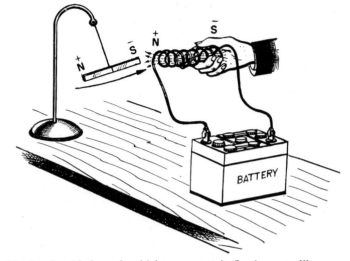

Fig. 91. A solenoid through which a current is flowing acts like a magnet.

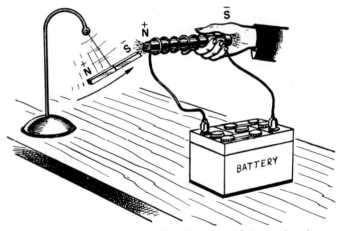

Fig. 92. Inserting an iron core within the solenoid intensifies the magnetic action. Iron has a higher permeability than air; therefore, the lines of force can be concentrated and thus "intensified."

ductor. Iron is 'an excellent conductor of magnetic lines of force, compared to air.

The direction of the circular lines of force around a conductor can be determined by the *left-hand rule*. If the wire is grasped in the *left* hand with the thumb pointing in the direction of the *electron flow*, the fingers will point in the direction of the lines of force (Fig. 94).

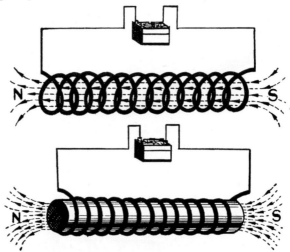

Fig. 93. The iron core concentrates the lines of force thus strengthening the magnetic effect.

The polarity of a solenoid can also be determined by the *left-hand* rule*. If the coil or solenoid is grasped in the *left* hand so that the fingers follow around the coil *in the direction of electron movement*, the *thumb* will point toward the *north* pole (Fig. 95). The electron movement is from a point of *negative* potential to one of positive potential. Hence, electrons enter the coil at the

* The student should not be confused by the term *right-hand rule* used in many texts. Before the advent of the electron theory, electricity was supposed to flow from positive to negative. As we know, only *negative* electrons move from atom to atom. Hence, in this textbook, we consider electricity as flowing from a point of *negative* potential to a point of positive potential.

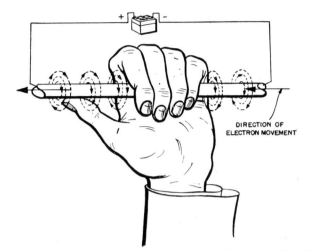

Fig. 94. The left-hand rule. This rule can be used to determine the direction of the lines of force around a conductor.

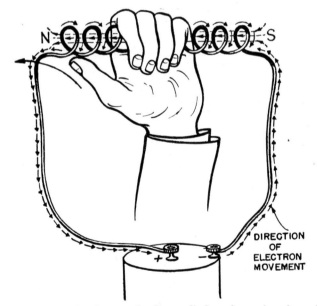

Fig. 95. The left-hand rule can also be applied to determine the polarity of a solenoid.

point of contact with the negative terminal of the source of e.m.f.

8. Magnetic Units

The term *flux* is generally used to describe the lines of force comprising a magnetic field. The strength of the flux (corresponding to the number of lines of force forming the field) is, in turn, determined by the *magnetomotive force* (m.m.f.). Magnetomotive force corresponds in a sense to the e.m.f. needed to produce a flow of current, and the flux can be considered as corresponding to the current that results when an e.m.f. is applied. The resistance that is apparent in any substance to the creation of a flux is called *reluctance*. A material such as iron has very little reluctance and is, therefore, easily magnetized.

Thus, it can be seen that in dealing with magnetism, we have three units corresponding to the three units of Ohm's Law.

$$I = \frac{E}{R} \text{ (Ohm's Law)}$$

$$\text{Flux } (\Phi) = \frac{\text{magnetomotive force (m.m.f.)}}{\text{reluctance } (R)}$$

Magnetomotive force is determined by multiplying the current in amperes by the number of turns of wire forming the solenoid. This is known as the *ampere turns*. If a solenoid has 100 turns of wire carrying 1 amp., the m.m.f. generated would be the same as if a solenoid of 10 turns were carrying 10 amp.

$$\text{M.m.f.} = I \times T = 1 \times 100 = 100$$
$$\text{M.m.f.} = I \times T = 10 \times 10 = 100$$

Permeability is the reciprocal (opposite) of reluctance. Reluctance referred to the degree of resistance to magnetization. Therefore, permeability is the degree of acceptance of magnetization. The higher the permeability of a core, the greater the strength of a given electromagnet. Nonmagnetic substances are considered to have a permeability of 1. Magnetic materials have permeabilities much higher than that figure. In computing the strength of an electromagnet having a metallic core, which is generally the rule, the factor of the permeability of the core metal must also be considered.

When a magnetic substance has been magnetized to its fullest extent, it is said to be *saturated*. This occurs when the orbits of *all* the electrons have been turned around so that their axes are

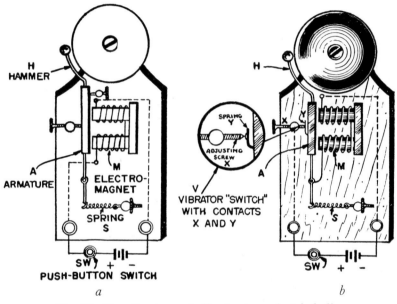

Fig. 96. Nonvibrator and vibrator type electric bells.

all in line and acting in a single direction. When a magnetic substance has reached the saturation point, the use of any additional magnetomotive force cannot increase the magnetic field further.

9. Use of Magnetic Fields

Magnets of all kinds and their magnetic fields play an extremely important part in electricity. The principles involved are an integral part of the construction and operation of many pieces of electrical equipment such as the ordinary bell, the telegraph, the relay, electric meters, the telephone, generators, motors, and many other devices.

1. *The Electric Bell.* In Fig. 96*a*, the electromagnet *M* is activated when the push-button switch *SW* is pressed. This causes the armature *A* upon which the hammer *H* is mounted to be drawn down upon the magnet core. As this occurs, the hammer is compelled to hit the bell. In this bell, a single sound is heard each time the switch is closed. *Nonvibrator* bells of this type are often used for signals, such as certain fire alarms.

In order to have a sustained ringing as long as the switch is closed, another method must be used (Fig. 96*b*). This is known as a *vibrator* type of bell, such as is commonly used in the home. In order to follow its operation, trace the circuit carefully. In addition to the regular push-button switch *SW*, an additional switch *V* is connected in series. This is the *vibrator* and consists of one contact *Y* mounted on a spring, which is, in turn, fastened to the armature. The remaining contact *X* is attached to a point where it normally is in full contact with *Y*, closing the circuit at that point.

When the regular push-button switch is closed, the current flows through the solenoid *M*, then through the vibrator *V*, and back to the battery through the switch *SW*. As this occurs, the armature is attracted to the electromagnet, and hammer *H* hits the bell. Just as the armature moved to the right, however, contacts *X* and *Y* are drawn apart, and the electromagnet releases the armature since the circuit is opened. As the armature is released, contacts *X* and *Y* close, and the armature is re-attracted to the magnet, causing the hammer to hit the bell again. This action is repeated as long as the main push-button switch is held closed.

2. *The Simple Telegraph.* In the simple telegraph circuit, the single-sound type of bell is replaced by a *sounder*, and the push-button switch by a *key* (Fig. 97). Note that the symbol for the key is the same as for any switch because that is exactly what it is. Its physical construction is somewhat different, as it **is**

designed to be operated in a quick succession of code groups representing the letters of the alphabet.

When the key is open, the armature is normally in contact with the upper part of the sounder, but as the key is pressed, closing the circuit, it is drawn downward causing a sharp click. The length of the click or group of clicks indicates to the operator what letter of the alphabet is being transmitted.

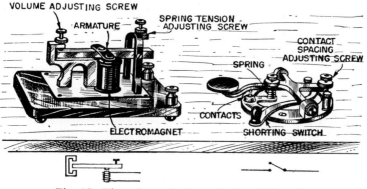

Fig. 97. The telegraph "sounder" and "key."

Suppose the letter *A* were to be transmitted. The code for this letter is one dot (a short click) followed by one dash (a long click). The key in this case would be pressed down for a brief period, released, and then held down for a period approximately three times as long, and then released. The operator, hearing one short and then one long click from the sounder would record the combination as the letter *A*. In this manner, entire messages are sent.

In practical operation, in order to transmit to more than one location, a number of keys and sounders are connected in series (Fig. 98). When a message is *not* being transmitted, all keys must be closed. If any one key were left open, and the operator at another position tried to communicate with the other station, he could not send a current through the line. In other words, the circuit would be open.

In Fig. 99 the same type of circuit is shown using a *ground return*. By using the earth as one "leg" or conductor of the circuit, a good deal of wire can be saved. A ground-return circuit, however, offers operational difficulties under certain conditions and, therefore, is not in general use. The full *metallic pair* (the use of two complete conductors) is the preferable procedure.

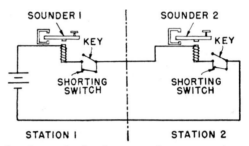

Fig. 98. A basic telegraph circuit connecting two stations. Note that the keys are kept closed electrically by the shorting switches. The switch is opened when the key is to be used.

3. *The Relay.* On long telegraph circuits, the resistance of the line may be so high that the amount of e.m.f. required to force a current through to another position may be too great for economical operation. The high voltage may also be dangerous. To avoid this, a relay, which is an electrically operated switch, may be used (Fig. 100). Relays may be made very sensitive, that is, capable of responding to a small amount of current. In turn, they may control circuits in which high voltages and cur-

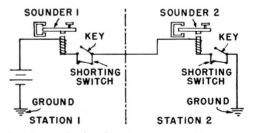

Fig. 99. A basic telegraph circuit using a ground-return circuit instead of a return wire.

rents may exist. When the key is closed, the armature is attracted by the relay electromagnet closing contact XY.

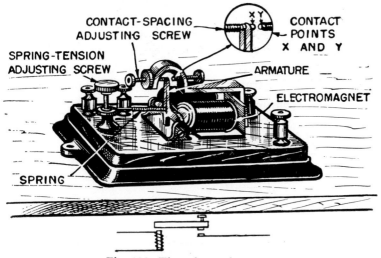

Fig. 100. The telegraph relay.

These contacts, in turn, close the second circuit operating the sounder in exactly the same manner as if a key were used (Fig. 101).

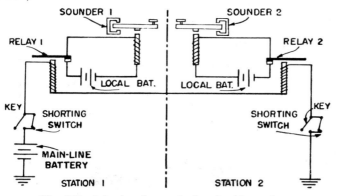

Fig. 101. A basic telegraph circuit using relays.

Relays may be of the open-circuit type as indicated in the telegraph circuit, that is, have contacts normally open. Such units are also called *make* relays as contact is made when the electromagnetic operation occurs. Closed circuit (break) relays have their contacts normally closed, opening (breaking) the circuit when the relay is activated. Such relays are often used as *overload* devices to break a circuit when an excessive current appears. This is illustrated in Fig. 102, where the overload relay

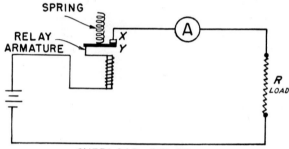

OVERLOAD RELAY

Fig. 102. An overload relay circuit. The contacts separate and open the circuit when there is an excessive current.

is connected in series with a load. Note that the solenoid of the electromagnet forms part of the complete circuit, the current flowing from the battery, through the solenoid, through the contact points X and Y and, thence, through the meter and load back to the battery.

As long as a predetermined amount of current flows through the circuit, the relay being adjusted accordingly, the magnetic strength of the relay solenoid is insufficient to draw the armature down and break the contact at XY. When a higher amount of current appears, the magnetization is sufficient to break the contacts and open the circuit. Used in this manner, overload relays replace or supplement fuses.

Underload relays operate in exactly the opposite manner. Here, the contacts are normally kept closed, but are opened if the voltage across the solenoid drops below a given value. This device is often used in battery-charging circuits to prevent the battery from discharging into the generator if the charging voltage drops too low. The charging voltage is normally higher than the battery voltage. The current furnished by the charger reaches the battery through the contacts on the overload device. However, in this instance, contact points X and Y are *only* held together if there is sufficient current to magnetize the relay,

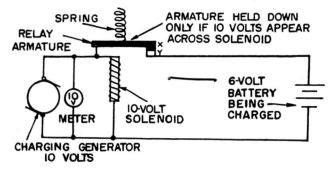

Fig. 103. An underload relay circuit. The spring will lift the armature and separate the contacts when the current in the solenoid drops too low.

and hold the armature down (Fig. 103). If the current drops, as would occur if the charging voltage decreased, the magnetic effect weakens, releasing the armature and breaking the circuit. In the use of this type of relay, it is generally necessary to close the circuit by pushing the contacts together manually. Otherwise, no current could flow through what would actually be an open circuit.

Overload and underload relays are often called *circuit breakers*, since they are used as safety devices to break a circuit when an excessive or insufficient current flow exists, as the individual case requires.

4. *The Basic DC Meter*. The basic DC meter, known as the *D'Arsonval* type, also depends upon the operation of magnets and their magnetic fields. In this type of meter, there are actually two magnets; one is a fixed permanent magnet of horseshoe shape; the other is an electromagnet (Fig. 104). The electro-magnet, consisting of a spool of wire wound on a frame, is mounted on a pivot and held in place by a spring directly between the poles of the fixed magnet. When a current is caused to flow through the coil, it becomes a magnet with a north pole opposite the north pole of the fixed magnet. Since like poles repel, it is forced to move on its pivot away from its normal position. The degree of repulsion will depend upon the amount of current flowing

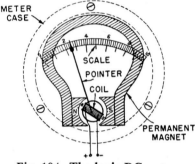

Fig. 104. The basic DC meter.

through the coil, which determines its strength as a magnet. The needle mounted on the coil will, of course, move with it, and the degree of movement will be recorded on a calibrated scale.

In order to be certain that a north pole appears on the proper side of the coil, the polarity of the current entering it must be carefully observed. The polarity of any electromagnet operating on direct current will depend upon the direction of current flow. Hence, all DC meters are marked with the symbols + and − and must be connected to a circuit properly. The rule, just as in connecting a battery charger, is "Plus to plus; minus to minus."

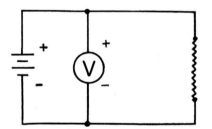

Fig. 105. A voltmeter is always con-nected in *parallel* to the source of e.m.f. to be measured. In DC circuits, the polarity must be observed.

Other types of meters will be studied later, but for the present we should know that the basic DC meter just described may be used as either a voltmeter

(to measure e.m.f. or volts) or as an ammeter (to measure cur-rent or amperes).

When used as a voltmeter, the resistance of the coil must be high, or a series resistor (called a *multiplier*) must be used with it. This is due to the fact that a voltmeter is always connected in *parallel* to a source of e.m.f. (Fig. 105), the e.m.f. or voltage representing a difference of potential between two points of a

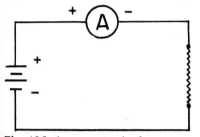

Fig. 106. An ammeter is always connected in *series* with the circuit.

circuit. If the resistance were too low, an excessive current would flow through the coil, burning it out. In addition, a low resistance drawing a considerable amount of current would, in itself, act as a considerable load on the source of e.m.f., and thus lower the available voltage automatically. This prevents an accurate indication of the voltage actually available for useful work.

On the other hand, an ammeter, which measures the rate of current flow past a given point within the circuit, must be of low resistance, as it is always connected in *series* with a circuit (Fig. 106). Low resistance will not prevent the free flow of current and thus does not produce a high voltage drop (*IR* loss) across the meter itself. This avoids a wastage of power where it serves no useful purpose, since it is intended that all available power be delivered to the load.

5. *The Simple Telephone Circuit.* The operation of the simple telephone circuit is of particular interest as it not only illustrates an additional way in which a magnetic field plays an important part in communications, but illustrates as well how a message may be transmitted by a pulsating direct current. A direct current flows in one direction and is uniform in magnitude, while a pulsating direct current is one in which the magnitude varies, even though the direction of flow remains the same. In the telegraph circuit, as the key was closed the DC impulse transmitted reached its full magnitude almost instantly and returned to zero quickly as the key was opened. This is shown in Fig. 107, in which the current change from zero to maximum is plotted in graph form against the time element involved in transmission.

The moment the key is pressed the DC current begins to rise to its full value, maintains itself at that magnitude while the

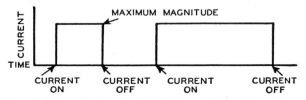

Fig. 107. Pure DC impulses reach their full magnitude almost instantly. The *square wave* illustrates a perfect telegraph signal.

circuit is closed, and drops to zero quickly as the key is again opened. In reaching its full magnitude, and in dropping back to zero from that point, a certain time element is involved though it appears to be instantaneous.

The graph in Fig. 107 indicates the wave shape of the transmitted signal. For purposes of simplicity, a square wave is

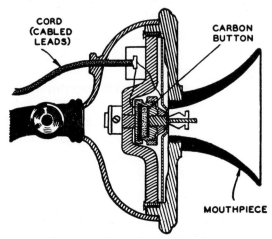

Fig. 108. The carbon microphone.

indicated, but this ideal wave form is seldom obtained in practice due to a number of factors, which will be studied in later chapters.

By the use of a carbon microphone (Fig. 108), it is possible to vary the magnitude of a DC current above and below a given level as sound strikes the diaphragm (Fig. 109).

When a person speaks, he causes the air to move forward in a series of waves in all directions, just as a pebble causes waves to appear when dropped into a pool. The waves of sound advance outward, causing the column of air to vibrate back and

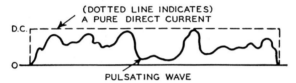

Fig. 109. A pulsating direct current varies in magnitude but not in direction.

forth. As the wave advances, it compresses the column. As it moves backward slightly, the pressure is reduced, and this is called *rarefaction* (Fig. 110).

This vibrating wave collides with the microphone diaphragm and causes it to vibrate in exactly the same way as did the column of air. When the diaphragm is moved in on the carbon granules (comprising the *button*), they are pressed more closely together and the button resistance is decreased. When the diaphragm moves in the opposite direction, the granules occupy more space, thus *increasing* the resistance. This varying resistance causes the normal value of DC current to pulsate or vary above and below the current value when the diaphragm is motionless.

If the construction of a telephone receiver (Fig. 111) is now examined, it will be found to include a metal diaphragm so mounted within a case that it is affected by two magnetic fields. One field is produced by a fixed magnet and exists at all times, thus keeping the diaphragm under a constant strain. The other field is produced by an electromagnet and appears, of course, only when the electromagnet is activated by a current.

If the windings of this electromagnet are connected in a

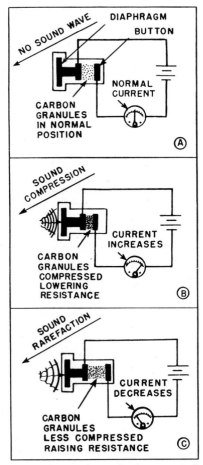

Fig. 110. Sound compression and rarefaction vary the resistance of the carbon button. This action produces a pulsating direct current.

series with a microphone and battery, the pulsating direct current that appears as the resistance of the circuit is varied will alternately weaken and strengthen the electromagnetic field, which, in turn, will cause the metal diaphragm to vibrate back and forth as the field varies in strength. This vibration

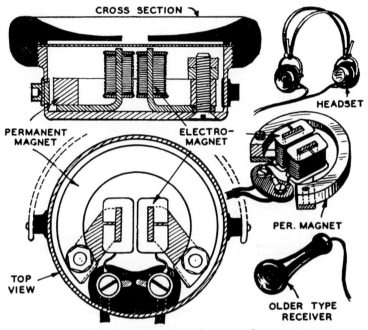

Fig. 111. The telephone receiver.

against the air will reproduce the original sound wave that caused the microphone diaphragm to vibrate in the first instance (Fig. 112).

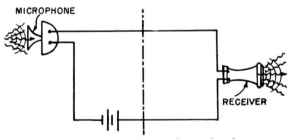

Fig. 112. The basic telephone circuit.

Modern telephone construction usually calls for the inclusion of both carbon microphone and the receiver in a single assembly for greater convenience (Fig. 113).

6. *Motors and Generators.* Motors and generators, as well as other types of meters and electromagnetic devices, will be studied in detail in subsequent chapters. Their importance in the field of

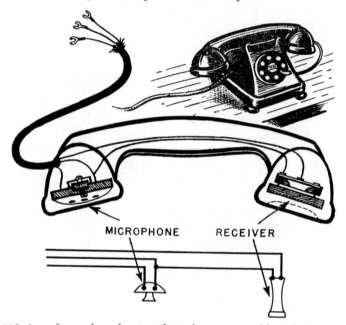

MICROPHONE   RECEIVER

Fig. 113. A modern microphone and receiver mounted in a single assembly.

electricity is so great that separate and complete treatment is desirable.

SUMMARY

1. A dielectric field consists of lines of force emanating from a charged body.

2. An electromagnetic field consists of lines of force emanating from a conductor through which a current is flowing.

3. A magnetic field consists of lines of force emanating from any magnet, and the term is used interchangeably with *electromagnetic field*.

4. The electromagnetic field is distinguished from the dielectric field in that the former possesses magnetic properties, that is, the ability to attract iron and its alloys.

5. A substance possessing inherently, or having artificially created, the property to attract iron is known as a *magnet*.

6. An electromagnet is a coil or solenoid, usually with an iron core, that has its electromagnetic field created when a current is passed through the winding.

7. The lines of force in a magnetic field comprise the flux. The flux is created by the action of the magnetomotive force, and both bear a relationship to the reluctance (magnetic resistance) of the substance being magnetized.

$$\text{Flux } (\Phi) = \frac{\text{magnetomotive force (m.m.f.)}}{\text{reluctance } (R)}$$

8. Permeability is the degree of acceptance of magnetization, and is the reciprocal of reluctance. The higher the permeability of the core, the greater the strength of a magnet, which in an electromagnet is also dependent upon the ampere turns.

9. Saturation occurs when a substance can accept no additional magnetization.

10. The poles of a magnet are the regions where the magnetic lines of force are most concentrated and the magnetic effect most pronounced. The north pole of a magnet is the point where the lines of force seem to leave the magnet; the south pole is the point where the lines of force seem to enter.

11. To determine the polarity of a solenoid, the left-hand rule can be used. The rule states: "If the coil or solenoid is grasped in the *left* hand so that the fingers follow around the coil in the direction in which the *electrons* are flowing, the thumb will point toward the *north pole*."

Quiz: Electromagnetism

This quiz will help you review the material just studied. See the quiz directions given on page 24 before answering the questions below.

1. In order to reproduce sound through the telephone receiver, it is necessary to use: *a.* 60-cycle DC; *b.* a nonpulsating direct current; *c.* a pulsating direct current; *d.* a highly damped wave.

2. The poles of a magnet are the regions where the: *a.* magnetic lines of force are most concentrated; *b.* magnetic lines of force are least concentrated; *c.* dielectric effect is most pronounced; *d.* dielectric effect is least pronounced.

3. One of the following statements is correct: *a.* Electrical energy cannot be stored in a dielectric field. *b.* Electrical energy can be stored in a dielectric field. *c.* Electrical energy can be stored in a conductor connected to a ground. *d.* Electrical energy can be stored in a conductor under a load.

4. The term *flux* means most nearly the: *a.* magnetic resistance of a magnetized substance; *b.* strength of the magnetomotive force; *c.* conductance of the magnetized substance in a magnetic field; *d.* lines of force in a magnetic field.

5. A *dielectric field* may be defined as the: *a.* area occupied by the lines of force radiating from an artificial magnet; *b.* area through which electronic movement occurs within a conductor; *c.* area occupied by the lines of force radiating from a charged object; *d.* area through which electronic movement occurs within an insulator.

6. Magnetism is that property of a substance that permits it to attract: *a.* lead; *b.* copper; *c.* carbon; *d.* iron.

7. An electromagnetic field will penetrate through: *a.* copper; *b.* glass; *c.* brass; *d.* silver.

8. In order to form an electromagnet, it is necessary to use a: *a.* solid piece of iron; *b.* copper wire wound around a glass rod; *c.* copper wire wound around an iron core; *d.* horseshoe-shaped magnet made from copper.

9. A magnetic field is associated with: *a.* a conductor; *b.* an insulator; *c.* a dielectric; *d.* a nonconductor.

10. The fields produced by an electromagnet and a fixed magnet are: *a.* entirely different; *b.* somewhat different; *c.* almost the same except for their action; *d.* exactly the same.

11. When the core of an electromagnet is removed, it retains some of its magnetic properties. This is due to the: *a.* internal resistance; *b.* residual magnetism; *c.* magnetic reluctance; *d.* dielectric field.

12. In order to form a solenoid, it is necessary to: *a.* rub steel on loadstone; *b.* insert steel into an electrolyte; *c.* wind a coil of wire; *d.* use a core of solid iron.

13. The *polarity* of an electromagnet will depend upon the: *a.* strength of current; *b.* voltage of source; *c.* ampere turns of coil; *d.* direction of current flow through coil.

14. An *ammeter* is connected in *series* with a load. This is done because: *a.* A parallel connection would require a low-resistance meter. *b.* The resistance of the meter is very high. *c.* A series connection prevents a voltage drop from forming across the meter. *d.* Current is measured in amperes, representing the rate current flows past a given point within the circuit.

15. The Electron Theory of Magnetism assumes that magnetic action is due to the: *a.* inability of protons to move within the atom; *b.* electron movement and arrangement of the electron orbits; *c.* force of the repulsion between electrons accumulated on the dielectric; *d.* presence of free electrons in a dielectric.

16. The basic DC meter utilizes: *a.* two iron magnets; *b.* one movable iron magnet; *c.* one fixed coil through which a current must flow; *d.* one permanent magnet and one electromagnet.

17. The strength of an electromagnetic field is *not* affected by the: *a.* number of turns of wire forming the solenoid; *b.* strength of the current in amperes flowing through the solenoid; *c.* type of insulation covering the wire forming the solenoid; *d.* size of the core.

18. Permeability is the opposite of: *a.* magnetic reluctance; *b.* magnetic attraction; *c.* ohmic resistance; *d.* magnetomotive force.

19. A *voltmeter* is connected in *parallel* to the source of voltage. This is done because: *a.* Resistance of a parallel circuit is always less than that of a series circuit. *b.* Voltage represents the difference of potential between two points in a circuit. *c.* A parallel connection allows less current to be drawn from the source. *d.* Resistance of the meter is very low.

20. When a person speaks into a telephone, the carbon granules within the button are: *a.* alternately compressed and released; *b.* always under compression; *c.* always in a position of strain; *d.* automatically under less compression.

21. If a solenoid has 1,000 ampere turns, the magnetomotive force (m.m.f.) developed would be the same as a solenoid wound with 500 turns and drawing: *a.* 200 ma.; *b.* 20 amp.; *c.* 2 amp., *d.* $\frac{1}{2}$ amp.

22. A pulsating direct current is one in which the: *a.* magnitude is constant but the direction of flow changes; *b.* magnitude varies but the direction of flow is unchanged; *c.* direction of flow changes as the resistance is varied; *d.* direction of flow changes in periodic pulses.

23. The resistance of a microphone button: *a.* remains at a fixed value at all times; *b.* increases to twice the normal value during sound rarefaction; *c.* increases during sound compression; *d.* varies to a greater or lesser degree during the periods of sound compression and rarefaction.

24. A *circuit breaker* may be a: *a.* sounder; *b.* relay; *c.* meter; *d.* microphone.

25. The diagram is intended to show a basic telephone circuit. It has: *a.* no errors; *b.* one error; *c.* two errors; *d.* three errors.

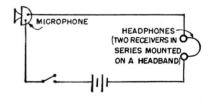

MICROPHONE

HEADPHONES—
(TWO RECEIVERS IN
SERIES MOUNTED
ON A HEADBAND)

26. When a sensitive relay is used to control the action of a separate electric circuit, the current in the relay solenoid: *a.* must exceed the current in the controlled circuit; *b.* must equal the current in the controlled circuit; *c.* cannot be less than the current in the controlled circuit; *d.* may be less than the current in the controlled circuit.

27. The diagram below is intended to show a basic telegraph circuit. It has: *a.* three errors; *b.* two errors; *c.* one error; *d.* no errors.

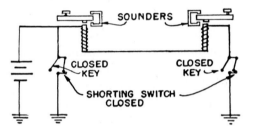

28. When a *magnetic substance* has reached the saturation point, its magnetic field: *a.* cannot be increased; *b.* can be increased by an increase in the ampere turns; *c.* cannot be increased unless the m.m.f. is increased; *d.* can be increased by using additional wire around the solenoid.

29. The diagram below shows two voltmeters and two ammeters connected within a circuit. With reference to the polarities of the meters and their position within the circuit, the number of errors in the diagram is: *a.* one; *b.* two; *c.* three; *d.* four.

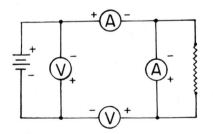

30. In connecting a DC meter, the rule is: *a.* positive to negative, negative to positive; *b.* positive to positive, negative to negative; *c.* positive to ground, negative to negative; *d.* positive to positive, negative to ground.

31. According to the Electron Theory of Magnetism, those substances can be magnetized whose: *a.* reluctance to magnetism is greatest; *b.* electron orbits can be lined up so that their individual fields aid each other; *c.* electron orbits can oppose and neutralize each other; *d.* electron orbits can periodically increase the reluctance of the substance.

32. The essential difference between a voltmeter and an ammeter is that the: *a.* voltmeter has a high internal resistance; *b.* ammeter has a high internal resistance; *c.* voltmeter has a low internal resistance; *d.* ammeter has no internal resistance.

33. A solenoid is being used as an electromagnet. If it is necessary to increase the electromagnetic effect, it is best to use a core of: *a.* glass; *b.* copper; *c.* iron; *d.* silver.

34. The reason that the north pole of a compass turns toward the North Pole of the earth is that the earth's North Pole: *a.* is really its South Pole; *b.* is neutral in relation to the north pole of the compass magnet; *c.* repels the north pole of the compass magnet; *d.* is nonmagnetic.

35. If the polarity of a DC meter is not observed and is therefore incorrectly connected, the meter needle will: *a.* not move from zero position; *b.* move directly across face of scale; *c.* remain fixed at center of scale; *d.* attempt to move to left of scale, assuming scale reads from left to right.

36. The diagram is intended to show an overload relay in operation. It has: *a.* no error; *b.* one error; *c.* two errors; *d.* three errors.

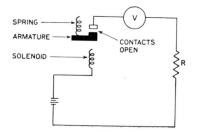

37. The diagram of an underload relay circuit has: *a.* no errors; *b.* one error; *c.* two errors; *d.* three errors.

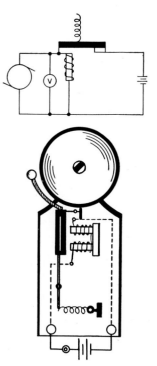

38. In order to convert the nonvibrator type of bell shown in the illustration to a vibrator type, it would be necessary to: *a.* replace the push-button switch with a knife switch; *b.* install an additional switch on the armature; *c.* replace the double solenoid with a single-coil unit; *d.* reverse the polarity of the battery.

39. One of the wave forms drawn in the diagrams below illustrates most nearly that of a pulsating wave. The correct diagram is: *a*; *b*; *c*; *d.*

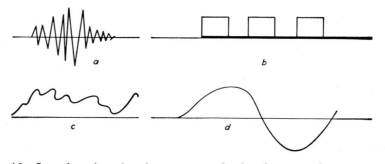

40. In electric circuits, an *overload relay* supplements or replaces: *a.* fuses; *b.* sounder; *c.* insulators; *d.* batteries.

Chapter 5. Alternating Current

1. Definition

In considering the flow of an electric current in a single direction, we have been using the term *direct current* (DC) to distinguish it from a form of electricity in which the direction

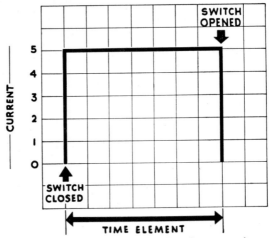

Fig. 114. Direct current is unidirectional and constant in magnitude.

of current flow is periodically reversed. Further, in noting the action of direct current, we have found that it reaches its maximum value very quickly after the circuit is established. This maximum value, once attained, remains at a given magnitude unless the circuit constants are changed. Direct current can, therefore, be defined as a current that flows at a uniform value (magnitude) in a single direction (Fig. 114).

Another form of electricity in motion is also available. This type is called *alternating current* (AC) because, as its name implies, the direction of flow is alternately in one direction and then in another.

Further, unlike direct current, which remains at a uniform value the instant it reaches its full magnitude, alternating current is continually changing in magnitude from zero to maximum, back to zero, and then to a new and equal maximum in an opposite direction, from which point it drops to zero

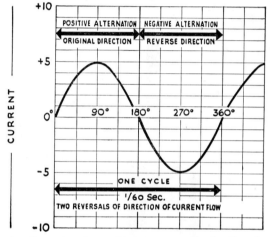

Fig. 115. During its cycle, alternating current varies its direction of flow and magnitude.

again. This action from zero to zero magnitude in one direction and then in an opposite one, completing a circle of travel in a given period of time, is called a *cycle*. Thus, a cycle represents two complete reversals of direction (Fig. 115).

The number of cycles completed in a given period of time is called the *frequency*. Ordinary alternating current used for lighting, for instance, has a frequency of 60 cycles. This simply means that the direction of current flow has been reversed 120 times in 1 second (1 sec.).

Alternating current is, therefore, defined as current that continually changes in magnitude and periodically reverses its direction of flow.

2. Sources of AC E.M.F.

1. *Induced Currents.* It has been seen how electrons in motion set up a magnetic field around a conductor. Conversely, a *change* in a magnetic field around a conductor tends to set electrons in motion. The mere existence of a field is not enough; there must be some form of *change* in the field.

If a bar magnet is held above a coil connected to a sensitive

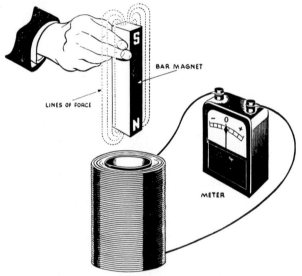

Fig. 116. With the magnet at some distance from the coil and with the magnetic lines of force stationary, no voltage will be induced across the coil, therefore, no current will flow through the meter.

meter with a zero reading on the center of the scale (Fig. 116), no indication of a current in the coil will exist until the magnet is plunged downward into the coil's center. As this occurs, the magnetic field surrounding the magnet "cuts" the coil, and the meter needle moves to *one* side of the scale and then, as the magnet remains stationary, returns to its zero setting. If the magnet is now withdrawn, the meter needle swings to the *opposite* side, returning to zero again as the lines of force, now moving in the opposite direction, no longer cut the coil.

Let us carefully examine what has happened.

1) When the coil was outside of the magnetic field, there was no current flow in the circuit as evidenced by a zero reading of the meter (Fig. 116).

2) When the magnetic lines of force were in motion, approaching and surrounding the coil, a current appeared (as shown by the me-

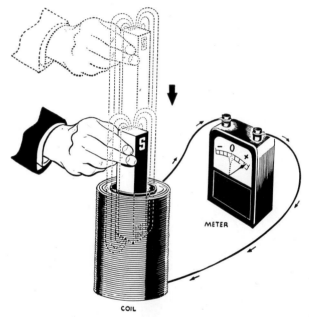

Fig. 117. With the magnetic field in motion and "cutting through" the coil, a voltage is induced across the coil and a current flows through the meter.

ter), and this current flowed in a single specific direction (Fig. 117).

3) *When the magnetic lines of force were no longer in movement* (at the time the magnet remained stationary within the coil), the current dropped back to zero. This demonstrates that the mere existence of a magnetic field around a conductor will not induce a current in the conductor (Fig. 118). *The field must be in a state of change.*

4) When the magnet was withdrawn, the field around the coil was being changed and a current again appeared, but moving in the opposite direction (Fig. 119).

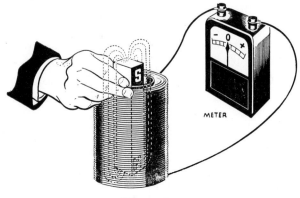

Fig. 118. The mere existence of a magnetic field around a coil will not induce a voltage across it. The field must be in a state of change.

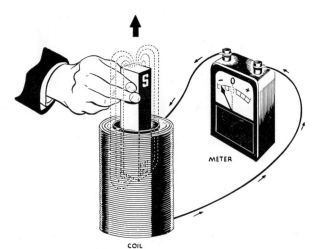

Fig. 119. The withdrawal of the magnet produces the field change necessary for current flow. This action reverses the direction of the lines of force and the resulting flow in the circuit.

5) As soon as the coil was no longer within the influence of this changing field, the current disappeared (as evidenced by the meter reading zero once again) (Fig. 120).

This form of electricity in motion is known as an *induced current*, because it was forced into being (in a circuit where it did not exist originally) by the action of magnetic lines of force. An induced current is always an alternating current, that is, a current that periodically changes its direction of flow.

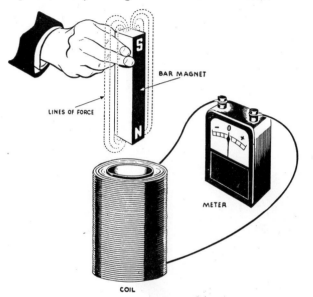

Fig. 120. When the coil is no longer within the influence of a changing field, the meter pointer returns to zero. There is no longer an induced voltage, hence, a current cannot be present.

2. *The Alternator* (*AC Generator*). In the illustration we have used, the coil remained in a fixed position, and the magnet was alternately inserted and withdrawn from the center of the coil. Just as the number of lines of force *cutting* the coil can be changed by bringing the magnet to the coil, a similar result can be obtained by bringing the coil to the magnet (Figs. 121 and 122).

As the coil approaches the magnet, it cuts more and more magnetic lines of force. As the coil cuts through more and more lines of force, the meter begins to indicate a current flow in one direction and shows an increase in magnitude until no additional lines of force are being cut or until the coil is brought to rest. At that instant, the current drops to zero. If the coil is then withdrawn, a current again appears, moving in the opposite direction, dropping to zero as the coil leaves the magnetic field.

In the first illustration, there was an actual movement of the

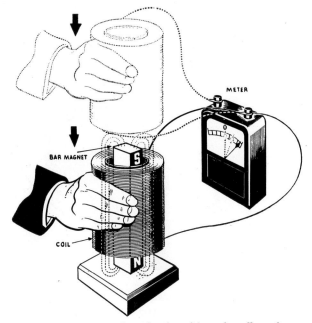

Fig. 121. With the bar magnet in a fixed position, the effect of a varying field can be obtained by moving the coil onto the magnet.

magnetic field. In the second, the field was stationary, but the coil moved in and out of the field, producing the same result. In the alternator (AC generator), this second method is used because it is mechanically simpler to operate.

The basic alternator (Figs. 123 and 123*a* to *e*) is a coil of wire (an *armature*) mounted on a shaft that permits its rotation within a magnetic field. In Fig. 123*a*, an armature consisting of a single loop *ABCD* is shown for clarity. *N* and *S* are the poles of a magnet, which may be a permanent magnet as is used in a *magneto* (a small AC generator used in telephony for ringing purposes) or an electromagnet, which is standard practice where large amounts of power must be generated. The electromagnet must be excited (energized) by a DC source such as a battery or DC generator in order to produce a field in which the lines of force move in a single direction.

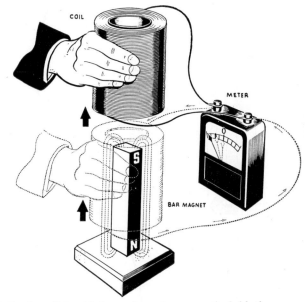

Fig. 122. As the coil is withdrawn from the magnetic field, the current changes its direction of flow.

The two ends of the armature coil are connected to *collector*, or *slip* rings, R_1 and R_2 (Fig. 123a), permanently mounted on, but insulated from, the shaft so that they rotate with the coil. In order to contact the rings, carbon *brushes* B_1 and B_2 make a wiping contact onto the rings and connect the alternator armature to the load.

The strength of the magnetic field between the poles of the magnet is one of the factors that will determine the alternator's output voltage. If an electromagnet is used, the strength of this

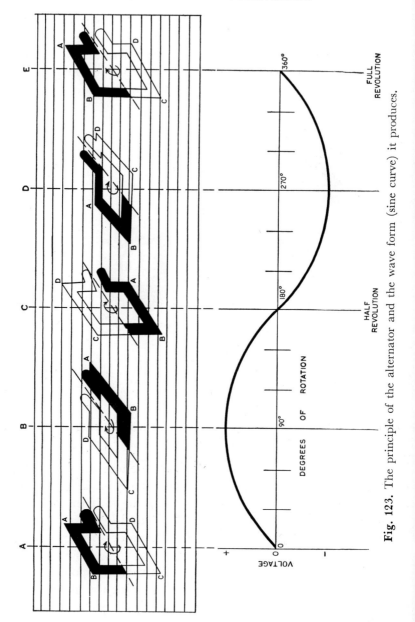

Fig. 123. The principle of the alternator and the wave form (sine curve) it produces.

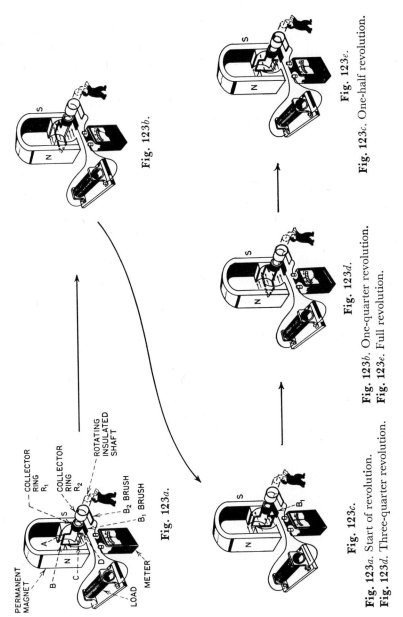

Fig. 123b.

Fig. 123c.

Fig. 123e.
Fig. 123e. One-half revolution.

Fig. 123a.

Fig. 123d.

PERMANENT
MAGNET
COLLECTOR
RING
R₁
COLLECTOR
RING
R₂
ROTATING
INSULATED
SHAFT
B₂ BRUSH
B₁ BRUSH
LOAD
METER

Fig. 123a. Start of revolution.
Fig. 123d. Three-quarter revolution.

Fig. 123b. One-quarter revolution.
Fig. 123e. Full revolution.

field can be varied by the use of a rheostat in series with the field (solenoid) windings.

The output voltage will also depend upon the speed of rotation, which factor will affect the AC frequency obtained. An increase in speed will increase both the voltage and the frequency.

To understand the operation of the alternator, assume that the armature *ABCD* is initially in a vertical position and is moving clockwise at a given rate of speed. At this initial position, no e.m.f. is being produced because the conductors forming the loop are parallel to the lines of force (Fig. 123a). *Therefore, none of the lines are being cut.* As rotation proceeds in a clockwise direction, the position of the loop is changing, and conductor *AB* begins to cut the field in a downward direction (Fig. 123b). At the same instant, *CD* cuts the field in an upward direction. The meter begins to record a current flow in one direction, the current reaching a peak value in this direction as the armature reaches the 90-degree position. At this point, it is cutting through the greatest number of lines of force. Passing this point, the current begins to drop to zero, as fewer lines of force are being cut through in a given distance of rotation.

At the 180-degree point, conductor *CD* is now moving downward and *AB* upward (Fig. 123c). *This is exactly the reverse of the situation so far described.* As would be expected, a current flow in the *reverse* direction occurs, reaching its maximum value at the 270-degree point (Fig. 123d) and dropping to zero as the 360-degree circle of rotation is completed (Fig. 123e). The cycle then reoccurs as long as rotation is maintained.

Changes of position of the armature and resultant induced voltage in the armature at any instant of time are shown in Fig. 123. When the voltage is induced in one direction, it is *positive;* when reversed, it is *negative.* The positive voltages on the graph are plotted above the center line, called the *zero axis,* while the negative voltages are plotted below this line. The resulting curve, termed *sine curve,* illustrates *AC* wave forms.

The *frequency* of the alternating current produced by an alternator will depend upon the number of magnetic poles used to produce the field and the speed of rotation per minute (r.p.m.). The formula is

$$\text{Frequency in cycles per second} = \frac{\text{number of poles} \times \text{r.p.m.}}{120}$$

In the basic alternator just studied, there were only two poles, and if the speed were 1,800 revolutions per minute (1,800 r.p.m.), the AC frequency would be 30 cycles (30 ∼).

$$F = \frac{2 \times 1,800}{120} = \frac{3,600}{120} = 30 \sim$$

The electromagnets used to produce the field in any generator

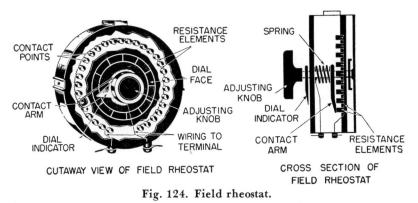

CUTAWAY VIEW OF FIELD RHEOSTAT

CROSS SECTION OF FIELD RHEOSTAT

Fig. 124. Field rheostat.

are called *field magnets*. Their solenoids are called *field windings* or *field coils*. The rheostat used to regulate the output voltage by controlling the strength of the field is termed a *field rheostat* (Fig. 124).

The field strength will depend upon the amount of current passing through the field coils. The higher the current, the stronger the field; the stronger the field, the greater the value of induced voltage. Since the rheostat is in series with the field windings, its resistance value at a given setting will determine the amount of current flowing in the circuit. Less resistance allows more current to flow; more resistance decreases the current.

At a given speed of rotation, the output voltage of an alternator may be charted as follows:

Rheostat resistance value	Field current	Field strength	Output voltage
Higher................	Lower	Lower	Lower
Lower.................	Higher	Higher	Higher

This chart also applies to DC generators, which will be studied later. The output voltage will also depend upon the load across

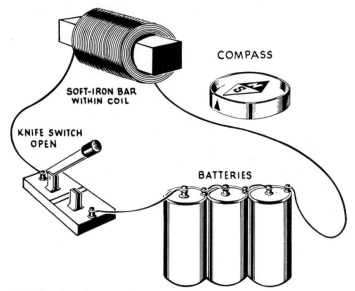

Fig. 125a. In the absence of a current flow through the coil, no magnetic field is produced. The position of the compass needle remains unchanged.

the armature. A heavy load, that is, one drawing a high current, will lower the voltage and will require an adjustment of the field rheostat to a lower value of resistance in order to increase the output. This will compensate for the heavier load. The reverse holds true if the load is very light.

3. *The Transformer.* An induced alternating current can be produced when an inductor (coil or solenoid) is made to cut lines of force, as was demonstrated in the action of the alternator. Either the lines of force must be in motion (as was the case when the magnet was moved in and out of a coil), or if the field is stationary, the coil itself must vary its position within the field.

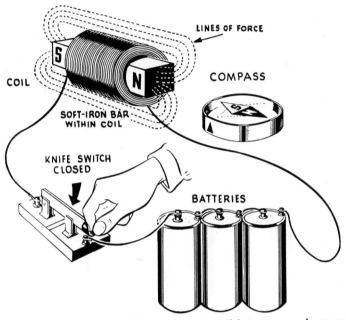

Fig. 125b. With the closing of the switch, the coil becomes an electromagnet as current flows through it. The south pole of the compass turns to face the magnet as the lines of force expand.

Exactly the same results can be obtained if a field is caused to *expand* and *contract*.

The coil in Fig. 125 should be connected to the battery so that a north pole appears on the side facing the compass when the switch is closed. (This is an application of the left-hand rule.) The small compass should initially be so placed that the needle comes to rest at right angles to the coil when the switch is open. If the switch is now closed, the *south* pole of the compass will change its position and point toward the north pole of the solenoid as the electromagnetic field is created. To the observer, this seems to occur almost instantaneously, but actually a period of time is involved during which the field is being developed. The lines of force formed by the current flowing through the solenoid

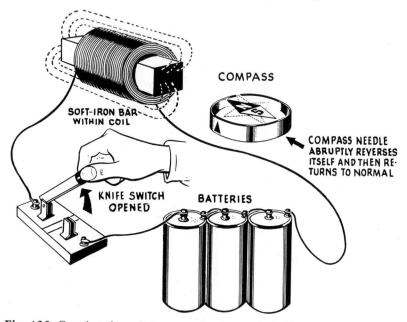

Fig. 126. Opening the switch causes the magnetic field to contract and disappear. In that instant, the compass needle abruptly reverses and returns to its normal position.

began to move outward (expand) and continued to do so until the flux reached its maximum strength and occupied its greatest area.

If the switch is now opened, the compass needle abruptly swings around in the opposite direction so that its *north* pole momentarily faces the coil and then returns to its normal position (Fig. 126). This reverse action occurred when the flux began to disappear. The field is said to have *contracted* (moved inward) and finally *collapsed* (disappeared entirely).

Note carefully that the solenoid's polarity was completely reversed when the field contracted. The polarity of any solenoid is dependent upon the direction of the lines of force. When they are expanding, the direction of *movement* is exactly opposite to that which is evident when they are contracting.

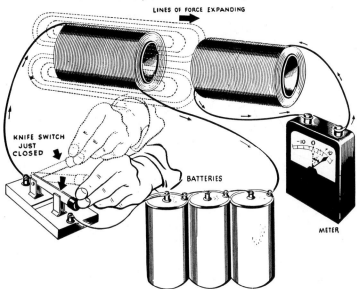

Fig. 127. An expanding field around one coil will induce a voltage across another coil to which it is inductively coupled. As soon as expansion of the field is complete, the induced voltage disappears.

If another coil is now *inductively coupled* to the first coil, that is, placed in such a relationship that the expanding and contracting field around the first or *primary* coil will cut through the space occupied by the second or *secondary* coil, a voltage will be induced in the secondary circuit each time the switch is closed and opened (Fig. 127). As the switch is closed, the meter reads in one direction and returns to zero setting; as the switch is opened, the meter reads in the opposite direction, and returns to zero (Fig. 128). This is, in effect, the same situation that existed when a magnet was moved in and out of a coil. The difference is that the permanent magnet had to be moved back and forth to create the requirement of lines of force in motion. In this case, we are using an electromagnet whose field moves in and out by turning the field current on and off.

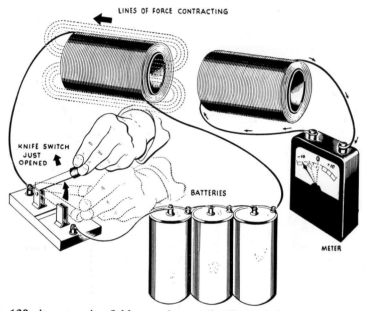

Fig. 128. A contracting field around one coil will also induce a voltage across another coil to which it is inductively coupled. As soon as contraction of the field is complete, the induced voltage disappears.

Any induced current always flows in such a direction that the field it sets up opposes any change in the original field that produced it. This is known as *Lenz's Law.*

When the current in the primary coil started to flow in one direction, the induced current in the secondary flowed in the *opposite* direction. Hence, the polarity of the secondary solenoid is always the reverse of the primary coil, and the newly created field tends to oppose the very formation of the original field as long as that field is still expanding. The moment the expansion ceased, an induced current no longer existed, and neither did its opposing field. Only the original field remained and existed unopposed.

When the current in the primary begins to drop as the switch is opened, an induced current again appears, but this time it is

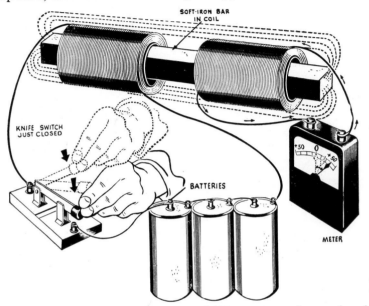

SOFT-IRON BAR
IN COIL

KNIFE SWITCH
JUST CLOSED

BATTERIES

METER

Fig. 129. If the two coils in Figs. 127 and 128 are mounted on an iron bar, the magnitude of the induced voltage will be greatly increased.

flowing in the opposite direction from the originally induced current. This flow of current in a new direction reverses the polarity of the secondary. This new reversed field opposes the contraction of the primary field by setting up a field of its own in the same direction as the one being destroyed. In each case, the induced field (set up by the induced current) opposed the change that was taking place in the original field. Here, too, the action ceased as soon as the original lines of force disappeared entirely.

In other words, *the lines of force comprising a field must be in motion to induce a current, and this induced current sets up a field of its own that opposes any change in the existing field.* The importance of this phenomenon will be further illustrated in later chapters.

If a bar of iron is now inserted within the coils and the experiment repeated, the magnitude of the induced current will be found to be much greater. This is due to the fact that the lines of force have been concentrated and, hence, the strength of the magnetic field has been increased in exactly the same way we increased the strength of an electromagnet by using an iron core (Fig. 129).

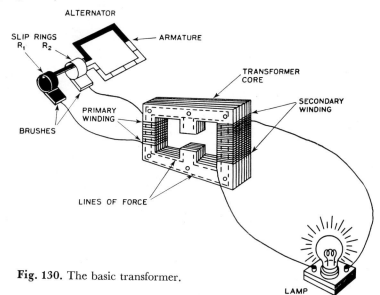

Fig. 130. The basic transformer.

Two coils inductively coupled together, that is, so placed that the varying magnetic field around one will induce a voltage in the other, form the basic *transformer* (Fig. 130). Note that there is no electrical contact between the coils other than through the magnetic field.

Some transformers, however, are designed with but a single winding, part of which is used as the primary and the other as the secondary. This is known as an *autotransformer*. Its action is identical to that of an ordinary transformer, the varying field set up in the primary circuit inducing a voltage in the secondary (Fig. 131a). In this type of transformer, used in special devices where *separation of the windings is not essential*, there is an actual electrical contact between the primary and secondary, which are connected in series.

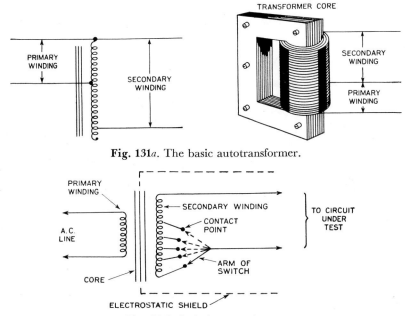

Fig. 131*a*. The basic autotransformer.

Fig. 131*b*. Isolation transformer.

Under certain circumstances, it is desirable to have the secondary winding of a transformer completely free of any connection with the primary or the ground. Such a transformer is called an *isolation transformer*. In some cases, the output voltage of this device is variable by means of *tapping* (making contact with certain sections of) either or both the primary and secondary windings (Fig. 131*b*). The setting of a control knob and contact point switch may be used to obtain the desired voltage, or the different output sections may be connected directly to receptacles into which a plug may be inserted to obtain contact. It is also common practice to shield the secondary winding by the use of a suitable metal screen. This *electrostatic shield-*

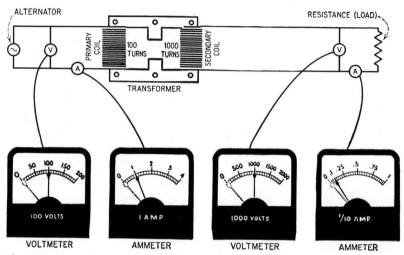

Fig. 132. The relationship of voltage and current values in the windings of a "perfect" transformer.

ing limits the transfer of certain unwanted frequencies from the primary winding (or surrounding area) to the secondary.

Isolation transformers are particularly valuable when it is necessary to test a piece of apparatus with all voltages applied. The regular AC source is usually grounded, but by using the isolation transformer, this side of the AC-line source is automatically removed from the apparatus being tested. Shock hazard is therefore reduced considerably because contact with a live (higher than ground) voltage point will not necessarily result in a flow of current sufficient to cause serious injury to a person. This might be the case if the AC source (which is usually capable of supplying very large amounts of current) were directly contacted accidentally.

It will be noted (Fig. 131*b*) that the *secondary* winding of the isolation transformer serves as the AC source for the apparatus under test. Its primary is connected to the regular AC source.

4. *Transformer Operation on Alternating Current.* Since alternating current varies in magnitude and direction of flow continuously, transformers find ready use where alternating current is available. The varying current through the input (primary) winding of the transformer automatically produces a constantly expanding and contracting field, the rate of change depending entirely upon the AC frequency.

The transformers used are known as *step-up* transformers if the output (secondary) winding has more turns on it than the primary, and as *step-down* transformers if the secondary winding has fewer turns. Increasing or decreasing the amount of voltage needed from an AC line is one of the common uses for transformers.

Suppose a transformer primary has 100 turns of wire and the secondary 1,000 turns. The secondary voltage would be ten times the primary voltage ($100 \times 10 = 1,000$ or $1,000 \div 100 = 10$). The *current* capacity, however, would be only one-tenth of the value drawn by the primary, as there is a definite power relationship (as well as voltage relationship) between the windings. (Fig. 132).

The relationship between voltage and turns may be expressed as follows:

$$\frac{E_p}{E_s} = \frac{T_p}{T_s}$$

where E_p = primary voltage
E_s = secondary voltage
T_p = primary turns
T_s = secondary turns

Example: A transformer designed to operate on 100 volts AC is wound with 100 turns of wire on the primary and 20 turns on the secondary. What is the available secondary voltage?

Step 1. $\dfrac{E_p}{E_s} = \dfrac{T_p}{T_s}$ *This is the formula.*

Step 2. $\dfrac{100}{E_s} = \dfrac{100}{20}$ *Here we have substituted the known values.*

Step 3. $100 \ E_s = 100 \times 20$
$= 2,000$

To solve the problem, we multiply the first numerator ($E_p = 100$) by the second denominator ($T_s = 20$), and then the second numerator ($T_p = 100$) by the first denominator (E_s). Note that we put the unknown combination on the left side to make the solution easier.

Step 4. $E_s = \dfrac{2,000}{100} = 20$ volts (*Ans.*)

To obtain E_s, we now divide the figure on the right side of the equation by the figure on the left side.

The answer is 20 volts and since this is a lower voltage than that connected to the primary, we obviously have a step-down transformer.

To determine the current-carrying capacity of the secondary winding, we must remember that the *power* developed in the secondary bears a close relationship to the power drawn by the primary. For a given value of power ($W = EI$) in any circuit, if voltage is stepped down, the current (I) is stepped up; contrari-wise, if voltage is stepped up, the current must be stepped down since the relationship between voltage (E) and current (I) must be maintained. This ratio may be expressed as follows:

$$\frac{E_p}{E_s} = \frac{I_s}{I_p}$$

where E_p = primary voltage
E_s = secondary voltage
I_s = secondary current
I_p = primary current

Example: A transformer operating on 100 volts and drawing 1 amp. from the line delivers 20 volts in the secondary. What secondary current is available?

Step 1. $\dfrac{E_p}{E_s} = \dfrac{I_s}{I_p}$

This is the formula.

Step 2. $\dfrac{100}{20} = \dfrac{I_s}{1}$

Here we have substituted the known values.

Step 3. $20I_s = 100 \times 1 = 100$ *To solve the problem, we multiply the first numerator ($E_p = 100$) by the second denominator ($I_p = 1$), and then the second numerator (I_s) by the first denominator ($E_s = 20$).*

Step 4. $I_s = \dfrac{100}{20} = 5$ amp.   *To obtain I_s, we now divide the figure on the right side of the equation by the figure on the left side.*

                 (Ans.)

This problem can be proved by determining the comparative power available in both primary and secondary circuits.

$$\text{Watts (primary)} = E_p \times I_p$$
$$W = 100 \times 1 = 100 \text{ watts}$$
$$\text{Watts (secondary)} = E_s \times I_s$$
$$W = 20 \times 5 = 100 \text{ watts}$$

The power in both the primary and secondary is the same in this ideal case. In practice, an efficiency of 100 per cent cannot be obtained, owing to losses, but transformers can be made with efficiencies approaching 98 per cent—the highest efficiency of any electrical device.

Losses in a transformer are of three main types: (1) eddy currents, (2) hysteresis, and (3) I^2R loss (also called *copper losses*).

Eddy currents are formed when the changing magnetic field induces currents in the iron core, sections of the core acting as "secondaries" in exactly the same way as does the regular secondary winding. Since these unwanted "secondaries" act as if they were under a constant short circuit, they consume power from the primary, thus reducing efficiency. Eddy currents are avoided to a large extent by breaking up their paths. To attain this end, the use of laminated cores, made up of sheets of metal, rather than a solid core is standard practice (Fig. 133). The thin sheets (laminations) are insulated from one another but bound together solidly. Loose laminations produce considerable "hum" as the magnetic field varies.

Hysteresis loss is the result of the energy wasted in reversing the magnetization of the core every time the current direction reverses and magnetizes the core in a different direction. It will be recalled that the axes of the atoms in a magnetized substance are all pointed in a single direction. Hence, in an AC circuit, as the direction of the current flow is reversed, the atoms reverse their positions. This process going on many times per second (120 times if 60 cycles is used) produces the hysteresis effect. To offset hysteresis loss, core material is made from special iron and steel or alloys of silicon and steel that magnetize readily.

Copper losses arise from exactly the same cause that produces

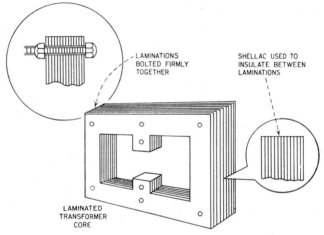

LAMINATIONS BOLTED FIRMLY TOGETHER

SHELLAC USED TO INSULATE BETWEEN LAMINATIONS

LAMINATED TRANSFORMER CORE

Fig. 133. The use of a laminated core in a transformer aids in reducing eddy-current losses.

I^2R losses in any conductor, that is, they are due to the current flowing through an opposing resistance.

All these losses are evidenced by heating effects. Hence a transformer must be designed to radiate the heat properly.

A transformer may have more than one primary and one secondary winding. Some of the secondary windings may be of the step-up and some of the step-down variety, or all of one kind. The resulting action is in no way changed, but it must be noted that the total power consumed by the primary winding or windings will necessarily be the total of all the power consumed by all the secondary windings.

3. Transformer Operation on Direct Current

Transformers are designed for service on AC lines as a general rule and *ordinarily must not be connected to a DC line.* Transformer operation under certain conditions on direct current is possible, however, where it is necessary to step up the available DC

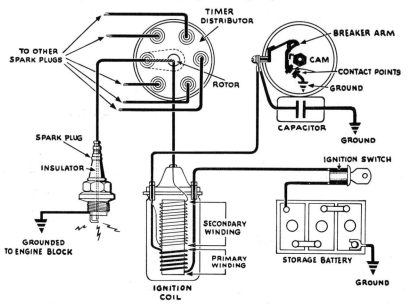

Fig. 134. The basic ignition system used in automobiles. The ignition coil is simply a transformer.

voltage. A typical example is the ignition system of an automobile, where the 6 or 12 volts furnished by the storage battery must be stepped up to a very high voltage to operate the spark plugs. Since DC current flows in a single direction, it can be seen that the requirement of an expanding and contracting field emanating from the primary winding would not result (as it does in the case of alternating current connected to the primary) unless some means of regularly breaking the primary circuit were used.

In the auto, the *ignition coil* (transformer) has its primary circuit broken at regular intervals by a set of contacts operated by a cam. Opening and closing this circuit causes the field to expand

and contract, inducing a voltage in the secondary winding. This high voltage is fed to the spark plugs causing them to flash over and ignite the gasoline (Fig. 134).

In Fig. 135, another method is shown that allows transformer operation on direct current. Here, a vibrator is used to make and

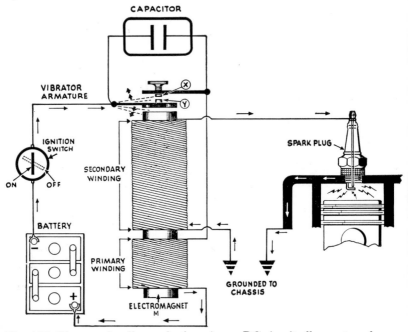

Fig. 135. The use of a vibrator in the primary DC circuit allows a transformer to function as if alternating current were applied. This method is no longer in common use for ignition work but is used in principle in many automobile radio receivers to furnish the high voltages required.

break the primary circuit. It consists basically of an electromagnet M, which attracts and releases an armature upon which one or more contacts are mounted. When the current is turned on, it flows through the primary of the transformer and also through the solenoid of the electromagnet. The current through the primary creates an expanding field, and at the same time, the electromagnet is being energized. As the electromagnet becomes energized, it attracts the armature, and the contacts X and Y are forced apart, opening the circuit. The primary field then collapses, and simultaneously, the electromagnet also loses its magnetism, releasing the armature. The circuit is thus again closed automatically and the process repeated.

4. Characteristics of Alternating Current

1. *Peak Value.* Once a DC circuit is established, the current

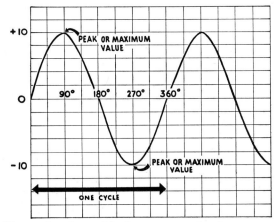

Fig. 136. The peak values of both current and voltage are reached twice during each AC cycle.

and voltage are at a uniform value. Hence, the power in the circuit can be determined by simply multiplying the current value (I) by the voltage (E).

In an AC circuit, the current and voltage values are continually changing. There is a peak or maximum value twice during each cycle (Fig. 136). Similarly, the values drop to zero during the cycle. Therefore, the instantaneous value at any given instant of time may be anywhere from zero to maximum. It can therefore be seen that when alternating current is flowing, we must select certain values to represent standards to work on. Such a standard is used by referring to the power developed in an AC circuit as compared to the power developed in a DC circuit.

2. *Effective or Root-mean-square Value.* Suppose we had an electrical device that was designed to operate on either alternating or direct current, but, for effective operation, absolutely required 100 watts of power. If we connected this device to a 100-volt *DC* source, with all other factors being normal, the instrument would perform properly. If an AC source whose *peak* value was 100 volts were substituted, we would find that the operation of the device would be seriously handicapped, and, in fact, it might not operate at all. Apparently, then, the *power* developed on an AC supply with a peak value of 100 volts is less than that obtained on a 100-volt DC supply. An instrument measuring the power developed in the AC circuit would show a consumption of only 70.7 watts in contrast to 100 watts drawn from the DC line. By mathematical analysis it has been found that an AC voltage or current that will give a *power value* equivalent to that obtained from a DC supply equals 0.707 times the *maximum* or *peak* AC value. This is known as the *effective* value. The term *r.m.s. value,* meaning *root-mean-square,* is sometimes used, as it describes the mathematical method of obtaining the figure used, that is, 0.707.

If an alternator produced a peak AC voltage of 10 volts, only 0.707 times this voltage or 7.07 volts ($10 \times 0.707 = 7.07$) would deliver *effective* power. In AC circuits, we are usually solely concerned with the effective value, and AC meters are designed to read in terms of effective voltages or current. *The effective value of alternating current, then, is the equivalent of a DC value that under identical conditions will produce the same amount of power.* The effective value of AC is normally used in computations, and is the value read on AC meters.

Since AC meters read the effective value, it is sometimes necessary to be able to determine the peak value. This is particularly the case when safety precautions must be taken to prevent an insulation breakdown. Suppose an AC meter showed a reading of 1,000 volts in a given circuit. If this were direct current, we know that the insulation would not have to stand a greater

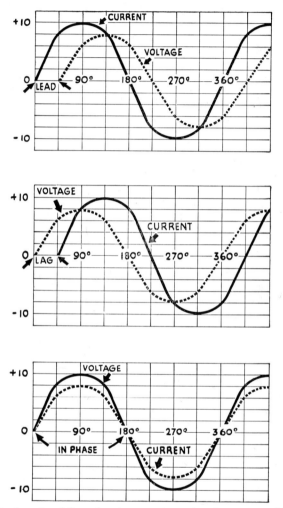

Fig. 137. During the AC cycle, the current and voltage may either lag or lead each other depending upon circuit conditions. When they reach given values simultaneously, they are said to be *in phase*.

voltage at any time. The maximum value would be 1,000 volts DC. We know, however, that in an AC circuit, the peak value goes above the effective value, the exact figure being 1.41 times the effective value. Hence, in the example given, a peak voltage of 1,410 volts (1,000 × 1.41 = 1,410) will appear. The insulation, therefore, must be suitable to withstand this peak value, not only the lower effective value that would be read by the AC meter.

3. *Average Value.* If reference is made to the sine curve of an AC current (Fig. 136), it will be seen that there is just as much current value *above* the zero axis as there is *below*. If all the positive values were added up, and all the negative values similarly added up, they would cancel each other out. The true *average value* of alternating current is therefore *zero*.

In practice, however, only the average value of *half* the cycle is considered. This value, it has been determined mathematically, is 0.636 times the peak value, or 0.9 times the effective value. This average value is used in the solution of certain complex problems.

4. *Phase.* In a DC circuit, the voltage and current simultaneously reach their respective values. In dealing with alternating current, however, it has been found that the voltage and current values may not "keep in step." When they are in step, they are considered to be in *phase*, that is, in *time* with each other, just as an orchestra is said to be keeping in time with the leader or a column of soldiers is keeping in step on a march. When the current reaches a certain value *before* the voltage in an AC circuit, the current is said to *lead* the voltage. If the current reaches a certain value *after* the voltage, it is said to *lag* (Fig. 137). The causes of these phenomena will be studied later.

SUMMARY

1. Direct current is a form of electricity in which the current flow is of a uniform magnitude and in a single direction.

2. Alternating current is a form of electricity in which the direction of current flow is periodically reversing itself, and the magnitude is continually changing.

3. A cycle (∼) represents *two* complete reversals of direction, and the number of cycles completed within a second is called the *frequency*.

4. An alternating current is an induced current, that is, a current set up in a conductor when magnetic lines of force cut through, or are cut by, the conductor. To obtain this cutting effect, the conductor may be moved in and out, or be rotated within, a magnetic field.

5. An alternator (AC generator) is a mechanically operated device in which a conductor (called the *armature*) is rotated within a magnetic field set up by either a permanent magnet or an electromagnet.

6. The solenoids of an electromagnet used in a generator are called *field coils* or *field windings*.

7. The rheostat connected in series with the field coils is called a *field rheostat*.

8. The AC frequency of an alternator is determined by the formula

$$\text{Frequency in cycles} = \frac{\text{number of poles} \times \text{r.p.m.}}{120}$$

9. The voltage of an alternator under a given load will depend upon the speed of rotation and the field strength.

10. A transformer is an electrical device consisting of two or more coils mounted on a common core. An AC current, or a *varying* DC current in the primary, will induce an AC voltage in the secondary winding.

11. An autotransformer has its primary and secondary windings connected in series as well as being inductively coupled.

12. A step-up transformer is one that has a greater number of turns in the secondary. A step-down transformer is one that has fewer turns in the secondary.

13. Transformer efficiency may be reduced by eddy currents (currents induced in the iron core), hysteresis (due to "magnetic friction" as the axes of the atoms are reversed continually), and copper losses (the I^2R loss as the current flows through the windings).

14. Laminating the core reduces eddy-current losses, and the use of special iron, steel, or silicon-steel alloys reduces hysteresis losses.

15. The effective value of alternating current is equivalent to the DC value in so far as the power developed is the consideration. It is the value read by AC meters.

$$E_{\text{eff.}} = 0.707 \times E_{\text{max.}} \qquad E_{\text{avg.}} = 0.636 \times E_{\text{max.}}$$
$$E_{\text{eff.}} = 1.11 \ \times E_{\text{avg.}} \qquad E_{\text{avg.}} = 0.9 \ \ \times E_{\text{eff.}}$$

$$E_{\text{max.}} = 1.414 \times E_{\text{eff.}} \qquad E_{\text{max.}} = \frac{E_{\text{avg.}}}{0.636}$$

$$E_{\text{max.}} = 1.57 \ \times E_{\text{avg.}} \qquad E_{\text{max.}} = \frac{E_{\text{eff.}}}{0.707}$$

To compute values of current in amperes, substitute I for E ($I_{\text{max.}}$, $I_{\text{eff.}}$, $I_{\text{avg.}}$) in the above formulas.

16. *Phase* refers to the relationship between AC voltage and current values at a given instant of time. Current *leads* the voltage when it reaches a given value *before* the voltage does. It *lags* when it reaches a given value *after* the voltage.

Quiz: Alternating Current

This quiz will help you review the material just studied. See the quiz directions on page 24 before answering the questions below.

1. In a given solenoid, the strength of its field will *not* be affected by the: *a.* applied voltage; *b.* current through the coil; *c.* type of core; *d.* type of wire used in constructing solenoid.

2. In order to operate an electromagnet, the solenoid must be *excited* by the: *a.* alternator; *b.* AC source of 25 cycles; *c.* AC source of 60 cycles; *d.* DC source.

3. An autotransformer differs from other types of transformers in that: *a.* Its primary winding is always larger than its secondary winding. *b.* Its primary and secondary windings form a continuous electric circuit. *c.* It can be used only in automobiles. *d.* It must be wound with a heavier wire.

4. Operation of a transformer on direct current is possible only if the: *a.* direct current in the primary is periodically interrupted; *b.* transformer is made large enough to dissipate the heat produced by heavy eddy currents; *c.* direct current does not exceed the value of current appearing in the secondary; *d.* transformer is to be used only to decrease incoming voltage.

5. The *insulation* of a transformer is designed to withstand voltages up to 1,000 volts. A meter placed across the secondary reads exactly 1,000 volts. The insulation is: *a.* sufficient because the peak voltage is 1,414 volts; *b.* sufficient because the effective voltage is 1,000 volts; *c.* insufficient because the peak voltage is 1,414 volts; *d.* insufficient because the average voltage is 636 volts.

6. In a circuit consisting of a solenoid in series with a battery and a switch, the moment the switch is closed and current flows through the coil the field around the coil: *a.* contracts; *b.* expands; *c.* vanishes; *d.* is interrupted.

7. *Eddy currents* are caused by the: *a.* constant reversal of the magnetic lines of force in the iron core; *b.* leakage between windings; *c.* formation of shorted "secondaries" within the core; *d.* use of direct current on the primary.

8. Alternating current is distinguishable from direct current in that: *a.* Its direction of flow and magnitude are never varied. *b.* It periodically reverses its direction of flow, but its magnitude never varies. *c.* Its magnitude varies periodically, but its direction of flow is unchanging. *d.* Its magnitude and direction of flow are periodically changing.

9. A transformer is connected across a 100-volt AC source, and the 100-turn primary winding is drawing 1.00 amp. At 100 per cent efficiency, what is the voltage across the secondary winding, which has 5,000 turns of wire? *a.* 5,000 volts; *b.* 500 volts; *c.* 5,000,000 volts; *d.* 50 volts.

10. The transformer that operates on *direct current* in an automobile is called the: *a.* ignition coil; *b.* distributor; *c.* rotor; *d.* timer.

11. A *cycle* represents: *a.* one complete reversal of direction; *b.* two complete reversals of direction; *c.* three complete reversals of direction; *d.* four complete reversals of direction.

12. The basic alternator consists of: *a.* two field magnets acting upon each other so that their fields add; *b.* an armature capable of rotating within a magnetic field; *c.* an armature occupying a fixed stationary position within a magnetic field; *d.* a single-pole magnet acting upon a variable, rotating armature.

13. An alternator is: *a.* an AC motor; *b.* a DC motor; *c.* a DC generator; *d.* an AC generator.

14. The term *frequency* refers to the: *a.* effective value of the current at a given moment; *b.* number of poles on an alternator; *c.* number of cycles completed in a given period of time; *d.* effective voltage at a given moment.

15. In the action of an alternator, an increase in the speed of rotation will: *a.* affect the frequency only; *b.* not affect the frequency but will affect the voltage; *c.* not affect the frequency or the voltage; *d.* affect the frequency and voltage.

16. The effective value of alternating current is the equivalent of: *a.* an AC value that under identical conditions will produce the same amount of voltage; *b.* a DC value that under identical conditions will produce the same amount of voltage; *c.* an AC value that under identical conditions will produce identically the same amount of power; *d.* a DC value that under identical conditions will produce the same amount of power.

17. "An induced current always causes current flow in such a direction that the field it sets up aids any change in the original field that induced it." This statement of Lenz's Law is: *a.* incorrect; *b.* correct; *c.* correct if the word *always* is changed to *never;* *d.* correct if the words *induced current* are changed to *direct current.*

18. The polarity of a solenoid: *a.* remains fixed whether the field is expanding or contracting; *b.* changes at a given rate only during expansion of the field; *c.* depends upon the size of the coil; *d.* depends upon the direction of the lines of force.

19. If a heavy load is placed upon an alternator, the voltage output may be increased by: *a*. increasing the value of resistance in the field rheostat; *b*. decreasing the speed of rotation; *c*. decreasing the value of resistance in the field rheostat; *d*. adding a number of poles to the field magnets.

20. An induced voltage will *not* be created when a solenoid: *a*. is being cut by an expanding and contracting field; *b*. is moved into and out of a fixed field; *c*. is rotating within a fixed field; *d*. remains stationary within a fixed field.

21. When both the voltage and the current values of an alternating current attain simultaneous values at a given time, the circuit is said to be: *a*. out of phase; *b*. in phase; *c*. lagging; *d*. leading.

22. To induce a voltage across a solenoid, there must be: *a*. a current of very large value; *b*. a voltage of very large value; *c*. a change in the field cutting the coil; *d*. no change in the field at any time.

23. An alternator may be physically identified by the: *a*. polarity of its field windings; *b*. type of brushes used; *c*. collector or slip rings; *d*. commutator bars.

24. An induced voltage is always: *a*. AC; *b*. DC; *c*. AC acting as DC; *d*. pulsating DC.

25. In order to vary the output of an alternator operating under a fixed load, it is possible to use a field rheostat: *a*. in series with the field winding; *b*. connecting the armature to the field coils; *c*. to cut out one of the field coils; *d*. in series with the field coils and the load.

26. An alternator's normal speed of rotation is 3,000 r.p.m. If the machine has four poles, what is the frequency? *a*. 400 cycles; *b*. 300 cycles; *c*. 200 cycles; *d*. 100 cycles.

27. A transformer is connected across a 100-volt AC source. The primary is drawing 2 amp. and has 100 turns of wire. At 100 per cent efficiency, what current can be drawn from its secondary, which has 50 turns of wire? *a*. 1 amp.; *b*. 4 amp.; *c*. 8 amp.; *d*. 12 amp.

28. A transformer rated as having an efficiency of 95 per cent is drawing 1 kw. from the line. What wattage is available from the secondary? *a.* 95 watts; *b.* 750 watts; *c.* 950 watts; *d.* 9,500 watts.

29. In order to make contact with the armature coil of an alternator, the *collector*, or *slip rings*, touches: *a.* glass rods; *b.* carbon brushes; *c.* iron cores; *d.* silver points.

30. Hysteresis is due to the: *a.* constant reversal of the magnetic lines of force in the iron core; *b.* leakage between windings; *c.* formation of shorted "secondaries" within the core; *d.* use of direct current on the primary.

31. Most transformers use laminated cores in order to reduce the losses caused by: *a.* I^2R losses; *b.* hysteresis; *c.* eddy currents; *d.* overloading.

32. An isolation transformer is one that: *a.* is located on a remote pole in a long line circuit; *b.* can be used only on direct current; *c.* is completely insulated and has no connection whatsoever with any other part of the circuit; *d.* has primary and secondary windings without any connection between the two or to the core.

33. An alternator produces a *peak* voltage of 1,000 volts. What is the *effective* voltage? *a.* 636 volts; *b.* 707 volts; *c.* 1,110 volts; *d.* 1,414 volts.

34. A transformer secondary winding may be *tapped* in order to: *a.* vary the output voltage as required; *b.* vary the input voltage as required; *c.* ground the core intermittently as required; *d.* ground the main line intermittently as required.

35. Two coils are inductively coupled and, therefore, can form a basic transformer if there is a: *a.* steady flow of current in one coil; *b.* direct connection between the two coils by the use of a common core; *c.* fixed field around the coil in which no current flowed originally; *d.* changing field around one coil.

36. In a circuit in which the effective voltage is 707 volts, the maximum voltage is: *a.* 707 volts; *b.* 1,414 volts; *c.* 1,000 volts; *d.* 636 volts.

37. In practice, the effective current in an AC circuit is the current actually read on: *a.* a DC ammeter; *b.* an AC ammeter; *c.* a DC voltmeter; *d.* an AC voltmeter.

38. In a circuit, the measured AC current is 70.7 amp. The maximum current, therefore, is: *a.* 63.6 amp.; *b.* 14.14 amp.; *c.* 2.22 amp.; *d.* 100.0 amp.

39. An alternator produces a peak voltage of 1,414 volts. The maximum voltage is: *a.* 1,414 volts; *b.* 707 volts; *c.* 636 volts; *d.* 222 volts.

40. In a circuit in which the average voltage is 636 volts, the maximum voltage is: *a.* 707 volts; *b.* 1,414 volts; *c.* 1,000 volts; *d.* 636 volts.

Chapter 6. Inductance

1. Physical Inertia

Suppose a person had to move a very heavy object from its original position. As the force is applied, the object seems to resist any attempt to move it. This opposition to a change in position is called *inertia*. As the force is continued, the inertia is

Fig. 138a. An object in a state of rest tends to resist any attempt to move it from its original position. This resistance to change is called *inertia*.

finally overcome, and the object can gradually be moved until a desired speed of motion is obtained. At this point only the resistance between the object and the ground need be overcome (Fig. 138). As the speed reaches its maximum, the inertia appears to be at a minimum; but, if the pressure is decreased, the inertia increases and finally again becomes maximum as the force is removed. If an effort is made to stop the object's movement once it is in motion, it will be found that it tends to

174

oppose the attempt. This tendency must be met with additional force in the opposite direction. In other words, once the inertia has been overcome to compel movement in one direction, the object develops a counterforce that opposes any attempt to change its new condition (Fig. 139).

Exactly the same thing takes place in an electric circuit. The

Fig. 138b. As the inertia is overcome by some force, the object tends to move in a direction opposite to the direction of the applied force.

applied force is the e.m.f., and its effort to force a current through must be great enough to overcome the circuit's resistance to the flow of current *and also the circuit's inertia to the setting up of a magnetic field*. A field is always produced when a current flows through a circuit, and energy is required to produce this field as well as to cause the current to flow.

2. Electrical Inertia or Inductance

The inertia exhibited by an electric circuit in opposing the *creation*, *destruction*, or *variation* of its magnetic field is known as the property of *inductance*. Since every conductor produces a magnetic field when current is flowing through it, it follows that every conductor necessarily possesses some degree of inductance. The property of inductance is always associated with magnetic fields, and specifically, with any *change* that may take place in the field. This last fact, that of a changing field, is to be particularly noted, as it is under such conditions of change that the effects of inductance must be considered.

A magnetic field is formed when current flows. Any action,

Fig. 139. Once the inertia of an object at rest is overcome and the object is in motion, it tends to resist any change in its motion. Force must now be applied in a direction opposite to its direction of motion in order to bring it to a state of rest once again.

therefore, that opposes the field will directly affect the current that produced the field. This being the case, it is also possible to define inductance as that property of a circuit which opposes any *change* in the current flowing through a circuit.

A full definition of inductance may now be stated as follows: Inductance is that property which opposes any *change* in the current flow or in the magnetic field of an electric circuit.

The magnetic field around a coil or solenoid is far stronger than that existing in a straight wire. The property of inductance in such a device is, therefore, more pronounced, and because of this, coils and solenoids are often called *inductors* or *inductances*. Various types of inductors and their symbols are shown in Fig. 140.

3. Unit of Inductance

An induced current, as we have seen, always flows in such a direction that its field opposes any change in the condition of the field that induced it. The induced e.m.f. in the new circuit is, therefore, of opposite polarity to the applied e.m.f. and tends

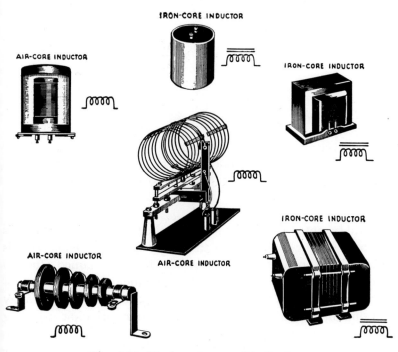

Fig. 140. Various types of inductors.

to oppose it. If the applied voltage is 100 volts and the induced voltage is 50 volts, the actual available voltage to force the current through the circuit will be the difference between them, 50 volts. Because the induced voltage operates in this counter fashion, it is called a *counter-e.m.f.* or a *back-e.m.f.*

The e.m.f. (E') of self-induction bears a constant ratio to the rate of change of current $(\Delta I/\Delta t)$. This *ratio* is termed the *inductance* (L) of the coil or the circuit and is sometimes expressed by the following formulas:

$$L = \frac{E'}{\dfrac{\Delta I}{\Delta t}}$$

$$E' = L \times \frac{\Delta I}{\Delta t}$$

where L = *property* of inductance
E' = e.m.f. of self-induction (or self-inductance of circuit)
I = current change in amperes
t = time during which a current change is occurring
Δ = symbol representing a constantly changing value

It will be noted that in the formulas the *property* of inductance is indicated by the letter L, but the *unit of inductance measurement* is commonly expressed as the *henry*. The henry is named after an American, Joseph Henry, who discovered the principle of electromagnetic induction in 1831. The same year, Michael Faraday in London, England, discovered the same principle working independently.

One henry of inductance (L) is present when a current *change* of 1 ampere per second in a circuit produces an induced e.m.f. of 1 volt. Since 1 henry represents a unit too large for many practical purposes, the units *millihenry* $(1/1,000$ henry) and *microhenry* $(1/1,000,000$ henry) are commonly used. The symbol for the millihenry is mh, and the symbol for the microhenry is μh.

The *inductance value* of a coil is determined by (1) the rate of current change through the coil (that is, its frequency), (2) the *square* of the number of turns of wire comprising the coil, and (3) if an iron core is used, the amount and type of iron in the core. All these factors affect the magnetic field; hence all must be considered in determining the value of inductance. In practice, the inductance value as operative in a circuit is computed as the *inductive reactance* described in greater detail in Chap. 8.

4. Self-inductance

When the effect of inductance is such as to cause the induced voltage to take effect in the very circuit where the current is flowing, the term *self-inductance* is often used. *Inductance* is the general term referring to the effects of a varying magnetic field and the resultant induced voltages that affect circuit operation, whereas *self-inductance* is a specific term referring to the effect produced in the same circuit where the original current is flowing. It may also be defined as the tendency of an inductor to induce a counter-voltage within itself that opposes any change in its existing condition.

In a transformer, for instance, the effects of inductance are noted mutually between the primary and secondary windings. The current in the primary induces a voltage in the secondary. A condition of *mutual inductance* is said to exist. If, on the other hand, we refer to the action of a single solenoid directly, we would speak of its *self-inductance* in describing its action. It should be remembered, however, that *inductance* and *self-inductance* are really the same, and that the terms are used interchangeably.

The effect of self-inductance can be shown by connecting an iron-core inductor in parallel to a lamp (Fig. 141). When the switch is closed, the lamp lights up brightly for a brief moment, and then becomes quite dim. As the current initially started to flow through the parallel load, most of the current passed through the lamp since the self-inductance of the inductor is initially very high. This self-inductance built up a large counter-e.m.f. that opposed the flow of current through the coil.

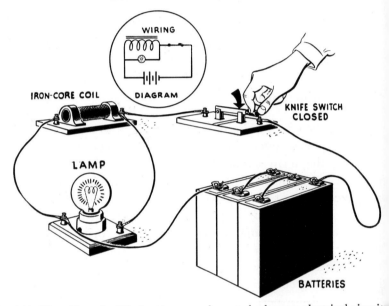

Fig. 141. The effect of self-inductance can be noted when an electrical circuit is initially closed—the lamp lights brightly and then dims.

As the current finally overcame the effect of the coil's self-inductance and reached its maximum strength, the magnetic field being built up around the coil could expand no farther. At that instant, the counter-e.m.f. disappeared and, like the lamp, the coil acted only as a resistor drawing off some of the current.

If the switch is opened, the lamp again flashes brightly and then goes out. Here again, it was the self-inductance of the coil that played the important part. When the circuit was broken, the magnetic field around the solenoid began to collapse. The collapsing field, now moving in the opposite direction, induced a current in the coil that set up a field trying to sustain the original field. The self-induced voltage set up by a rapidly collapsing field can be much higher than the initial voltage

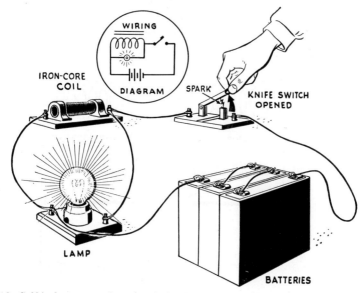

Fig. 142. Self-inductance of a circuit is also evidenced when the circuit is initially opened—the lamp lights very brightly and then goes out entirely.

activating the circuit as its value depends upon the rate at which the lines of force cut the coil. This fact explains why the lamp lights so brightly when the switch is opened and also explains why, when a switch is opened, a spark or flash often occurs (Fig. 142). The self-inductance of a circuit tends to induce a voltage that acts to sustain the current flow.

5. Inductors in Series and Parallel

Just as resistors (which are devices intended to introduce *resistance* into a circuit) can be connected in series, in parallel, or in series-parallel, so can inductors (which are used to introduce *inductance* into a circuit), as required.

The total inductance of several inductors in series is equal to the sum of the inductances of the individual inductors ($L_{\text{total}} = L_1 + L_2 +$ etc.) *provided there is no magnetic coupling between the inductors. Coupling* is a term that refers to the transfer

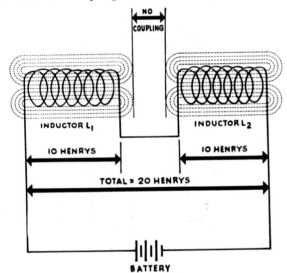

Fig. 143. In the absence of mutual coupling between two inductors connected in series in a circuit, the total inductance is the sum of their individual values.

of energy from one circuit to another by lines of force. *Unity coupling,* or *100 per cent coupling,* exists when the entire magnetic flux of one inductor cuts another inductor. If only half the flux cuts the other coil, the percentage of coupling is 50 per cent. At unity, the *coefficient of coupling* (K) is said to be one. The K would be 0.5 at 50 per cent coupling.

When coupling exists, the total inductance will depend upon whether the individual fields *aid* or *oppose* each other. Hence, if two inductors of 10 henrys each are placed in series and no mutual coupling exists, the total inductance will be 20 henrys ($L_{\text{total}} = L_1 + L_2 = 10 + 10 = 20$) (Fig. 143). If coupling *does* exist, the situation is changed drastically. It will be recalled that one of the factors in computing the inductance of any coil was "the *square* of the number of turns." If the two 10-henry inductors are connected in series and so placed that there is

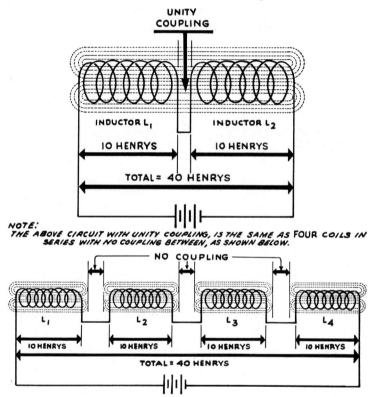

UNITY COUPLING

INDUCTOR L_1 — 10 HENRYS

INDUCTOR L_2 — 10 HENRYS

TOTAL = 40 HENRYS

NOTE:
THE ABOVE CIRCUIT WITH UNITY COUPLING, IS THE SAME AS FOUR COILS *IN SERIES WITH NO COUPLING BETWEEN, AS SHOWN BELOW.*

NO COUPLING

L_1 — 10 HENRYS
L_2 — 10 HENRYS
L_3 — 10 HENRYS
L_4 — 10 HENRYS

TOTAL = 40 HENRYS

Fig. 144. Where coupling does exist between two inductors in a circuit and their respective fields are aiding each other, the total value of inductance is greater than the sum of their respective values.

unity coupling between them, it is just as if the coils were really wound as one. Since we would then have *twice* the number of turns, the square of this number (2) would make the total inductance of the two coils *four times* as great as the single unit, or 40 henrys. It is just as if *four* individual 10-henry coils were connected in series but no coupling existed (Fig. 144).

This may be made clearer if we think first of the two coils (L_1 and L_2) representing 10 henrys each. Now the flux from L_1 at unity coupling is cutting all the turns of L_2. This induces a current in L_2, which in turn produces its own field, giving

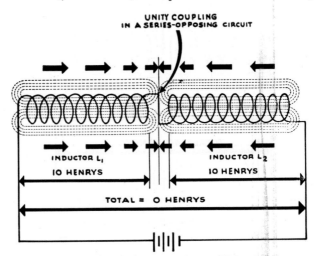

Fig. 145. In an ideal case, seldom obtainable in practice, the total inductance offered by two coils of equal value connected in a series-opposing circuit would be zero at unity coupling.

L_2 an additional inductance of 10 henrys. This additional inductance can be called L_3.

At the same time this is occurring, the flux around L_2 is causing the same effect on L_1, creating the effect of a fourth inductance of 10 henrys, which we can call L_4. We now have L_1 (10 henrys) + L_2 (10 henrys) + L_3 (10 henrys) + L_4 (10 henrys), or 40 henrys in all. Since L_3 and L_4 are the result of the mutual inductance between L_1 and L_2, L_3 and L_4 can be combined into one term $2M$ with a plus sign before it ($+2M$) to indicate a *series-aiding* field and a minus sign ($-2M$) to indicate a *series-opposing* field. The letter M stands for *mutual inductance*, and its value must be known before applying the basic formula.

In the ideal *series-aiding* circuit just described, where unity coupling existed (Fig. 144), the computation could have been:

$$L_{total} = (L_1 + L_2 + 2M) \times K$$
$$L_{total} = (10 + 10 + 20) \times 1$$
therefore, $\quad L_{total} = 40$

where $M = 10$ henrys and $K = 1$

In a similar ideal case, where unity coupling existed but the coils were connected in a *series-opposing* circuit (Fig. 145), the resultant inductance would be zero.

$$L_{total} = (L_1 + L_2 - 2M) \times K$$
$$L_{total} = (10 + 10 - 20) \times 1$$
therefore, $\quad L_{total} = 0$

where $M = 10$ henrys and $K = 1$

In practice, unity coupling is never fully approached except in the very highest quality transformers using the best type of core material. The use of a good core assures practically no magnetic leakage, which is the condition in which some of the flux fails to cut through the inductor. Transformers can thus be designed with a coefficient of coupling of 0.98, just 0.02 (2 per cent) below unity. Air-core inductors, or iron-core inductors with poorly designed cores, have much lower values of K since most of the lines of force are lost in space.

Inductors in parallel follow the same formula as resistors in parallel if no coupling exists. $L_{total} = 1/[(1/L_1) + (1/L_2) + \text{etc.}]$

If coupling does exist, the formula must include the M factor of mutual inductance. $L_{total} = 1/[(1/L_1 \pm M) + (1/L_2 \pm M) + \text{etc.}]$

6. Magnetic Shielding and Neutralization

When it is necessary to prevent magnetic coupling between circuits, or when it is desirable to avoid the creation of an inductance effect in a device where it might prove harmful, a number of methods are used.

Magnetic shielding makes use of a suitable metal enclosure around the inductor, the shield usually being grounded. The flux around the inductor is thus prevented from reaching another circuit. When a shield is placed around an inductor, the total inductance of the device is decreased, owing to the

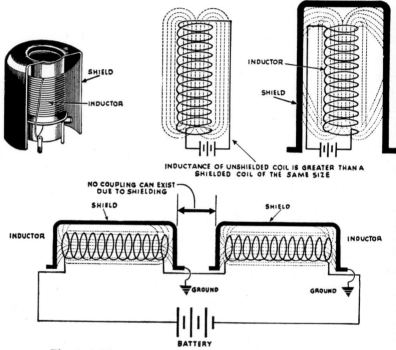

Fig. 146. The effect of a shield on the inductance of a coil.

fact that some of the flux enters the shield and has no effect in building up the coil's inductance (Fig. 146). It will be noted that magnetic shielding is really identical to electrostatic shielding described in Chap. 5.

Wire-wound resistors, consisting of suitable resistance wire wound in coil form on insulating material, may have considerable inductance. To prevent this in cases where such inductance is undesirable, a *noninductive winding* is used. By this method, the resistor is so wound that the turns of wire do not form a continuous circular winding, and thus do not constitute in effect, an inductor (Fig. 147). The field around each section opposes the field alongside, thus *neutralizing* (balancing out) the inductive effect.

A similar neutralizing effect is obtained by *transposing* (twisting) lengths of wire so that the field set up by one conductor opposes and neutralizes that of the other (Fig. 148).

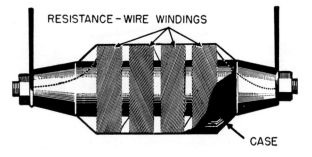

RESISTANCE – WIRE WINDINGS

CASE

TYPE OF NONINDUCTIVE RESISTOR WINDING

Fig. 147. To reduce the effect of inductance in such devices as wire-wound resistors, the individual windings comprising each section of the device are so wound that the field of each section opposes that of the adjacent section. This arrangement approaches the condition illustrated in Fig. 145.

7. Saturation

An air-core inductor maintains a practically constant value of inductance, but an iron-core inductor will vary in value as the core becomes more or less magnetized. It will be recalled that a magnet could be magnetized only to a certain point, beyond which it was said to be *saturated*. At the point of saturation, no greater magnetic field can be produced, and since inductance is a property of a circuit resulting from changes in magnetic fields, it logically follows that this property will be affected when the saturation point is reached. This is exactly the case. At saturation, the value of inductance will drop greatly (Fig. 149).

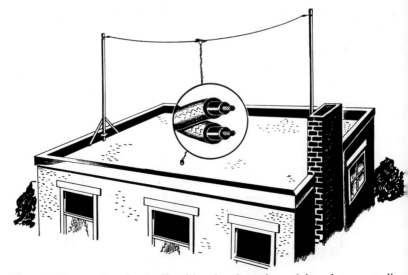

Fig. 148. Transposing the dual lead-in wires from the aerial tends to neutralize their respective fields. This aids in reducing the pickup of unwanted energy in the vicinity of the leadin and allows the energy picked up by the aerial to be transmitted with a minimum of loss.

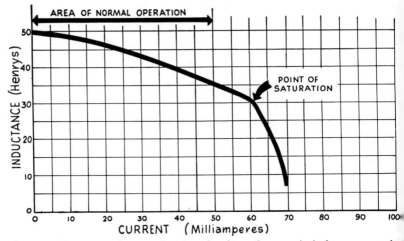

Fig. 149. Exaggerated curve showing the sharp decrease in inductance at the point of saturation.

To offset the effects of saturation in an iron-core inductor, an air gap (Fig. 150) is used. Since air has a far higher reluctance to magnetization than iron, the combined air and iron core that results prevents saturation from occurring to the same degree as when an iron core is used alone. When an air gap is used, the inductance is somewhat decreased. The higher reluctance of the circuit decreases the flux, but it tends to keep the inductance within limited values as current changes occur.

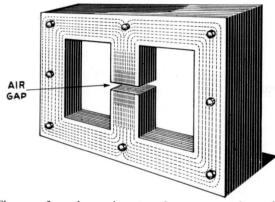

AIR GAP

Fig. 150. The use of an air gap in a transformer core reduces the possibility of core saturation where saturation is undesirable under specific operating conditions.

8. Types of Inductors

Inductors vary greatly in size and shape depending upon their designs and the functions they are to serve. Various names are also used to designate their specific functions when used in a circuit. As an example, *loading coil* refers to an inductor used in an electric circuit or line to increase the line's inductance. This is called *loading* or *loading the line*; hence the term *loading coil*. As various uses for inductors and other electrical devices are studied in later chapters, their trade names will be emphasized in order to accustom the student to their use. A knowledge of "trade terms" or names is extremely helpful when one is actually working in a trade or occupation.

Inductors may be divided into two general classifications: (1) the air-core type and (2) the iron-core type. Iron-core inductors are ordinarily used where *high* values of inductance are required. Air-core inductors are used where *low* values of inductance are needed. Iron-core inductors are available with ratings of many henrys; air-core inductors are usually available in units rated in millihenrys only (Fig. 140).

The term *iron-core inductor* is commonly used to designate all types of inductors using metal cores, as iron was the original core material used. Modern inductors, however, have cores composed of various types of iron and steel as well as of highly magnetic alloys that increase the over-all efficiency greatly.

The term *air-core inductor* includes units wound on solid nonmagnetic forms as well as those so wound that the core is mainly air. Such solid forms of nonmagnetic material do not affect the coil's inductance.

SUMMARY

1. Inductance is that property of an electric circuit which tends to oppose any change in the flow of current through the circuit. Because a flow of current through a conductor always produces a magnetic field, the effects of inductance are such that it also opposes the creation, destruction, or variation of the magnetic field.

2. The magnetic field around a coil is far stronger than that existing in a straight wire. Therefore, such devices possess a higher degree of inductance and because of this fact are called *inductors* or *inductances*.

3. The unit of measurement for inductance (L) is the henry (h). One henry (1 h) of inductance (L) is said to exist when a current change of 1 ampere per second produces an induced e.m.f. of 1 volt.

4. In practice, the terms *millihenry* (mh) and *microhenry* (μh) are often used, since the henry is too large a unit for many purposes.

5. The inductance value of a coil as measured in henrys is determined by

  a. The rate of current change through the coil (frequency)
  b. The square of the number of turns
  c. The type and size of iron core (if used)

Self-inductance refers to the tendency of a circuit to induce a voltage within itself that opposes any change in its existing condition. *Self-inductance* and *inductance* are actually identical terms.

6. Inductors may be connected in series or in parallel, and if no magnetic coupling between the individual units exists, the formulas used are

$$L_{\text{total}} \text{ (in series)} = L_1 + L_2 + \text{etc.}$$

$$L_{\text{total}} \text{ (in parallel)} = \frac{1}{\dfrac{1}{L_1} + \dfrac{1}{L_2} + \text{etc.}}$$

7. If magnetic coupling exists, the following factors must be considered:

  a. Coefficient of coupling (K), which at unity coupling equals 1
  b. Mutual inductance $(\pm M)$

8. A shield may be used to avoid magnetic coupling between circuits. This consists of a suitable magnetic material completely surrounding the inductor and is usually grounded. The use of a shield to avoid coupling also reduces the total inductance of the device.

9. A noninductive winding is one in which the turns of wire do *not* form a continuous circular winding.

10. In an iron-core inductor, the inductance is affected by the degree of core saturation, which in turn depends on the amount of current flowing through the coil. The use of an air gap aids in maintaining the inductance value through large variations of current values.

Quiz: Inductance

This quiz will help you review the material just studied. See the quiz directions on page 24 before answering the questions below.

1. When a coil is shielded, its inductance is: *a.* completely eliminated; *b.* decreased; *c.* increased; *d.* unaffected.

2. The unit of inductance *measurement* is the: *a.* henry; *b.* milliampere; *c.* microvolt; *d.* ohm.

3. Where the effects of inductance are noted within the same circuit in which the original current exists, it is called: *a.* mutual inductance; *b.* self-inductance; *c.* variable inductance; *d.* stationary inductance.

4. "Inductance is that property which opposes any change in the current flow or in the magnetic field of an electric circuit." This definition is: *a.* correct if word *field* is changed to *flux;* *b.* correct if word *opposes* is changed to *aids; c.* incorrect as stated; *d.* correct as stated.

5. Transposing or twisting lengths of wire: *a.* has no effect on its inductance; *b.* increases the inductance; *c.* doubles the inductance; *d.* decreases the inductance.

6. The magnetic field surrounding a conductor is the result of: *a.* resistance of the wire; *b.* insulation covering the wire; *c.* inertia of the metal; *d.* current flow through the wire.

7. The induced voltage that opposes the original e.m.f. applied to the circuit is called the: *a.* counter-e.m.f.; *b.* terminal e.m.f.; *c.* load e.m.f.; *d.* circuit e.m.f.

8. Unity coupling exists when the coefficient of coupling (K) equals: *a.* 0.5; *b.* 0.75; *c.* 1.0; *d.* 1.5.

9. When two inductors are connected in series and no magnetic coupling exists, the total inductance may be found by the following formula: *a.* $L = L_1 - L_2$; *b.* $L = L_1 + L_2$; *c.* $L = L_1 + L_2 - 2M$; *d.* $L = L_1 + L_2 + 2M$.

10. One 10-henry coil is connected in parallel to a 20-henry coil in a *series-aiding* circuit. If $K = 1$ and $M = 10$, the total effective inductance is: *a.* 48; *b.* 36; *c.* 24; *d.* 12.

11. The inductance value of a coil is *not* affected by the: *a.* size and type of core; *b.* square of the number of turns; *c.* resistance of the wire; *d.* frequency of applied voltage.

12. The inductance of a solenoid is greater than that of the same length of uncoiled wire. This is due to the: *a.* greater amount of current needed to flow through a solenoid; *b.* heavier weight of a solenoid compared to straight wire; *c.* weaker magnetic field around a solenoid; *d.* stronger magnetic field around a solenoid.

13. Two 60-henry coils are connected in a *series-aiding* circuit. If $K = 0.5$ and $M = 20$, the total inductance is: *a.* 80; *b.* 60; *c.* 40; *d.* 20.

14. "An air-core inductor maintains a practically constant value of inductance, but an iron-core inductor will vary in value as the core becomes more or less magnetized." This statement is: *a.* correct as stated; *b.* incorrect as stated; *c.* correct only if the air-core inductor has an exceedingly small core; *d.* correct if the air-core inductor has an exceedingly large core.

15. Two 20-henry coils are connected together in a series-aiding circuit. If $M = 10$ at unity coupling, the total inductance is: *a.* 10 henrys; *b.* 40 henrys; *c.* 80 henrys; *d.* 100 henrys.

16. When a switch is opened in an electric circuit that is carrying a current of 10 amp., a heavy spark is noted across the gap between the blade and the jaw of the switch. This spark is due to the: *a.* heavy current flowing in the circuit; *b.* self-induction of the circuit; *c.* high applied e.m.f.; *d.* low resistance of the circuit.

17. Inductive effects are *not* noted when a field is: *a.* expanding; *b.* contracting; *c.* collapsing; *d.* stationary.

18. Generally, iron-core inductors are used where: *a.* low values of inductance are required; *b.* high values of inductance are required; *c.* shielding is not required; *d.* alternating current alone is used.

19. A millihenry equals: *a.* 1/1,000 henry; *b.* 1/10 henry; *c.* 1,000 henrys; *d.* 1,000,000 henrys.

20. At *saturation*, the value of inductance will: *a.* increase slightly; *b.* increase greatly; *c.* decrease considerably; *d.* remain unaffected if the e.m.f. is increased.

21. The term *air-core inductor* refers to units wound on: *a.* magnetic forms of all kinds; *b.* iron forms only; *c.* nonmagnetic forms; *d.* hollow forms only.

22. The symbol for a *millihenry* is: *a.* mh; *b.* μh; *c.* *L*; *d.* *K*.

23. A wire-wound noninductive resistor is one in which the winding is: *a.* impregnated with an insulating varnish; *b.* circularly wound; *c.* insulated from the form; *d.* noncircularly wound.

24. All other factors being equal, the use of an air gap in an iron-core inductor: *a.* has no effect on its inductance; *b.* increases the inductance; *c.* decreases the inductance; *d.* doubles the inductance.

25. Two 40-henry coils are connected together in a *series-opposing* circuit. If $K = 1$ and $M = 10$, the total inductance is: *a.* 60; *b.* 40; *c.* 20; *d.* 0.

Chapter 7. Capacitance

1. Capacitance

Just as inductance is associated with the magnetic field of a circuit, another circuit property, called *capacitance*, is associated

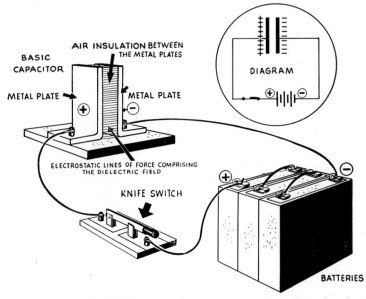

Fig. 151. A dielectric field is formed when a source of e.m.f. is placed across conductors separated by some form of insulation.

with the dielectric field. It will be recalled that a dielectric field is formed wherever an electric charge is found, and since, in an electric circuit, it is the movement of electric charges in the form of electrons with which we are directly concerned, it is apparent that dielectric fields are always encountered. As the word *dielectric* suggests, an insulator or dielectric is also always present when a dielectric field exists, since without such a dielectric, the charges would readily escape and the field collapse.

In creating an electric field, energy is necessarily expended, but a great deal of this energy is stored up within the field it-

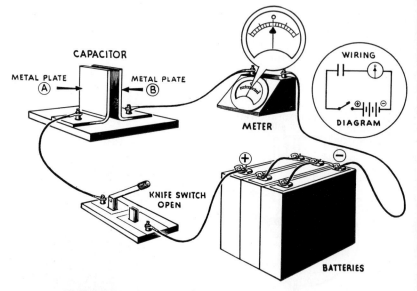

KNIFE SWITCH OPEN, METER READS ZERO.

Fig. 152. No charge appears on the plates of the capacitor since the circuit is open. No dielectric field is formed.

self. Hence, as in the case of the magnetic field, when any *current change* occurred that might affect the field, the stored-up energy within the field developed a counter-e.m.f. to oppose the current change.

In order to create a dielectric field, a source of e.m.f. or voltage must exist between two points separated by some form of insulation (Fig. 151). Once the field is created it tends to oppose any *voltage change* that would affect its original condition. Capacitance, then, is that electric property which opposes any change in *voltage*, whereas inductance is a property that opposes any change in *current*.

All circuits possess a degree of capacitance, just as all circuits possess a degree of inductance. The amount varies depending upon the circuit's constants, such as the length of the wire used, the distance between the wires, the type of insulation separating

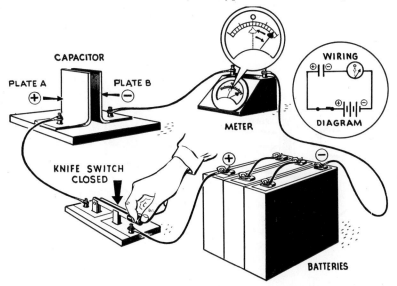

KNIFE SWITCH CLOSED. METER SWEEPS MOMENTARILY TO RIGHT AND THEN RETURNS TO ZERO.

Fig. 153. The capacitor plates accept a charge when the circuit is closed. The momentary movement of the meter pointer in one direction indicates a current surge (sudden flow) in that direction.

them, and the voltage applied. This will, perhaps, be better understood if we study the action of a *capacitor* (often called a *condenser*), which is a device designed to introduce the property of capacitance within a circuit.

2. The Capacitor

Basically, a capacitor consists of two conductors, called *electrodes* or *plates*, that are separated by a dielectric. The plates may be made of aluminum, copper, or tin. Alloys (mixtures of metals) or foils (metal that has been compressed into very thin sheets so that it may be readily folded such as the tin foil used to wrap packages) are also used. The dielectric may be air, glass, mica, or any other good insulating material. In some cases, an electrolyte that forms an insulating gaseous oxide film is used.

To observe the action of a simple capacitor (Fig. 152), we can use two sheets of metal separated from one another and

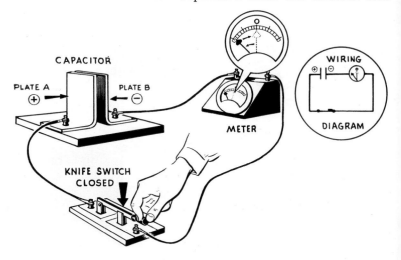

BATTERIES REMOVED AND KNIFE SWITCH <u>CLOSED</u> AGAIN, METER SWEEPS TO THE LEFT AND THEN RETURNS TO ZERO.

Fig. 154. The capacitor will retain its charge even when the battery is removed from the circuit. The shorting of the capacitor through the meter and a closed switch produces a momentary discharge-current surge in a direction opposite to that taken by the initial charging current.

connected through a switch and meter to a battery. The sheets of metal act as the plates of the capacitor; the air that separates them is the dielectric.

When the switch is closed, plate A is connected to the positive terminal of the battery and plate B to the negative terminal. The plates thus become charged—one positive and the other negative. As this is occurring, the meter shows a definite current surge in one direction but rapidly returns to the zero setting (Fig. 153). If the battery is now removed from the circuit, and the switch again closed, the meter again shows a momentary current surge, but this time in the *opposite* direction (Fig. 154).

Since an ordinary electric current flow requires a complete path along which the electrons can travel, we apparently have

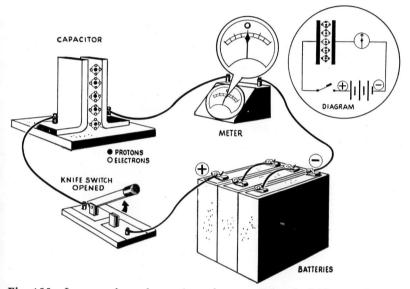

Fig. 155a. In an uncharged capacitor where no dielectric field can exist, the electron orbits within the dielectric remain in their normal undistorted state.

here a somewhat different phenomenon. The air dielectric is not a conductor; hence the circuit at this point is incomplete. The momentary current flow that appeared during *charging* of the capacitor plates was due to the distortion of the electron orbits within the dielectric.

A dielectric field was formed between the plates as they became charged. This field placed the dielectric separating them under a stress or strain, causing the positions of the electron orbits within the dielectric to become distorted (Fig. 155). Owing to the fact that the electrons within an insulator are firmly bound to their orbits, they could not be torn away entirely. The electrons simply moved closer to the positive plate and away from the negative plate. A *movement* of electrons *is* an electric current; hence the meter reading. The movement was only temporary until the plates received their maximum charge and the maximum field strength was created. Once it

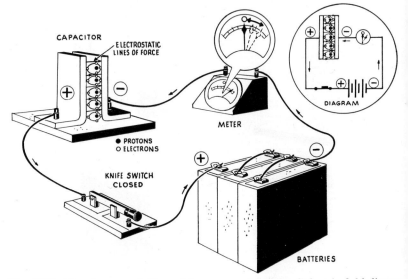

Fig. 155b. The electrostatic lines of force comprising the dielectric field distort the electron orbits. The movement of the electrons closer to the positively charged plate of the capacitor produces the surge current that is noted on the meter.

was created, the orbits remained distorted, and no further current flow occurred.

When the e.m.f. was removed, these orbits tended to remain in their distorted shapes, because electrons are not readily removed from their orbits within a dielectric and further because the plates themselves retain their charge. The moment a path was constructed that allowed the electrons on the negative plate to be conducted to the positive plate, the field was destroyed. The lines of force across the dielectric (representing stored-up energy) begin to collapse and thus to move in an opposite direction to the one they followed when the field was formed. This causes the electron orbits to return to their original shape. The movement of electrons within the dielectric in this opposite direction gives rise to the current observed, that is,

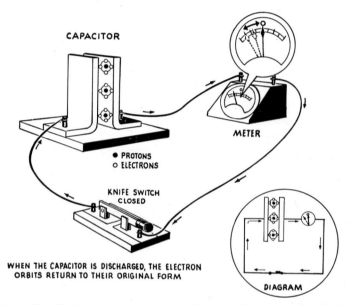

CAPACITOR

METER

● PROTONS
○ ELECTRONS

**KNIFE SWITCH
CLOSED**

WHEN THE CAPACITOR IS DISCHARGED, THE ELECTRON
ORBITS RETURN TO THEIR ORIGINAL FORM

DIAGRAM

Fig. 156. The discharge current produced by a charged capacitor is due to the return of the electrons to their normal orbits.

to the flow in a reverse direction, and is described as the *discharge* current (Fig. 156).

Charging the capacitor created a distortion of the electron orbits within the dielectric in one direction; discharging the capacitor returned the orbits to their original condition.

A definite voltage was needed to charge the plates and create the dielectric field. The energy represented by this voltage was stored within the dielectric field. When the capacitor was discharged, the dielectric field created a voltage of its own to oppose the change in its condition.

3. Capacitance Compared to Elasticity

Just as inductance has been compared to inertia, capacitance may be compared to elasticity or springiness.

A boxer training with a punching bag is a good illustration. Before the bag is punched, it remains in a vertical position (Fig. 157). This may be compared to the uncharged capacitor.

Fig. 157. Capacitance may be compared to the elasticity or "springiness" of a punching bag. Before the blow is delivered, the bag can be considered as being "uncharged" just as a capacitor is said to be uncharged before it has been connected across an e.m.f.

Fig. 158. Delivery of the boxer's punch causes the punching bag to move outward to an extent dependent upon the force exerted. Similarly a capacitor accepts a charge the strength of which is determined by the applied electrical energy.

As the punch is delivered, the bag is moved outward to an extent depending upon the force exerted (Fig. 158). This may be compared to the e.m.f. or voltage applied to the capacitor in order to charge it. When the bag reaches the maximum distance it can move in a given direction owing to the elasticity of its supports, it represents stored energy, which flings the bag backward with almost equal force (Fig. 159). This may be compared to the energy stored within a capacitor's dielectric and then released when discharge takes place.

Another analogy may be found in the action of two pistons or plungers connected through suitable pipes but separated from one another by a rubber gasket or diaphragm (Fig. 160). If piston A is pushed down, the water to the left of the diaphragm is under increased pressure and forces the diaphragm to expand to the right. In doing so, it increases the pressure on the water on that side and forces piston B upward. This action continues until the diaphragm elasticity has built up a sufficient counter-pressure to withstand the force exerted by piston A (Fig. 161a).

Fig. 159. When the punching bag reaches the maximum distance it can move in a given direction owing to the elasticity of its supports, it represents stored energy that flings the bag backward with almost equal force. This may be compared to the energy stored within a charged capacitor's dielectric field which is released when the capacitor is discharged.

Now, as piston A is released, the diaphragm forces its way back to its original position, driving the water to its left against the piston and causing it to rise. Simultaneously, pressure to its right drops, and piston B returns to its normal position also (Fig. 161b). It can be said that the diaphragm stored up the energy needed to force A down and B up, and returned the energy when the force on A was released.

If piston A is moved up and down within the elastic limit of the diaphragm, the *energy* will be transferred by the water from A through the diaphragm to B; *yet no water actually would flow through the diaphragm*. Similarly, in a capacitor, *no current flows through the dielectric*, but electrical energy can be stored up within it and released as required.

4. Measurement of Capacitance

The quantity of electricity (or number of electrons) that exists in a circuit is measured in units called *coulombs*. Six hundred and twenty-eight billion billion* electrons are contained in 1 coulomb, and if 1 coulomb per second flows through a circuit,

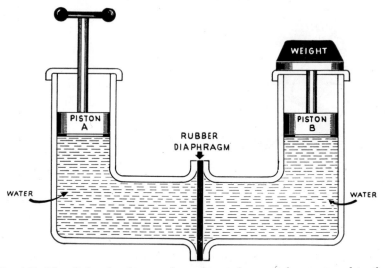

Fig. 160. The dielectric of an uncharged capacitor may be compared to the condition of the rubber diaphragm shown. The diaphragm is under no strain in the illustration. Similarly, the absence of a dielectric field in an uncharged capacitor allows the dielectric to remain undisturbed.

it is represented by the unit we already know as an *ampere*. In other words, in order to have current flowing at the *rate* of 1 ampere within a circuit, a *quantity* of electrons represented by 1 coulomb must pass through each second.

Since capacitance represents stored electric energy, the *quantity* of electricity stored is also measured in coulombs, but its ability or *capacity* to store this quantity of electricity is measured in a unit called the *farad*. A farad of capacitance is said to exist when 1 coulomb of electrical energy can be stored within a dielectric field as an e.m.f. of 1 volt is applied. In order

* Expressed as 6.28×10^{18}.

to store the potential energy of 628 billion billion electrons within a dielectric field under the pressure of but 1 volt, the dielectric would have to be of huge proportions; in fact, as large as a building of skyscraper proportions. Therefore, in practical usage, the terms *microfarad* (μf), one-millionth (or

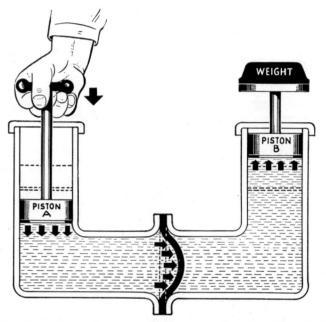

Fig. 161*a***.** Increasing pressure on the water to the left of the diaphragm exerts a distorting force on the rubber. This is similar to the condition of dielectric strain that exists when a capacitor is charged.

1/1,000,000) of a farad, and *micromicrofarad* (μμf), one million-millionth (or 1/1,000,000,000,000) of a farad, are used.

The word *capacity* is often used interchangeably with the word *capacitance*. Capacitance, however, is best used to represent the electrical *property* or effect on a circuit that opposes voltage changes, whereas *capacity*, if used, should be thought of as simply representing the *quantity* of electricity that can be stored within a capacitor.

5. Factors that Affect Capacitance

Capacitance depends upon

a. The total area of the plates

b. The distance between the plates (thickness of the dielectric)

c. The *dielectric constant* (K)

a. *Area of the Plates.* The greater the area of the plates, the greater the number of electric charges they can hold. If the plates of a capacitor measuring 1 sq. in. can hold, let us assume,

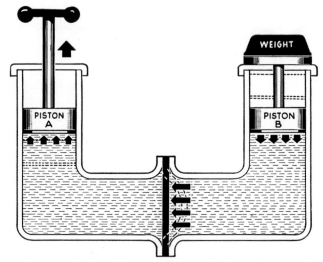

Fig. 161*b*. In its strained position, the rubber diaphragm represents stored-up energy. When pressure on piston *A* is released, the elasticity of the diaphragm forces the water under piston *A* in the opposite direction. This may be compared to the dielectric field's energy that is released by the discharge of a charged capacitor. It should be noted that no water flowed *through* the diaphragm; similarly, no current flows *through* the dielectric of a capacitor.

1 million electric charges at a given voltage, doubling the area will double the number of electric charges that can be accumulated on the plates. Another way to look at this is to remember that the dielectric field is the place where the energy is actually stored. Hence, enlarging the area of the plates allows the dielectric field to be proportionally enlarged (Fig. 162).

b. *Distance between the Plates, or Dielectric Thickness.* In the basic capacitor just studied, air was the dielectric used. Let

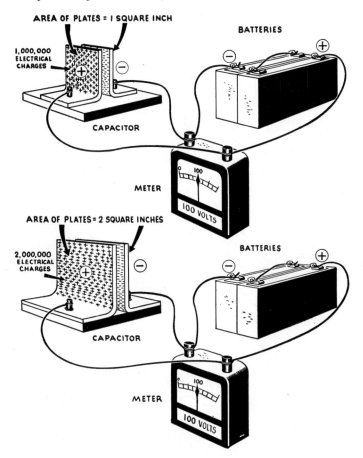

Fig. 162. Enlarging the area of the plates of a capacitor increases its capacity to "store" electrical charges even though the applied e.m.f. remains constant.

us assume this device had a capacity of 10 microfarads (10 μf) when the spacing between the plates was 1 in. If the experiment is again conducted with the plates only $\frac{1}{2}$ in. apart, a larger current surge will appear, and if the capacitance were measured, it would be found to be 20 μf. If the spacing is doubled to 2 in., the current surge will be less. The distance between the plates, or, in other words, the thickness of the air dielectric, affected

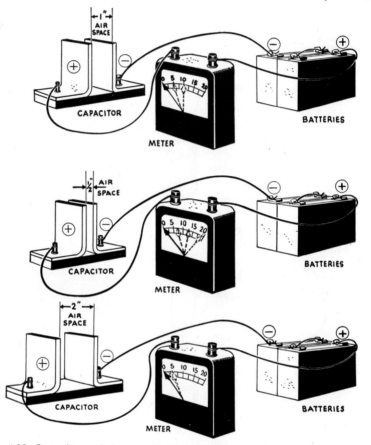

Fig. 163. Capacitance is increased when the plates are brought closer together and decreases as the plates are placed farther apart.

the total capacitance in direct proportion to the distance or thickness. This is due to the fact that the dielectric field between two charged plates is strongest when the distance of separation is the least (Fig. 163).

c. *Dielectric Constant.* The strength of the dielectric field between the plates of a capacitor will also depend upon the type of material used as the dielectric. As a basis of comparison, dry air is used and has been assigned a *dielectric constant* (a term symbolized by the letter K and representing the comparative effect of a substance on capacitance when used as a dielectric)

Fig. 164. When the potential between the clouds and the earth exceeds the dielectric strength of the atmosphere, lightning flashes through the air. This phenomenon often occurs during storms particularly in warm weather.

of 1. K represents the increase in capacitance when a particular type of dielectric is used, in comparison to air. A high grade of mica, for example, has a dielectric constant of 8. Hence, a capacitor of a given size and at a given voltage using mica as the dielectric would have a capacitance eight times as great as a similar capacitor using air as the dielectric.

6. Dielectric Strength

Dielectric strength is the ability of an insulator to withstand the electric stress across it without breaking down, that is, allowing current to pass through it. It is expressed in volts per inch. Dry air, used as a standard of comparison, will stand about 25,000 volts per inch thickness. This means that if 25,000 volts had been placed across the plates of the basic capacitor just studied, and the distance between the plates had been 1 in., a current would have passed through the air dielectric and the device would no longer have been acting as a capacitor. The electrons would have been torn from their orbits within the dielectric under the pressure of the e.m.f. across the plates. The lightning flashes that occur in a storm are the result of the breakdown of the air dielectric separating the "plates" of a huge capacitor—one "plate" being the storm clouds, and the other, the earth. The tremendous voltages involved are evident when one sees the terrific intensity of the flash, as well as its length (Fig. 164).

The dielectric strength of other substances varies greatly. Rubber, for instance, has a dielectric strength of approximately 150,000 volts per inch thickness, and the dielectric strength of mica is some eight times greater. Such figures are not completely accurate under all conditions, as temperature, degree of compression, moisture, condition of the surface, as well as the frequency of the voltage applied, greatly affect this characteristic. Heat lowers the breakdown voltage, as do moisture and a poor surfacing. The application of higher AC frequencies tends to heat the dielectric and thus reduce the dielectric strength as compared to lower frequencies.

Dielectric strength and dielectric constant should not be confused. Materials having great dielectric strength do not necessarily possess a high dielectric constant, nor does the reverse hold true. Distilled water, for example, has a very high dielectric constant (81) but will break down at comparatively very low voltages.

Capacitors are normally rated for operation at specific voltages (termed the *working voltage*), and such voltages should

not be exceeded if breakdown is to be avoided. Both the AC
and DC ratings are usually given, since, it will be recalled, the
AC peak voltages are higher than the effective DC equivalent.
A capacitor rated at 1,000 volts DC should not be used on
1,000 volts AC, as the peak voltage of 1,410 volts ($AC_{peak} = 1.41$
$\times AC_{eff.}$ or DC) would break down the dielectric.

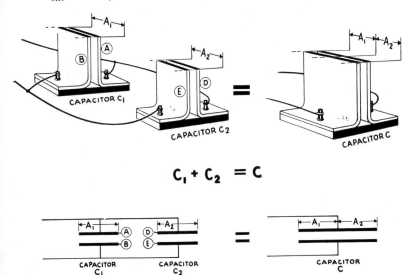

$$C_1 + C_2 = C$$

Fig. 165. The total capacitance of capacitors connected in a parallel circuit
is found by determining the sum of the individual capacitances.

7. Capacitors in Series and Parallel

Just as batteries, resistors, and inductors can be used in series
or in parallel (also in series-parallel when needed) to attain
certain combinations, so can capacitors.   When capacitors are
connected in parallel, the effect is to increase the area of the
plates (Fig. 165). Therefore, to find the total capacitance, the
individual capacitances are added together.

$$C_{total} = C_1 + C_2 + \text{etc.}$$

Example: Two capacitors, one of 5 μf and the other of 10 μf, are
connected in parallel. What is the total capacitance?

Step 1. $C_{\text{total}} = C_1 + C_2$ *This is the formula.*

Step 2. C $= 5 + 10$ *Here we substitute the actual values of C_1 and C_2.*

Step 3. C $= 15 \ \mu f$ *Ans.*

In the example illustrated, both capacitors were rated in microfarads. In cases where one is rated in microfarads and the other in micromicrofarads, it is necessary to convert one form into the other. Suppose one capacitor is rated at 5 μf and another at 5,000 $\mu\mu f$. If an answer in micromicrofarads is desired, the 5 μf must be converted to micromicrofarads before the two are added together. A microfarad is one million times as great as a micromicrofarad, and therefore 5 μf is the equivalent of 5,000,000 $\mu\mu f$ (5 $\times$ 1,000,000 = 5,000,000). Conversely, if an answer in microfarads is required, it would be necessary to convert the 5,000 $\mu\mu f$ into microfarads. A micromicrofarad is only one-millionth (1/1,000,000) as great as a microfarad. Hence, 5,000 $\mu\mu f$ would be the equivalent of 5/1,000 or 0.005 μf.

$$\frac{5,000}{1} \times \frac{1}{1,000,000} = \frac{5}{1,000} = 0.005$$

The *voltage* across each *parallel* capacitor is the same, just as is the case with parallel resistors or dry cells. Since capacitors have varying voltage breakdown ratings, it is necessary to select units with suitable ratings for the purpose required. A capacitor designed to operate on 100 volts, for example, may be placed in parallel with units rated at higher voltages provided that the entire combination is not used at any higher voltage than 100 (Fig. 166).

In practice, capacitors are placed in parallel when the total capacitance within a circuit must be *increased*. They are connected in series when the total capacitance must be *decreased*, or when the voltage rating of a particular unit is too low for circuit requirements.

When capacitors are connected in *series*, the total capacitance is always less than that of the smallest unit in the combination, but the voltage rating of the series combination is normally higher. The effect here is as if the thickness of the dielectric had been increased or the plates placed further apart (Fig. 167). As the outer plate of C_1 is charged negatively, the inner plate

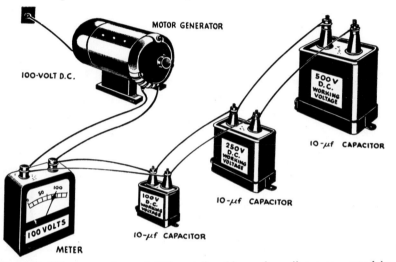

Fig. 166. When capacitors of different "working voltages" are connected in parallel, the voltage across the circuit must not exceed the working voltage of the lowest rated unit.

assumes a positive charge. In C_2, however, the outer plate received a positive charge, causing its inner plate to become negative. The two inner plates of the combination thus neutralize each other and have no effect on the action of the capacitor combination. The series combination acts as a single capacitor equivalent to a capacitor having a total dielectric thickness equal to the sum of the dielectric thicknesses of the individual units.

The voltage breakdown of capacitors connected in series will be higher than that of the individual units. Theoretically, it should be equal to the sum of the voltage breakdown ratings for each capacitor. This is not the case, however, when direct current is applied, as the DC voltage will divide in direct proportion to the DC resistance of the two dielectrics. If both dielectrics have the same resistance, the voltage drop across each capacitor will be the same, but if they do not, a higher voltage drop will occur across the unit of higher resistance.

Suppose two 5-μf capacitors (A and B) each rated at 500 volts

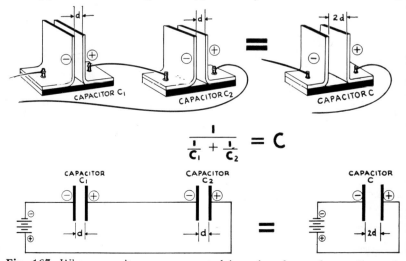

$$\frac{1}{\frac{1}{C_1} + \frac{1}{C_2}} = C$$

Fig. 167. When capacitors are connected in series, the total capacitance is less than that of the smallest unit (in capacitance) and is the reciprocal of the sum of the reciprocals.

DC were connected in series and placed across a 1,000-volt source (Fig. 168). If both units had an *equivalent* DC resistance, the total voltage rating for each unit would not be exceeded, and satisfactory results would be obtainable. Let us assume, however, that one capacitor has a DC resistance of 25 megohms (25,000,000 ohms), and the other, 75 megohms (75,000,000 ohms). The voltage drop across the capacitor (A) having a higher resistance would be three-fourths of the total voltage across the circuit, or 750 volts, while the voltage drop across the low-resistance capacitor (B) would be only 250 volts. Capacitor A would most likely break down quickly, as its rated voltage would be exceeded

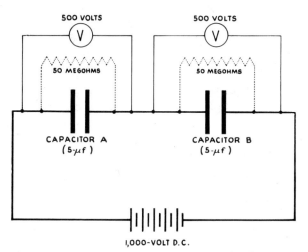

Fig. 168. Where capacitors of equal capacitance also have equivalent DC resistances, the voltage drop across each unit in a series circuit will be the same.

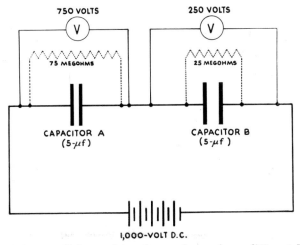

Fig. 169. Where capacitors of equal capacitance have different DC resistances, the voltage will be higher across the unit of higher resistance when they are connected in series.

by 250 volts (Fig. 169). Where two capacitors, A and B, of different values of capacitance are placed in series, the voltage across the smaller unit B will be *higher*. This is due to the fact that its resistance is higher as compared to a larger capacitor of the same type. Hence, the voltage drop across it is also higher. Capacitor A is of greater capacity than capacitor B, as the plates are closer together. The dielectric resistance of A is less than that of B. The voltage drop across A, the larger value of capacitance, is less than that across B, the smaller capacitance whose resistance is higher.

In order to find the total capacitance of capacitors connected in *series*, a formula equivalent to the one used to find the total resistance of resistors in *parallel* must be used.

$$C_{\text{total}} = \frac{1}{\dfrac{1}{C_1} + \dfrac{1}{C_2} + \text{etc.}}$$

Where capacitors are connected in parallel, a formula equivalent to the one used to find the total resistance of resistors in series is used.

$$C_{\text{total}} = C_1 + C_2 + \text{etc.}$$

Example: What is the total capacitance available when capacitors of 20 μf and 10 μf are connected in series?

Step 1. $$C = \frac{1}{\dfrac{1}{C_1} + \dfrac{1}{C_2}}$$ *This is the formula.*

Step 2. $$C = \frac{1}{\dfrac{1}{20} + \dfrac{1}{10}} \diagdown 20$$ *Here we substitute the actual values of C_1 and C_2 and obtain the least common denominator, 20.*

Step 3. $$C = \frac{1}{\dfrac{1 + 2}{20}}$$ *Here we mark down the fact that the denominator of one fraction (20) goes into 20 once, and the other denominator (10) goes into 20 twice.*

Step 4. $C = \dfrac{1}{\dfrac{3}{20}}$

Adding them up we have a total of $\dfrac{3}{20}$.

Step 5. $C = \dfrac{20}{3} = 6.6 \ \mu\text{f}$

(Ans.)

Here we solved the fraction below the main dividing line by inverting it. This is the reciprocal.

Note that the *total* capacitance is *less* than the smallest capacitance of the series combination.

8. Capacitor Losses

1. *Leakage Loss*. The dielectric used in a capacitor is selected on the basis of its dielectric constant and dielectric strength. In addition, the material has very high insulation qualities. As we know, this means that its resistance to the flow of current is very high, running into millions of ohms. This very high resistance prevents a flow of current *through* the dielectric. If the resistance becomes low owing to deterioration of the material, or owing to the use of a poor dielectric to start with, some current will pass through the dielectric. This is termed a *leakage current* and results in a *leakage loss*. Should the leakage loss become excessive, the value of the device as a capacitor is negligible. It will not retain its charge, and excessive heating due to the leakage current usually results in rapid deterioration.

2. *Dielectric Hysteresis Loss*. When an alternating current is applied to an iron-core solenoid, the rapid reversals of current produced hysteresis, that is, a loss in the form of heat as the electron orbits within the core were shifted around completely at each current reversal. In the dielectric of a capacitor, the electron orbits are subjected to the same treatment when alternating current is used, giving rise to a loss called *dielectric hysteresis*. The degree of dielectric hysteresis depends upon the type of dielectric used. Dry air, for example, has but little loss compared to paper dielectrics. Because of this, it is used as a standard of comparison for other dielectrics in the matter of *power factor*.

Power factor is a term that describes the efficiency of capacitor action. Theoretically, a perfect capacitor will return to a circuit all the energy stored within it. Such a perfect capacitor is said to have a power factor of zero (0.000); in other words, no loss of power has occurred. Other dielectrics, compared to air, have different power factors. Mica, for example, has a power factor of approximately 0.0005, which indicates that the loss within the capacitor would amount to five ten-thousandths of the total energy originally supplied. Dry fiber may have a power factor of 0.09, which indicates that 9 per cent (9%) of the energy is lost.

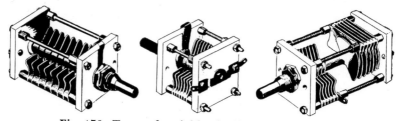

Fig. 170. Types of variable air-dielectric capacitors.

The power factor of a capacitor is mainly determined by the type of dielectric used and is not affected to any great extent by the capacitance of the unit, the voltages involved, or the frequency of the current. However, it is affected by the conditions under which the dielectric is caused to function. Moisture and heat, for example, will greatly affect the dielectric and, in turn, increase losses. This gives rise to a poorer power factor than would be the case under good conditions.

9. Types of Capacitors

1. *Variable Capacitors.* Variable capacitors (Fig. 170), used mainly in the field of radio, are generally of the air-dielectric type. These consist of a number of metal plates (the exact number depending upon the capacitance of the unit), some of which are mounted on a shaft, with others mounted in a permanent position. The plates that rotate within the fixed plates comprise the *rotor,* and the fixed position plates, the *stator*. The plates of the rotor, as are those of the stator, are in parallel with each other. The effective capacitance of the device is at maximum point when the plates of the rotor are completely enmeshed with the stator. Minimum capacitance exists when the rotor is completely unmeshed.

Two or more variable-capacitor units are often mounted on a

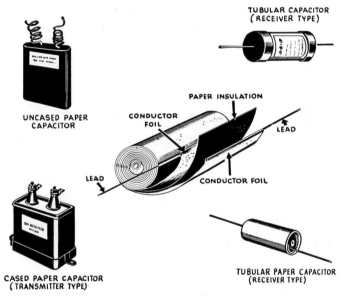

Fig. 171. **Types of fixed paper-dielectric capacitors.**

common shaft where capacitance variation within more than one circuit is simultaneously desired.

2. *Fixed Capacitors.* Fixed capacitors may be differentiated by the types of dielectric used, such as paper or mica.

Paper capacitors (Fig. 171) consist of strips of metal foil separated by a thin sheet of paper that is impregnated with a moisture repellent, such as wax or paraffin. The complete strips are rolled compactly and usually sealed within a container of cardboard or metal.

Paper capacitors may also be oil impregnated or may rest within a container holding a quantity of oil. Such capacitors are mainly used on high-voltage circuits.

The size of paper capacitors and their voltage ratings vary greatly.

Where fixed capacitors are to be used in circuits where the least possible losses are allowable and where voltages are consistently higher, mica is the preferred dielectric. Mica capacitors (Fig. 172) are made of layers of foil separated by mica strips.

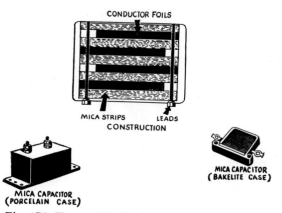

Fig. 172. Types of fixed mica-dielectric capacitors.

Just as in the air-dielectric variable capacitors, the strips are paralleled into two groups, each group serving as a plate of the complete unit.

Electrolytic capacitors (Fig. 173) are characterized by large capacitance in proportion to size. Their operation depends upon the fact that when certain metals (such as aluminum) are immersed in an electrolyte and have a positive voltage imposed upon them, the metals will form a gaseous oxide film, which will serve as an excellent dielectric. This dielectric film possesses a high capacitance per unit area because of its extreme thinness.

The electrolyte is actually the *negative electrode*, and its outside contact is often the metal container in which the positive plate and the electrolyte are housed. In other cases, the outside negative terminal is a separate sheet of metal contained within the unit. The entire device is then mounted within a metal and cardboard container.

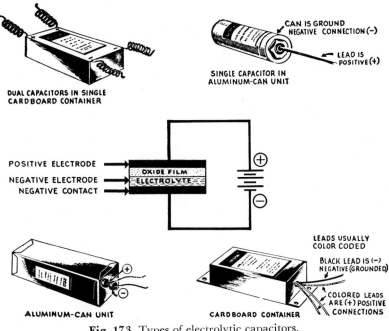

Fig. 173. Types of electrolytic capacitors.

An electrolytic capacitor has definite polarity and, hence, must always be connected within a circuit with this in mind. Since polarity must be observed (positive to positive, negative to negative), *regular* electrolytic capacitors must be used on direct current only. *Special nonpolarized* capacitors of this type are, however, available for use on AC current.

Electrolytic capacitors have a high leakage current and high power factor. Therefore, they cannot be used where the power available is small and must be conserved. Further, their capacitance tends to vary with age, applied voltage, and temperature. Where such factors are not paramount, however, their high capacitance per unit size proves of great value. Further, if the oxide film is punctured by an excessive voltage, they can often be made serviceable again by operating them at a lower voltage. This causes the dielectric film to re-form. Ordinary dielectrics,

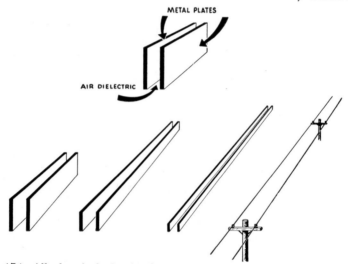

Fig. 174. All electrical circuits (such as the telephone line) contain some degree of capacitance.

once punctured, are irreparable, and capacitors using such dielectrics must be discarded.

10. Distributed Capacitance

Capacitance is found in all electric circuits and in every piece of electrical equipment, because there are always dielectrics separating conductors across which a voltage appears.

This capacitance is termed the *distributed capacitance*, as it appears apportioned over a greater area than is the "concentrated" capacitance of a capacitor.

To illustrate this, refer to Fig. 174 showing two metal plates forming a basic capacitor and then assume the plates to be stretched out, as shown, to form the conducting wires of an electrical circuit. The capacitance that was confined within the capacitor is now distributed over a greater length, but the basic principle remains the same, that is, we have conductors separated

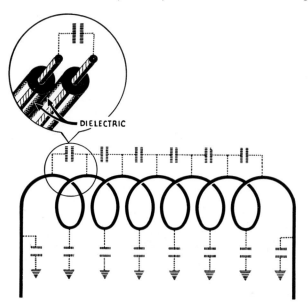

Fig. 175. Distributed capacitance of a coil is the resultant capacitance owing to capacitance between the turns of insulated wire and between the wire and the ground.

by a dielectric in both instances. In electric wiring, the wires may rest one upon the other separated by only a thin insulating cover of cotton or silk. In such cases, this insulating cover becomes the dielectric, and its thickness plus the length of the wires will determine the circuit's capacitance.

Inductors or coils are primarily designed to introduce the property of inductance within a circuit, but they will also possess a degree of distributed capacitance (Fig. 175). Each turn of the wire winding is insulated from every other turn, thus creating a capacitance effect. In addition, each insulated turn forms a capacitor in relation to the ground.

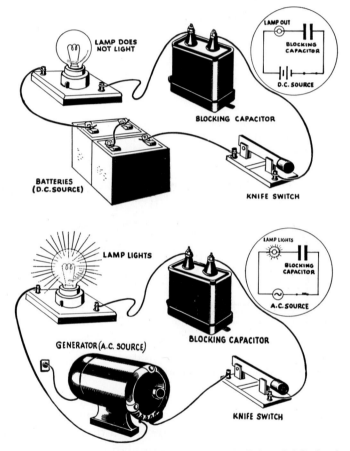

Fig. 176. The effect of a blocking capacitor in DC and AC circuits.

Where it is desirable to reduce the distributed capacitance found in inductors, the winding is so arranged that the spacing between adjacent turns is increased. Another method of reducing this capacitance is to *bank-wind* the coil, that is, wind the coil in layers so that the capacitance built up in one layer somewhat neutralizes that of the layer above or below.

11. The Blocking Capacitor

If a capacitor is connected in series with a lamp and a source of DC voltage, the lamp will not light. If, however, the voltage

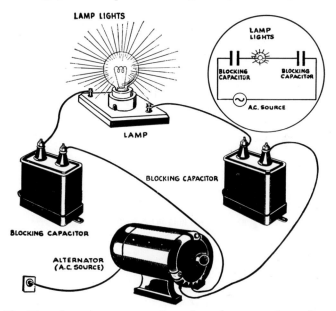

Fig. 177. Though current cannot flow through a capacitor, the charge-discharge process allows electrical energy to be obtained from AC sources even when blocking capacitors are in series with the load.

source is alternating current, the lamp will light and the degree of incandescence or brightness will depend upon the capacitance. The higher the capacitance, the more brilliant the light (Fig. 176).

This action does not mean, however, that an alternating current will flow *through* a capacitor, whereas a direct current cannot. When the direct current is applied, a momentary surge or flow does take place, but as soon as the capacitor receives its maximum charge, no further flow occurs. The dielectric acts just as any insulator does to prevent a flow of current in the circuit. The brief

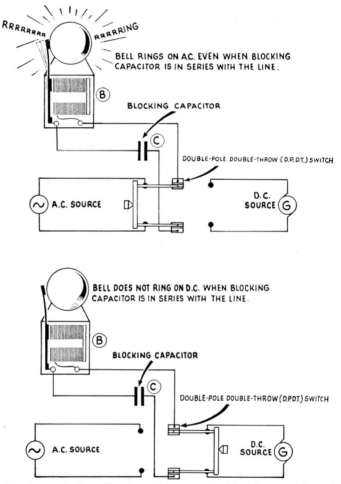

Fig. 178. A practical application of the use of a blocking capacitor. Circuits of this basic type are used in certain telephone ringing circuits.

current surge occurs so quickly that the lamp filament cannot be heated to incandescence, though the momentary flow can be observed on a sensitive meter.

However, when an alternating current is applied, the capacitor is automatically being charged, first in one direction, and then in another, as the AC cycle is completed. We therefore have a condition where a constant charging, discharging, and recharging process is taking place with a resultant flow of current in one direction, and then in another, the rate depending upon the AC frequency. This charging current flowing to and from the plates of the capacitor *but not through the dielectric* will also be flowing through the lamp, and this causes it to light.

If the lamp is connected between two capacitors (Fig. 177), exactly the same situation will result. Here, too, it must be remembered that no current is flowing *through* the capacitors, even though in trade language it is often common practice to say that an AC current will flow through such devices.

In many practical applications, advantage is taken of the fact that a capacitor will *block* the flow of a direct current but will allow an alternating current to pass. A capacitor used in this manner is called a *blocking capacitor*. This is shown in Fig. 178. Action of the circuit calls for operation of the bell *only* when the switch is thrown to the AC side of the voltage supply. When the switch is in this position, the alternating current appears across the capacitor *C* and the bell *B*, which are in series, and the bell will ring. However, when the switch is thrown to the DC side, the bell will not operate, as the blocking capacitor in series with the bell prevents a flow of current through the bell solenoid.

SUMMARY

1. Capacitance is that property of an electric circuit associated with a dielectric field which tends to oppose any change in voltage.

2. A capacitor (often called a *condenser*) is an electrical device designed to introduce capacitance within a circuit.

3. A basic capacitor consists of two metal plates (electrodes) separated by a suitable dielectric.

4. A voltage placed across the electrodes of a capacitor places a positive charge on one electrode and a negative charge on the other, causing a dielectric field to be formed between the plates. The dielectric field distorts the shape of the electron orbits within the dielectric. The capacitor is now charged. Discharge occurs as the external e.m.f. is removed and a conducting path from the negative to the positive plate is formed. The energy stored within the dielectric field is released.

5. The farad is the unit of measurement for capacitance. One farad is said to exist when 1 coulomb can be stored within a dielectric field as an e.m.f. of 1 volt is applied.

$$C \text{ (in farads)} = \frac{Q \text{ (coulombs)}}{E \text{ (voltage across plates)}}$$

6. Since a farad is too large for practical purposes, the microfarad (one-millionth of a farad) and micromicrofarad (one million-millionth of a farad) are generally used.

7. Capacitance is affected by

a. The total area of the plates

b. The distance between the plates (thickness of the dielectric)

c. The dielectric constant (K), which represents the comparative effect of a substance on capacitance, when it is used as a dielectric

8. Increasing the area of the plates increases the capacitance.

9. Using a dielectric of higher K increases the capacitance.

10. *Decreasing* the thickness of the dielectric *increases* the capacitance.

11. Dielectric strength refers to the ability of a dielectric to withstand electrical stress without breakdown. Dielectric *strength* must not be confused with dielectric *constant*.

12. When capacitors are connected in series, the total capacitance is less than that of the smallest unit and is the reciprocal of the sum of the reciprocals.

$$C_{total} \text{ (in series)} = \frac{1}{\dfrac{1}{C_1} + \dfrac{1}{C_2} + \text{etc.}}$$

13. The total capacitance of capacitors in parallel is found by determining the *sum* of the individual capacitances.

14. Leakage loss occurs when current passes *through* the dielectric. The better the insulating qualities of the dielectric, the less the possible leakage loss.

15. Dielectric hysteresis loss is due to the rapid reversal of the electron orbits within a dielectric when an AC voltage is across a capacitor.

16. Power factor is a term describing the efficiency of capacitor action. A power factor of zero is indicative of 100 per cent efficiency.

17. Distributed capacitance refers to the inherent capacitance found in circuit wiring as well as in inductors and other electrical devices. It is the result of the dielectric field formed between the conductors separated by the insulation.

Quiz: Capacitance

This quiz will help you review the material just studied. See the quiz directions on page 24 before answering the questions below.

1. The basic capacitor consists of: *a.* two electrodes separated by an insulator; *b.* two electrodes separated by a conductor; *c.* one electrode and one conductor; *d.* one electrode and one layer of insulation.

2. The amount of energy a capacitor can store is called its: *a.* resistance; *b.* capacitance; *c.* inductance; *d.* reactance.

3. Capacitance is that electric property which opposes any change in the: *a.* applied voltage; *b.* current flow; *c.* inductance of the circuit; *d.* circuit resistance.

4. The capacitance of a circuit is *not* affected by the: *a.* length of the wires forming the line; *b.* current flow through the line; *c.* distance between the wires; *d.* type of insulation separating the wires.

5. The unit of capacitance is the: *a.* henry; *b.* ohm; *c.* volt; *d.* farad.

6. In an electrolytic capacitor, the *dielectric* is the: *a.* electrolyte; *b.* oxide film; *c.* aluminum plate; *d.* insulating container.

7. As applied to a capacitor, the word *dielectric* means most nearly the: *a.* conducting material of the capacitor; *b.* metal used as the electrode; *c.* insulating material separating the plates; *d.* capacitance of the capacitor.

8. When the plates of a variable capacitor are fully meshed, the capacitance is: *a.* greatest; *b.* the same as when unmeshed; *c.* least; *d.* zero.

9. An electrolytic capacitor is characterized by a: *a.* large capacitance in a small-sized unit; *b.* low capacitance in a large-sized unit; *c.* large capacitance in a large-sized unit; *d.* low capacitance in a small-sized unit.

10. In an electrolytic capacitor, the negative electrode is the: *a.* insulating container; *b.* oxide film; *c.* electrolyte; *d.* aluminum plate.

11. Where voltages are high, capacitor plates should be: *a.* closer together than for low voltages; *b.* the same as for low voltages; *c.* farther apart than for low voltages; *d.* made of heavier conductors.

12. "An electrolytic capacitor must be used only on direct current." This statement is: *a.* entirely incorrect; *b.* absolutely correct; *c.* partially correct in that such capacitors can be used on direct current if the plates are not polarized; *d.* incorrect to the extent that it fails to mention the use of nonpolarized electrolytic capacitors for AC circuits.

13. The capacitance of a capacitor is *not* affected by the: *a.* total area of the plates; *b.* resistance of the plates; *c.* dielectric constant; *d.* thickness of the dielectric.

14. A capacitor is rated at 100 volts DC. To assure safe operation on alternating current, the AC voltage should be approximately: *a.* 100 volts; *b.* 90 volts; *c.* 70 volts; *d.* 60 volts.

15. Leakage current affects the efficiency of a capacitor inasmuch as it: *a.* increases the capacitance; *b.* prevents the retention of the charge; *c.* increases the resistance; *d.* prevents dielectric deterioration.

16. A perfect electrolytic capacitor has: *a.* losses equivalent to those of a perfect dry-air type; *b.* losses less than those of a perfect dry-air type; *c.* losses greater than those of a perfect dry-air type; *d.* losses much less than those of a perfect dry-air type.

17. Excessive voltage applied to an electrolytic capacitor will: *a.* not destroy it entirely and allow further use if the dielectric film can be properly re-formed; *b.* irreparably destroy it always; *c.* lower its capacitance; *d.* evaporate the electrolyte and, therefore, change the voltage rating of the unit.

18. The term *microfarad* means: *a.* 1,000,000 farads; *b.* 100 farads; *c.* 1/1,000 farad; *d.* 1/1,000,000 farad.

19. The term *dielectric strength* means most nearly the ability of: *a.* a conductor to handle high voltages; *b.* a conductor to store large voltage values; *c.* an insulator to withstand electric stress across it without breaking down; *d.* an insulator to pass high current values without breakdown.

20. One dielectric has a dielectric constant (K) of 10. Another has a K of 20. Assuming equal factors in all regards to exist, this means that: *a.* The capacitor in which $K = 20$ will withstand higher voltages. *b.* The capacitor in which $K = 10$ will withstand higher voltages. *c.* The capacitor in which $K = 20$ will have a higher capacitance. *d.* The capacitor in which $K = 10$ will have a higher capacitance.

21. One 20-μf capacitor and one 50-μf capacitor are connected in series. The total capacitance will be: *a.* 9.2 μf; *b.* 14.2 μf; *c.* 30 μf; *d.* 70 μf.

22. The *power factors* of four capacitors are 0.0, 0.01, 0.001, and 0.0001, respectively. The most efficient capacitor is the one having the power factor of: *a.* 0.0; *b.* 0.01; *c.* 0.001; *d.* 0.0001.

23. One 20-μf capacitor and one 50-μf capacitor are connected in series across a voltage source. Ordinarily, the voltage across the 20-μf capacitor will be: a. less than that across the 50-μf capacitor; b. exactly equal to that across the 50-μf capacitor; c. higher than that across the 50-μf capacitor; d. two-fifths of the value across the 50-μf capacitor.

24. A lamp connected in series with a capacitor and an AC voltage source will light up. This is due to the fact that: a. The dielectric is shorted out automatically when alternating current is applied. b. The peak AC voltage, being higher than a DC voltage, can temporarily break down the dielectric. c. The lamp is also acting as a capacitor when connected in series with an actual capacitor. d. The capacitor is automatically being charged and recharged, resulting in a flow of current through the lamp.

25. "When a voltage is applied to a capacitor, a current flows through it continuously." This statement is: a. absolutely correct; b. absolutely incorrect; c. correct if the word *voltage* is changed to *e.m.f.;* d. correct if the word *capacitor* is changed to *condenser*.

Chapter 8. Effects of Inductance and Capacitance

1. General

The effects of inductance and capacitance in a circuit are particularly pronounced when AC current is flowing owing to the constant variation in magnitude and direction that is taking place. In DC circuits, some effects are also noted when some change affecting the current flow occurs. This happens as the circuit is initially established and current *begins* to flow. It happens when the circuit is broken and the current attempts to *stop* flowing. It happens as well when the current value *pulsates*, that is, increases and decreases to a varying degree as the circuit remains closed.

2. Inductance and Capacitance in DC Circuits

To demonstrate the action of inductance in a DC circuit, let us refer to Fig. 179*a*, in which an inductor with a movable iron core is inserted in series with a 100-watt lamp, and then connected through a switch to a 100-volt DC supply. A DC voltmeter is connected across the lamp. Let us assume that the inductor has a DC resistance of 10 ohms. When the switch is closed, the lamp will light up, and if the voltage across the lamp is measured, it will be found to be 90 volts. A 10-volt drop or *IR* loss takes place in the inductor owing to its 10-ohm resistance. The 100-watt lamp draws 1 amp. ($E_{\text{(voltage drop)}} = IR = 1 \times 10 = 10$) (Fig. 179*b*).

If the iron core is now moved in and out of the inductor, thus increasing and decreasing its inductance, the lamp continues to remain incandescent to the same degree and the voltmeter still reads 90 volts. Apparently, then, different values of inductance in and of themselves have no effect on the DC flow as long as the current remains at a fixed value. The only effect the coil had was to introduce resistance into the circuit, and if we were now to

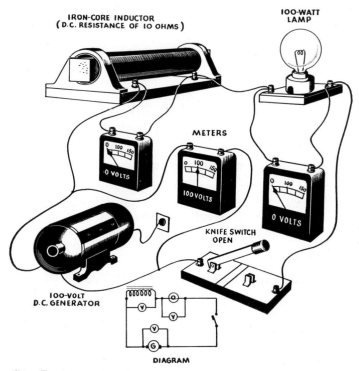

Fig. 179a. Equipment that can be used to show the effect of inductance in a DC circuit.

substitute a 10-ohm noninductive resistor for the coil, it can be shown that no change in the circuit constants occurs. In other words, the 10-ohm resistor and the 10-ohm inductor (regardless of the latter's value in henrys) act similarly in a DC circuit when no change in the current value appears.

When the circuit is initially closed as the switch contacts are brought together, the self-inductance of the coil builds up a counter-e.m.f., which tends to delay the current in reaching its full magnitude. Similarly, as the switch is opened, the inductance tends to maintain the current value, thus delaying its quick drop to zero. The spark that occurs across the switch contacts is due

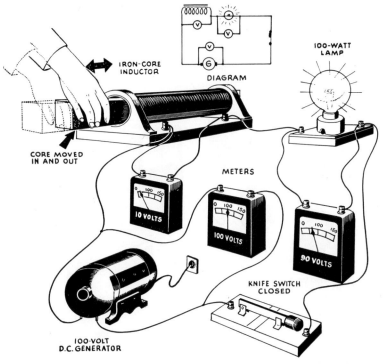

Fig. 179b. When the circuit is closed, the lamp lights. Varying the inductance value of the coil does not affect the brilliance of the lamp in a DC circuit.

to this fact. This spark can be eliminated by placing a capacitor across the contacts, the energy that would have been used to create the spark being used instead to charge the capacitor (Fig. 180).

Capacitance, as well as inductance, has a pronounced effect on the time lag observed when a direct current is attempting to reach its maximum magnitude or decrease to zero value. The

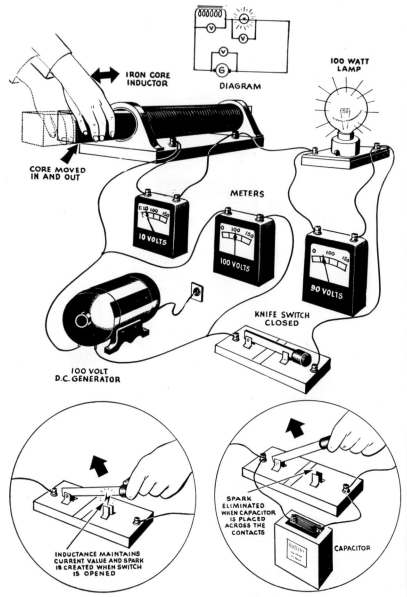

Fig. 180. Breaking the circuit containing inductance may produce a spark between the blade and the jaw of the switch. This can generally be eliminated or greatly reduced by placing a capacitor across the switch terminals.

distortion of a DC telegraph signal is perhaps the best illustration of the effect of inductance and capacitance together, or each of these properties individually.

The graph in Fig. 181*a*, in which current is plotted against the time required for the current's full magnitude to be reached, assumes that the circuit contains neither inductance nor capacitance. Note the almost instantaneous rise from zero to maximum

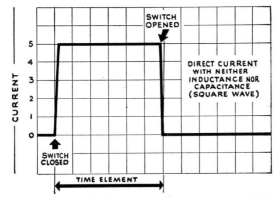

Fig. 181*a*. In the absence of inductance and capacitance, a DC voltage tends to reach its maximum magnitude extremely rapidly. Similarly, it drops very quickly to zero when the circuit is opened.

and then the sharp drop to zero as the circuit is opened. This almost perfect square wave is the ideal, but in practice the signal is distorted and appears more like the graph in Fig. 181*b*. This distortion is due to the effects of inductance and capacitance. Inductance within the circuit tends to oppose the creation of the magnetic field and thus builds up a counter-e.m.f. opposing the initial flow of current as the circuit is closed. Capacitance within the circuit, just as an ordinary capacitor would when placed across a source of e.m.f., takes a time interval to accept its full charge, and this affects the applied voltage and, in turn, the magnitude of the current.

As the circuit is opened, the circuit's inductance tends to sustain the original value of e.m.f.

To overcome this action, which may seriously disturb telegraphic communication, efforts are made to balance out, or neutralize the inductance and capacitance, or either one alone, as may be required. We shall shortly see how this is done in studying the effect of these electrical properties when alternating current appears in a circuit, as the conditions made apparent when making or breaking direct current are even more pro-

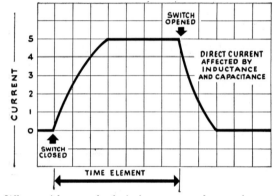

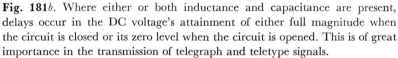

Fig. 181b. Where either or both inductance and capacitance are present, delays occur in the DC voltage's attainment of either full magnitude when the circuit is closed or its zero level when the circuit is opened. This is of great importance in the transmission of telegraph and teletype signals.

nounced where alternating current is present, owing to its ever-changing magnitude and direction of flow. In a pulsating direct current, where the magnitude varies but the direction does not, these conditions are similarly encountered.

3. Inductance in AC Circuits

If a 10-ohm "pure" resistor, that is, one having no inductance or capacitance, were inserted in the circuit shown in Fig. 179 and an AC voltage applied, the lamp would light up in exactly the same way it did when direct current was applied. Apparently, then, both alternating current and direct current act alike when inductance and capacitance are absent. Therefore, under such conditions, Ohm's Law applies equally well to both cases.

Now if the pure resistor were to be replaced by an inductor with a movable iron core and having a resistance of 10 ohms, an entirely different action will occur. If the inductance is at minimum (iron core removed from the coil) at the start of the experiment, the lamp will light but will not be as bright as when the

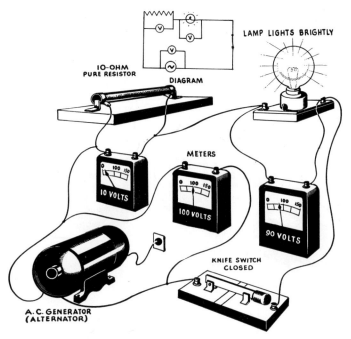

Fig. 182*a*. In an AC circuit containing no inductance, the operation is similar to DC operation. The resistance of the circuit alone affects its operating characteristics.

pure resistor was used (Fig. 182*a*). As the iron core is moved into the coil, thus increasing its inductance, the light becomes more and more dim, and a point may be reached where it will be extinguished entirely (Fig. 182*b*).

In a circuit where alternating current is flowing, the presence of inductance introduces another factor in addition to resistance. This additional factor is termed *inductive reactance*, or as it is sometimes called, *positive reactance* (X_L), and its effect, like that of resistance, is to oppose the flow of current. In other words, in a DC circuit, ohmic resistance alone opposes the current flow, but in an AC circuit, where inductance is present, the flow of current

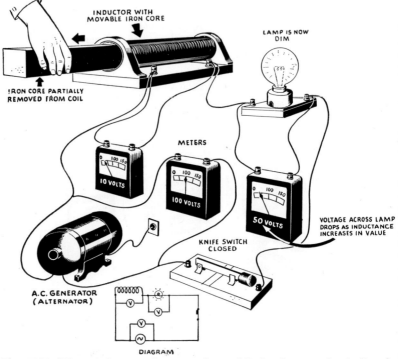

Fig. 182*b*. Where inductance is present in an AC circuit, operation is directly affected.

is opposed by both the ohmic resistance and the inductive reactance.

In order to determine the inductive reactance, the following formula is used:

$$X_L = 6.28FL$$

Here F represents the frequency in cycles and L the inductance in henrys.

Example: At 60 cycles, what is the inductive reactance of a loading coil rated at 10 henrys?

Step 1. $\qquad\qquad\qquad X_L = 6.28FL$

Step 2. $\qquad\qquad\qquad X_L = 6.28 \times 60 \times 10$

Step 3. $\qquad\qquad\qquad X_L = 3,768$ ohms $\qquad\qquad$ *Ans.*

Inductive reactance, like ohmic resistance, is measured in *ohms* because, like ohmic resistance, it opposes current flow.

We now can see that Ohm's Law, as it applies to DC circuits, must be modified to include the factor of inductive reactance as well as resistance. The combined effect of resistance and inductive reactance is called *impedance* (Z), which is also measured in ohms. Impedance, then, is the *total* opposition to the flow of alternating current, and Ohm's Law, for use where alternating current is concerned, is made to read as follows:

$$Z = \frac{E}{I}$$

or

$$I = \frac{E}{Z}$$

or

$$E = IZ$$

Before the formula can be applied, however, impedance (Z) must be determined. To do this, the resistance (R) and inductive reactance (X_L) of the circuit must be known and the values substituted in the following formula:

$$Z = \sqrt{R^2 + X_L{}^2}$$

Impedance (Z) representing the *total* opposition to the flow of alternating current is *not* the *sum* of the ohmic resistance plus the inductive reactance but the *square root* of the sum of their squares.

Example: What is the impedance of a solenoid whose ohmic resistance is 60 ohms and whose inductive reactance is 80 ohms?

Step 1. $Z = \sqrt{R^2 + X_L^2}$ *This is the formula for impedance where the resistance and inductive reactance are known.* *

Step 2. $Z = \sqrt{(60)^2 + (80)^2}$ *Here we substitute the actual values of R and X_L.*

Step 3. $Z = \sqrt{3,600 + 6,400}$ *Here we square the actual values.*

Step 4. $Z = \sqrt{10,000}$ *Here we have added the figures obtained in Step 3.*

Step 5. $Z = 100$ ohms   *(Ans.)*   *The square root of 10,000 is 100.*

In the example just given, the ohmic resistance and inductive reactance were known. In many instances, it may be necessary to first determine the inductive reactance, before Ohm's Law for alternating current can be applied.

Example: At 60 cycles, what is the impedance of a solenoid that is rated at 212 millihenrys and has a resistance of 60 ohms?

Note: In order to solve for Z in the formula $Z = \sqrt{R^2 + X_L^2}$, we must first find the value of X_L using the formula $X_L = 6.28FL$. Further, in the example, the inductance is given in *millihenrys* and this must be converted to *henrys*. Since 1,000 mh. = 1 henry, 212 mh. = 0.212 henry.

Step 1. $X_L = 6.28FL$

Step 2. $X_L = 6.28 \times 60 \times 0.212$

Step 3. $X_L = 79.8816$ *or approximately* 80 ohms

Step 4. $Z = \sqrt{R^2 + X_L^2}$

Step 5. $Z = \sqrt{60^2 + 80^2}$

Step 6. $Z = \sqrt{10,000}$

Step 7. $Z = 100$ ohms   *Ans.*

* See Appendix 1 for a review of the method of solving for the square root of a number.

4. Capacitance in AC Circuits

The action of capacitance in an AC circuit can best be illustrated by using different capacitors representing various values of capacitance in a circuit such as is shown in Fig. 183a and b. Assume that a capacitor of 10 μf is used initially (Fig. 183a). The

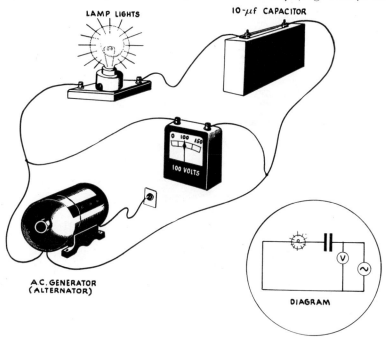

Fig. 183a. In this AC circuit, a 10-μf capacitor is in series with the lamp. The capacitive reactance is low enough to allow the lamp to light quite brilliantly.

flow of alternating current to and from the plates of the capacitor will allow the lamp to light. If a 5-μf capacitor is substituted, the light becomes dimmer (Fig. 183b); a 20-μf capacitor causes the lamp to become quite bright.

Apparently, then, an increase in capacitance offers less opposition to the current flow; a decrease in capacitance offers greater opposition. This effect is just the opposite of what occurred when inductance was being considered. Hence, the form of opposition that capacitance offers to the flow of alternating current is called *capacitive* or *negative* reactance (X_C).

Capacitive reactance (X_C) is determined by the formula

$$X_C = \frac{1}{6.28FC}$$

where F represents the frequency in cycles and C the capaci-

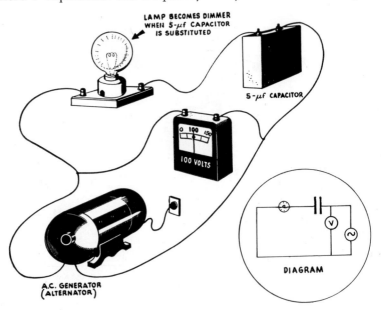

LAMP BECOMES DIMMER
WHEN 5-μf CAPACITOR
IS SUBSTITUTED

5-μf CAPACITOR

0 100 150
100 VOLTS

A.C. GENERATOR
(ALTERNATOR)

DIAGRAM

Fig. 183*b*. If a 5-μf capacitor is used in place of the 10-μf unit, shown in Fig. 183*a*, the lamp becomes dimmer owing to the greater capacitive reactance of the 5-μf capacitor.

tance in *farads*. Since farads are seldom used, the capacitance, generally given in *microfarads*, must always be converted to farads before the formula is applied.

Example: At 60 cycles what is the capacitive reactance of a capacitor rated at 5 μf?

Note: 5 μf equals 0.000005 or $\dfrac{5}{1,000,000}$ farad.

Step 1. $X_C = \dfrac{1}{6.28FC}$ *This is the formula.*

Step 2. $X_C =$ *Here we have substituted actual values*
$\dfrac{1}{6.28 \times 60 \times 0.000005}$ *for F and C, the latter in farads.*

Step 3. $X_C = \dfrac{1}{0.0018840}$ *Here we have multiplied all the figures together.*

Step 4. $X_C = 530.7$ ohms   *To solve the fraction in Step 3, we*
(*Ans.*)   *divided 1, the figure above the line, by the figure 0.0018840 below the line. This is done by making the number 0.0018840 a whole number, 18,840, and adding seven zeros after the figure 1 to compensate for moving the decimal point seven places to the right in converting the number 0.0018840 to a whole number.*

$$\frac{1}{0.0018840} = \frac{10,000,000}{18,840}$$

Since capacitive reactance acts in exactly opposite fashion to that of inductive reactance, it is reasonable to assume that in circuits where both are found, one will act to balance the other to a greater or lesser degree. Hence, in order to find the impedance of a circuit, the *total* effective reactance must be known. Note the formula used:

$$X = X_L - X_C$$

The value of capacitive reactance is shown as being subtracted from the value of inductive reactance. This is the case where the inductive reactance is greater. If it were less, it would be subtracted from the capacitive reactance, and the circuit would be said to be *capacitive*, whereas in the former case, it would be called *inductive*. This simply means that in one case the capacitive reactance played the larger part by overbalancing the inductive reactance and in the other, inductive reactance overbalanced the capacitive reactance. The formula for impedance can now be shown as

$$Z = \sqrt{R^2 + (X_L - X_C)^2}$$

or

$$Z = \sqrt{R^2 + X^2}$$

Example: A coil rated at 5 henrys and having a resistance of 10 ohms is connected within a circuit with a capacitor of 5 μf. At 60 cycles, what is the impedance?

Step 1. $Z = \sqrt{R^2 + X^2}$ *This is the formula for impedance. We know R (10 ohms) but must determine the value of X.*

Step 2. $X = X_L - X_C$ *This is the formula to determine the total reactance X. We must first find X_L and X_C.*

Step 3. $X_L = 6.28FL$ *This is the formula for X_L.*

Step 4. $X_L = 6.28 \times 60 \times 5$ *Here we have substituted actual values for F and L.*

Step 5. $X_L = 1,884$ ohms   *We now have X_L but must still find X_C.*

Step 6. $X_C = \dfrac{1}{6.28FC}$ *This is the formula for X_C.*

Step 7. $X_C = \dfrac{1}{6.28 \times 60 \times 0.000005}$ *Here we have substituted actual values of F and C. Note that 5 μf was converted to 0.000005 farad.*

Step 8. $X_C = 530.7$ *This is X_C and now this must be subtracted from X_L in Step 5 to find X.*

Step 9. $X = X_L - X_C$

Step 10. $X = 1{,}884 - 530.7$ *We now have X and can substitute in*
$\quad\quad\quad = 1{,}353.3$ ohms   *the Z formula in Step 1.*

Step 11. $Z = \sqrt{R^2 + X^2}$ *This is the formula for Z where R*
and X are known.

Step 12. $Z = \dfrac{}{\sqrt{(10)^2 + (1{,}353.3)^2}}$ *Here we substitute the values of R*
and X.

Step 13. $Z = \sqrt{100 + 1{,}831{,}420.89}$ *Now we square the numbers, add*
$\quad\quad\quad = \sqrt{1{,}831{,}520.89}$ *them together, and find the square root.*

Step 14. $Z = 1{,}353+$ ohms   *Ans.*

The importance of impedance in practical applications where alternating current is used may be illustrated clearly by con-

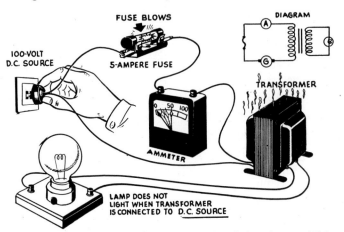

Fig. 184a. The transformer primary has a very low DC resistance. This causes the fuse to blow out when the heavy DC current surges through the winding.

sidering the action of a transformer primary. Assume that the primary winding of the transformer in Fig. 184a has a resistance of 2 ohms and an effective impedance of 100 ohms. It is designed to draw 1 amp. from the line, when under load.

If the winding is connected to a 100-volt DC line, the only factor that plays a part is the resistance. The 2-ohm winding will draw 50 amp., as indicated by Ohm's Law ($I = \dfrac{E}{R} = \dfrac{100}{2} = 50$ amp.). This heavy current will destroy the winding unless the fuse blows (burns) out immediately.

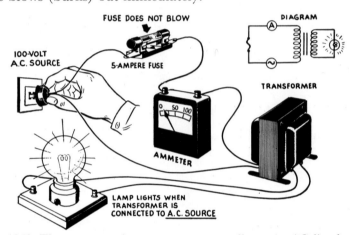

Fig. 184b. The same transformer operates normally on an AC line because its impedance is high even though its resistance is low.

If the same transformer is placed across a 100-volt AC line (Fig. 184b), resistance alone is not the deciding factor, but the impedance very definitely is. Impedance, as we now know, is a value representing the total effect in an AC circuit of resistance and reactance. The primary, therefore, would draw only 1 amp., which is the normal amount ($I = \dfrac{E}{Z} = \dfrac{100}{100} = 1$ amp.).

5. Resonance

In a DC circuit, the voltage and current reach their full values simultaneously, since resistance alone is generally the sole factor that affects the current flow.

In an AC circuit, however, inductive reactance and capacitive reactance affect the flow of current quite differently. Inductive reactance tends to oppose the flow of current, causing it to *lag* behind the voltage. This means that a certain voltage value will be reached before a given current value is obtained. This is shown in Fig. 185. In a purely inductive circuit containing no resistance whatsoever, the lag would reach 90 degrees, but this condition is not encountered because some degree of resistance is always present.

Capacitive reactance causes the current to *lead* the voltage, that is, a current value will be reached ahead of a given voltage

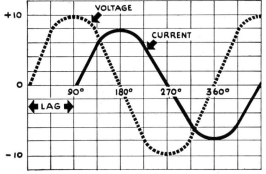

Fig. 185. The effect of inductive reactance.

value (Fig. 186). In a purely capacitive circuit containing no resistance, the lead would reach 90 degrees, but this situation also is never approached in practice.

When AC voltage and current values reach given values simultaneously (as in DC circuits), they are said to be *in phase*, and the circuit then acts as if resistance alone were the governing factor. This is the condition of *resonance*, and it can only occur when the inductive reactance and the capacitive reactance cancel each other out entirely. Resonance, therefore, is the condition existing when the resistance of an AC circuit is the main factor affecting the current flow, and all other factors (at that particular frequency) have been canceled out.

Resonance* can be produced with either series or parallel

* Resonant frequency $(F) = \dfrac{1}{6.28\sqrt{LC}}$

where L = inductance, henrys
C = capacitance, farads
F = frequency, cycles

circuits containing inductance and capacitance, but the effects they exhibit are quite different.

A series resonant circuit (Fig. 187) is one in which the applied

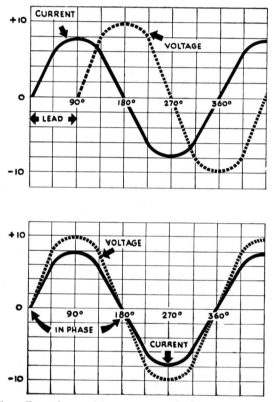

Fig. 186. The effect of capacitive reactance (*top*). The effect when voltage and current are "in phase" (*bottom*).

voltage is in series with both the inductor (*L*) and the capacitor (*C*).

A parallel resonant circuit (Fig. 188) is one in which the applied voltage is directly across both the inductor (*L*) and the capacitor (*C*). In both figures, the resistance (*R*) represents the inherent resistance of the circuit, since such resistance is inevitably present.

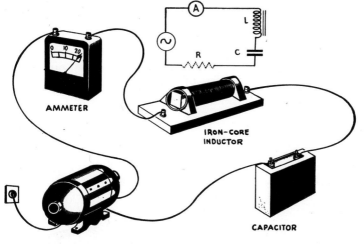

Fig. 187. An inductor (L) and a capacitor (C) connected to form a series resonant circuit. R symbolizes the entire resistance of the circuit. At resonance, the circuit draws a *high* value of current.

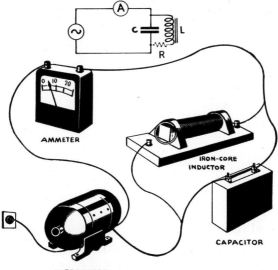

Fig. 188. An inductor (L) and a capacitor (C) connected in a parallel resonant circuit. R symbolizes the resistance of the LC combination. At resonance, the circuit draws a *low* value of current.

To illustrate the actual action of a series resonant circuit, a lamp, capacitor, and inductor can be connected in series as in Fig. 189, and a 100-volt 60-cycle AC voltage applied. If the values of *L* and *C* are adjusted so that a resonant circuit for the particular frequency is formed, the lamp will light up brightly.

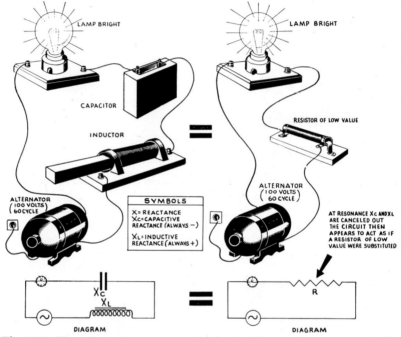

LAMP BRIGHT

LAMP BRIGHT

CAPACITOR

RESISTOR OF LOW VALUE

INDUCTOR

ALTERNATOR
(100 VOLTS)
(60 CYCLE)

ALTERNATOR
(100 VOLTS
60 CYCLE)

SYMBOLS

X = REACTANCE
Xc = CAPACITIVE
REACTANCE (ALWAYS −)

XL = INDUCTIVE
REACTANCE (ALWAYS +)

AT RESONANCE Xc AND XL
ARE CANCELED OUT
THE CIRCUIT THEN
APPEARS TO ACT AS IF
A RESISTOR OF LOW
VALUE WERE SUBSTITUTED

X_C
X_L

R

DIAGRAM

DIAGRAM

Fig. 189. The effect when resonance is obtained in a series resonant circuit.

At this point, the inductive and capacitive reactances are balanced out, and the circuit is acting as if a resistor of *low* value were taking the place of *L* and *C*. The impedance is therefore *low* as well, since impedance and resistance are equivalent when both inductive and capacitive reactance are absent.

The component parts, that is, inductor *L* and capacitor *C*, have not been changed in any way. They still represent units of, comparatively speaking, high reactance. Thus, the high current drawn by the series resonant circuit *as a whole* will produce a *high* voltage drop across these *individual* components. If the reactance of C were 200 ohms, and 1 amp. were flowing in this circuit, the voltage drop across C would be *200 volts*, even though the applied voltage is only 100 volts.

$$E = I \times X_C$$

where E is the voltage drop across C, I is the current in the circuit, and X_C is the capacitive reactance.

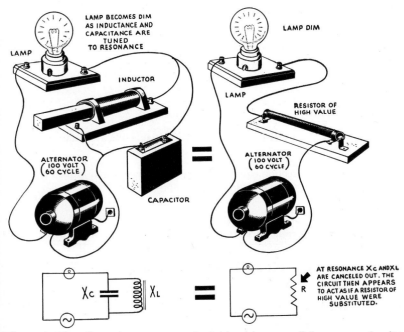

Fig. 190. The effect when resonance is obtained in a parallel resonant circuit.

To illustrate the action of a parallel resonant circuit, the circuit shown in Fig. 190 is used. As the values of LC are "tuned" (adjusted) to the 60-cycle resonant frequency by varying their values, the light becomes very dim (showing that a low value of current is now flowing in the circuit) and may go out entirely. This indicates that a parallel resonant circuit has a *high* impedance and is acting like a resistor of very high value. In other words, it is just as if a resistor of very great ohmic resistance were replacing the LC combination. Here too, however, the components, L and C, still act as reactances of given values when considered individually. Thus, if the applied voltage across LC is 100-volts, and the effective reactance of the parallel LC combination measures 100 ohms, the current in LC will be 1 amp. even though the line current is much lower.

$$I \text{ (current in } LC) = \frac{E \text{ (voltage across } LC)}{X \text{ (effective reactance)}} = \frac{100}{100} = 1 \text{ amp.}$$

Since parallel resonance acts in opposite fashion to series resonance, it is often called *anti-resonance*. The different action in each case may be charted as follows:

Series resonance	*Parallel resonance*
1. Impedance *low*.	Impedance *high*.
2. Circuit acts like a resistance of *low* value	Circuit acts like a resistance of *high* value.
3. Current in each section equal to applied current (current in main line)	Voltage across each branch equal to applied voltage.
4. *High voltages* developed across each inductive and capacitive section.	High *current* in each branch.

6. Resonant Circuit as an AC Generator

In studying the action of various sources of e.m.f. the alternator was mentioned as a source of alternating current. This is the device most commonly used where large amounts of AC power at fairly low frequencies (such as are used for lighting, heating, power, etc.) are needed.

In certain applications, particularly in the field of radio and in certain test equipment, alternating current of very much higher frequencies is required. A resonant circuit can be used to furnish such frequencies.

In Fig. 191, a battery is used as an exciter (source of potential). This is of interest because it will show how direct current can be converted to alternating current. Later, we shall see how alternating current is rectified to direct current. (*Rectification* is a term that applies only to the conversion of alternating

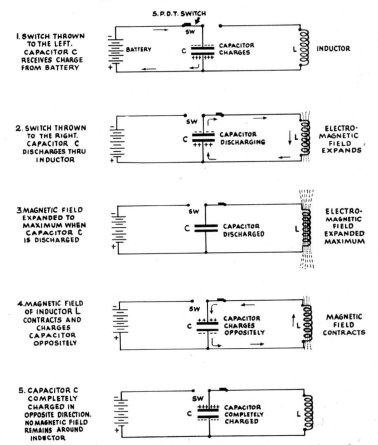

Fig. 191. A resonant circuit initially excited by a DC potential can be used to produce alternating current.

current to direct current; it is not used when direct current is being changed to alternating current.)

When the single-pole double-throw (s.p.d.t.) switch *SW* is thrown to the left onto the battery side of the circuit, the capacitor (*C*) receives a charge. If the switch is now thrown to the right, the capacitor discharges through the inductor (*L*). This discharge current flowing through *L* produces an electromagnetic field, and this field continues to expand as long as any energy remains in the capacitor.

When the capacitor is fully discharged, the electromagnetic field begins to collapse, and a voltage of opposite polarity is developed in the inductor (*L*), as the lines of force of the collapsing field now move in exactly the reverse direction. This newly produced voltage charges the capacitor in the direction opposite to that of the original charge until all the energy developed by the coil's field is expended. The capacitor, now charged in the opposite direction, again discharges across the inductor, and this process continues until all the originally stored energy is lost in the form of heat. Exciting the circuit again at this moment will renew the action. This back-and-forth discharge is called *oscillation* (vibration), and the AC frequency developed by this oscillation is dependent upon the frequency of the resonant circuit formed by the inductor-capacitor combination. If the resonant circuit were adjusted to 1,000 cycles, the oscillation would develop an AC voltage with a frequency of 1,000 cycles. If it were tuned to 1,000,000 cycles, the oscillation would occur at that rate.

7. Power in AC Circuits

In a DC circuit, power is determined by the formula $W = EI$. Thus, if 2 amp. were drawn at 100 volts, 200 watts would represent the power consumed.

In an AC circuit, this formula applies only if current and voltage are in phase. We have already seen that this condition can occur only when the factors of inductive and capacitive reactance are not involved. Under most conditions of operation, inductive and capacitive reactance are present to a greater or lesser degree.

When the reactance, either capacitive or inductive, is extremely high as compared to the resistance, the current is

90 degrees out of phase with the voltage, and the *actual* or *true* *power* is *zero*. Suppose a 100-volt AC source is connected to a circuit having such great reactance that this 90-degree phase relationship exists. If we check the sine curve in Fig. 192, we see that the voltage will have reached its full magnitude (100) at a time when the current is zero. The formula $W = EI$ would then give zero watts as the answer ($W = EI = 100 \times 0 = 0$).

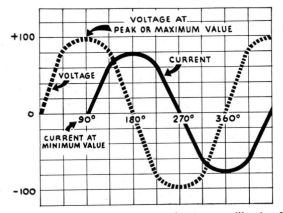

Fig. 192. The condition under which a *wattless current* will exist. Voltage and current are 90 degrees out of phase.

In circuits of this extreme kind, the energy delivered by the AC line is being stored in the form of either an electromagnetic or dielectric field during one part of the cycle and returned to the line on the other part of the cycle. This is called a *wattless current*.

This extreme condition is not ordinarily met, but it does indicate that the concept of power in AC circuits is somewhat different from that appearing in DC circuits. Simply multiplying volts times amperes will give the *apparent* power, but the *actual* or *true* power is gained by multiplying the figure thus obtained by a value called the *power factor* ($W = E \times I \times$ P.F.).

A power factor of 1.0 exists only when voltage and current are in phase, and this occurs only in a circuit containing resistance alone. Where inductance and capacitance are present, the power factor is always *less* than 1.0.

Example: A transformer primary connected across 100 volts AC is drawing 5 amp. The circuit has a power factor of 0.85. What is the apparent power? What is the actual power?

$$\text{Apparent power} = EI$$
$$= 100 \times 5$$
$$= 500 \text{ watts}$$

$$\text{Actual or true power} = EI \times \text{P.F.}$$
$$= 100 \times 5 \times 0.85$$
$$= 425 \text{ watts}$$

In rating electrical apparatus used on direct current, manu-facturers will mark them in watts or kilowatts, for example, a 500-watt electric iron or a 2-kw. DC motor. For AC appliances, similar practice is observed on many small pieces of apparatus, particularly those designed for household use, but for larger commercial needs, motors, generators, and other equipment, the ratings are in kilovolt-amperes. This indicates that such equipment operates on alternating current and will handle so many thousands of volts at so many amperes. The power factor of the actual circuit is then applied to determine the true power the circuit is consuming when the device is operating under normal load.

SUMMARY

1. Owing to the constant variation in magnitude and direc-tion of current flow, the effects of inductance and capacitance are particularly noted in AC circuits.

2. *Inductive reactance* (or *positive reactance*) is a term designating the effect of inductance in an AC circuit ($X_L = 6.28FL$).

3. *Capacitive reactance* (or *negative reactance*) is a term designating the effect of capacitance in an AC circuit $\left(X_C = \dfrac{1}{6.28FC}\right)$.

4. In a purely resistive circuit (one containing resistance alone and completely free of inductance and capacitance), Ohm's Law applies to AC as well as DC circuits. Where either inductance or capacitance, or both, are present, Ohm's Law is modified to include the factor of impedance. Impedance is the total opposition to the flow of an alternating current and includes the factor of reactance as well as resistance.

$$Z = \sqrt{R^2 + X^2} \quad \text{or} \quad Z = \sqrt{R^2 + (X_L - X_C)^2}$$

5. Inductive reactance causes the current to *lag* the voltage.

6. Capacitive reactance causes the current to *lead* the voltage.

7. When inductive reactance and capacitive reactance are not present or have been balanced out, the current and voltage are *in phase*. This is the condition of resonance, and the circuit acts as a resistive circuit.

8. A series resonant circuit is one in which the applied voltage is in series with both the inductor and the capacitor. At resonance, its impedance is very *low*.

9. A parallel resonant circuit is one in which the applied voltage is directly across both the inductor and the capacitor. At resonance, its impedance is very *high*.

10. A resonant circuit may be used as an AC generator. The circuit will oscillate at an AC frequency determined by the constants L and C.

$$F_{res.} = \frac{1}{6.28 \sqrt{LC}}$$

11. *Apparent power* in an AC circuit may be determined by the same formula used in DC circuits ($W = EI$).

12. *Actual* or *true power* is computed by multiplying the apparent power by a value called the *power factor*. A power factor of 1.0 exists only in a resistive circuit, that is, when current and voltage are in phase. A lesser value exists ordinarily, as some degree of inductance and capacitance is always present.

Quiz: Effects of Inductance and Capacitance

This quiz will help you review the material just studied. See the quiz directions on page 24 before answering the questions below.

1. Capacitive reactance is measured in: *a.* ohms; *b.* farads; *c.* henrys; *d.* coulombs.

2. Inductive reactance is measured in: *a.* ohms; *b.* farads; *c.* henrys; *d.* coulombs.

3. Impedance is measured in: *a.* ohms; *b.* farads; *c.* henrys; *d.* coulombs.

4. The term *in phase* indicates that the: *a.* current lags the voltage; *b.* current leads the voltage; *c.* current and voltage reach given values simultaneously; *d.* voltage is always higher than the current.

5. In an AC circuit in which inductance is present, the current flow is affected by: *a.* the resistance and the inductive reactance; *b.* the resistance alone; *c.* the inductive reactance alone; *d.* neither the resistance nor inductive reactance, as one cancels the other.

6. The formula for *capacitive reactance* is: *a.* $C = Q/E$; *b.* $X_c = 1/6.28FC$; *c.* $X_L = 6.28FL$; *d.* $X_{eff.} = X_L - X_c$.

7. The formula for *inductive reactance* is: *a.* $X_L = 6.28FL$; *b.* $X_c = 1/6.28FC$; *c.* $Z = E/I$; *d.* $X_{eff.} = X_L - X_c$.

8. *True power* is equal to: *a.* $W = I \times R$; *b.* $W = E \times I$; *c.* $W = E \times R \times P.F.$; *d.* $W = E \times I \times P.F.$

9. For determining the impedance of a coil, the formula is: *a.* $Z = E/I$; *b.* $X_{eff.} = X_L - X_c$; *c.* $X_L = 6.28FL$; *d.* $Z = \sqrt{R^2 + X^2}$.

10. When resistance alone is the governing factor in the flow of a current, the circuit is said to be: *a.* a resonant circuit; *b.* an inductive circuit; *c.* a capacitive circuit; *d.* a combined inductive and resistive circuit.

11. A transformer whose power factor is 0.98 is drawing 2 amp. at 100 volts AC. The *true* power is: *a.* 200 watts; *b.* 198 watts; *c.* 196 watts; *d.* 98 watts.

12. A transformer primary has a resistance of 10 ohms and an impedance of 200 ohms. When connected to a 100-volt AC line, the current drawn will be: *a.* 0.25 amp.; *b.* 0.5 amp.; *c.* 1.0 amp.; *d.* 1.5 amp.

13. What is the impedance of a circuit that has a resistance of 30 ohms and an effective reactance of 40 ohms? *a.* 10 ohms; *b.* 50 ohms; *c.* 70 ohms; *d.* 1,200 ohms.

14. *Oscillation* means most nearly: *a.* attenuation; *b.* reverberation; *c.* desensitization; *d.* vibration.

15. *Positive reactance* means most nearly: *a.* capacitive reactance; *b.* inductive reactance; *c.* thermal reactance; *d.* photoelectric reactance.

16. A transformer primary with a resistance of 10 ohms and an impedance of 300 ohms is accidentally connected across a 100-volt DC line. The primary fuse is rated at 1 amp. The transformer is, therefore: *a.* fully protected as the line current will be only $\frac{1}{3}$ amp.; *b.* protected as the line current will be 10 amp.; *c.* unprotected as the line current will be only $\frac{1}{3}$ amp.; *d.* unprotected as the line current will be 10 amp.

17. A capacitor having a reactance of 500 ohms is connected in series with an inductor having a reactance of 1,500 ohms to form a resonant circuit. The current in the line is 1 amp. and the applied voltage is 100. The voltage across the capacitor will be: *a.* equal to the applied voltage; *b.* less than the applied voltage; *c.* greater than the applied voltage; *d.* less than one-half the applied voltage.

18. In a DC circuit, the effects of inductance and capacitance are: *a.* nonexistent; *b.* apparent when a change in the current magnitude occurs; *c.* apparent only if the voltage value exceeds the current value; *d.* apparent only when the resistance of the circuit is negligible.

19. In an AC circuit, a power factor of 1.0 exists only when the: *a.* voltage and current are in phase; *b.* current leads the voltage; *c.* current lags the voltage; *d.* inductance exceeds the capacitance.

20. A parallel resonant circuit acts like a resistance of: *a.* very low value; *b.* very high value; *c.* low value; *d.* medium value.

21. When the reactance, either capacitive or inductive, is extremely high as compared to the resistance, so that the current is 90 degrees out of phase with the voltage, the actual or true power is: *a.* plus or minus 90; *b.* plus 90; *c.* zero; *d.* minus 90.

22. The circuit illustrated is intended to be a series resonant circuit. The diagram has: *a.* no errors; *b.* one error; *c.* two errors; *d.* three errors.

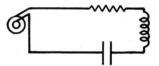

23. "All circuits possess a degree of resistance, but not all circuits possess a degree of reactance." This statement is: *a.* true only in AC circuits; *b.* true only in DC circuits; *c.* untrue; *d.* true.

24. If a resonant circuit is used to produce an alternating current, the frequency will depend upon the values of the: *a.* inductance alone; *b.* capacitance alone; *c.* inductance and capacitance together; *d.* resistance and capacitance.

25. An AC generator may be a: *a.* resonant circuit; *b.* purely reactive circuit; *c.* rectified circuit; *d.* pulsating circuit.

Chapter 9. The Electric Generator

1. The Dynamo

Dynamo is a term used in the field of electricity to describe an electrical device that converts one form of energy into another form. An electric motor may be called a *dynamo*, as it converts *electrical* energy into *mechanical* energy. The generator is also a dynamo, as it converts *mechanical* energy into *electrical* energy.

The word *dynamo*, therefore, is a fairly comprehensive term, taking in as it does all kinds of motors and all kinds of generators. For our purpose, however, we shall restrict our study to those motors and generators whose operation illustrates basically important principles of electricity.

Though electric motors, of course, are caused to rotate by applied electrical energy, generators must be rotated by mechanical means, such as steam turbines, water power, gasoline and diesel engines, as well as electric motors. Hand-rotated generators are also available. Since the rotating device and the generator proper are often combined into one unit, such terms as *motor generator* and *steam-turbine generator* are in common use.

2. The DC Generator

The basic *alternator*, as we have previously seen, consists of a coil of wire, called an *armature*, that can be rotated within a stationary magnetic field. The current induced within the armature reverses its direction of flow periodically as one side of the coil and then the other cuts through the field in a particular direction. Connection to the external load is made through *brushes* contacting *collector* or *slip rings*. Each brush is always in contact with the same collector ring, and therefore, as the current reverses in the coil, the current picked up by the brush contacting its own collector ring is similarly reversing its direction of flow.

The basic *DC generator* is similar in construction to the alternator in that it also has a field magnet and an armature. Instead of the collector rings, however, a mechanical switching device, called a *commutator*, is used. The simple commutator, like slip rings, is mounted on the armature shaft, but instead of consisting of two separate complete *rings*, it is constructed of two *half rings* separated from one another by insulating material, usually mica. Each half of the commutator is connected to one end of the armature coil, and the brushes are mounted so that they contact *opposite* sides of the commutator (Fig. 193).

Now let us see what happens as armature rotation occurs. Assume that the coil *ABCD* is initially in a vertical position and is moving clockwise. At this initial position, no e.m.f. is being produced because the conductors *AB* and *CD* forming the coil are parallel to the lines of force, and none of the lines are being cut. As that side of the coil which we have labeled *AB* begins to cut the field in an *upward* direction, the other side, *CD,* is moving downward.

The side of the commutator connected to *AB* is, at this point, in contact with brush B_1, and brush B_2 is in contact with the other side of the commutator connected to the *CD* part of the armature. The meter across the brushes begins to record a current flow in one direction reaching a peak value at the 90-degree position. As this position is passed, the current decreases, and at the 180-degree position drops again to zero. Note carefully that the meter showed a *positive* current during this period, that is, its indications, though varying in magnitude, were all to one side (the positive or + side) of the zero center scale.

As the 180-degree position is passed, the *other* side of the coil (*CD*) is now moving in an *upward* direction, and side *AB* is

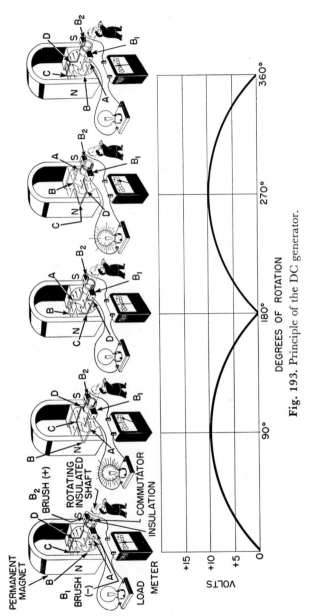

Fig. 193. Principle of the DC generator.

moving downward. *The current in the armature coil must now flow in the opposite direction, but the current read by the meter will show no change in direction.* This is due to the fact that brush B_1 is still contacting the *upward*-moving side of the armature, and brush B_2 is still contacting the *downward*-moving side. As the armature was rotated, the commutator also rotated, but the brushes in

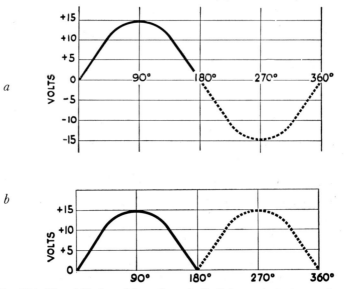

Fig. 194. The shifted position of one-half of the cycle is due to the action of the commutator.

their fixed position were now in contact with the *opposite* segments of the commutator. In other words, brush 1 *always* contacts that portion of the commutator connected to that part of the armature moving upward. Similarly, brush 2 *always* contacts that portion of the commutator connected to that part of the coil moving downward. The armature changes its position periodically, but the brushes, through the action of the commutator, only contact that part of the armature moving in a specific direction. Hence, the direction of current flow, *as it appears at the brushes*, does not change.

In effect, what the commutator has done is to switch the brushes around automatically so that one brush always contacts the *positive* side of the armature, and the other brush, the *negative* side. This automatic switching takes place just as the armature current changes its direction of flow.

In Fig. 194*a*, the sine curve produced by an alternator is shown. Part of the cycle is above the center line, and part

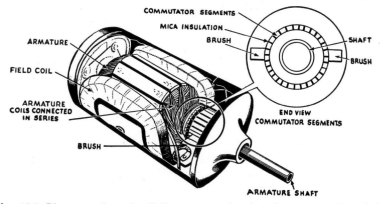

Fig. 195. Phantom view of a DC generator showing the construction of the armature and its commutator.

below. In a DC generator, owing to the action of the commutator, we can consider the lower part of the curve, shown in dotted lines, as being shifted to the upper side so that a curve representing the output current of the basic DC generator will appear as in Fig. 194*b*. As can now be seen, the direction of flow is always in one direction, but unlike the direct current produced by a battery, the magnitude is varying from zero to maximum, and then to zero again. Thus, the current appears to flow in *pulses*, and, in fact, this is a form of *pulsating direct current*.

Pulsating direct current is not desirable for most practical applications. For this reason, the armature of a DC generator is wound with a large number of coils connected in series. The ends of each coil are connected to the segments of a commutator that has many segments, the segments following each other in sequence. These metal segments are composed of wedge-shaped bars of copper separated by thin sheets of mica, and the whole unit is assembled in the form of a cylinder held together by strong clamps. The segments are insulated from the clamps as well as from the metal armature shaft (Fig. 195).

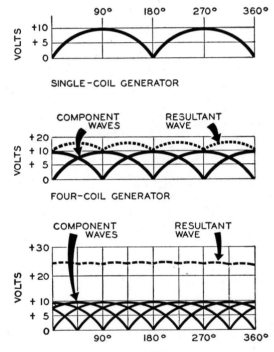

Fig. 196. The use of a multi-coil armature results in a more even flow of direct current.

The use of this multi-coil armature allows the generator to produce an almost steady direct current, the pulsations being reduced as the resultant pulses from each coil blend with one another. While one coil is at the zero position, another is at the maximum position, giving the effect of having the e.m.f. produced by one coil *fill in* as the e.m.f. produced by the other dropped out (Fig. 196).

However, even with a very large number of coils forming the armature, some of the pulsating effect remains. This effect is called *commutator ripple*. The ripple (representing small changes

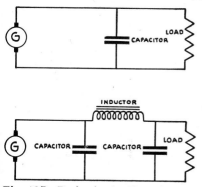

in current) can be almost entirely eliminated by the use of a *ripple filter*, which consists of a capacitor, or a capacitor-inductor combination (Fig. 197). It will be recalled that a capacitor tends to oppose voltage variations, and the inductance opposes current changes. The term *filter* indicates an electrical device

Fig. 197. Basic ripple-filter circuits.

that blocks the flow of undesired pulsations or frequencies and allows the passage of only the type of current required. Thus, by using a filter, the output of a DC generator can be made to resemble DC current as furnished by a battery (Fig. 198).

3. Types of DC Generators

Direct-current generators are classified according to the method used to excite their field windings. Four methods are available:

a. Separate excitation
b. Series winding
c. Shunt winding
d. Compound winding

a. *Separately Excited Generators.* In the separately excited generator, an external DC source such as a battery or another DC generator is connected across the field (Fig. 199). This type of generator has very good *regulation*, that is, the voltage variation as the load changes is not excessive, since the field strength is maintained at a constant value. Such generators are used where a very steady voltage is absolutely essential as, for example, in electroplating, in which a steady DC current flowing through a chemical solution will deposit a thin layer of metal on one of the electrodes. The separately excited DC generator does not, however, for reasons of economy in such factors as initial cost, maintenance, and space for installation, find general usage.

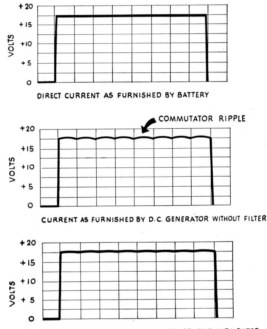

Fig. 198. By using a ripple filter, the output of a DC generator can be made to resemble direct current as furnished by a battery.

b. *Series-wound Generators.* In the series-wound generator, the field winding and the armature winding are connected in series without any external source of excitation (Fig. 200). When the generator is started, the residual magnetism of the field magnets is sufficient to induce a voltage within the armature, and as the speed of rotation increases, the current developed in the armature flows through the series field winding, increasing the field strength proportionately. This same current flows through the load. As a heavier current drain is called for, the heavier current flow through the series field winding increases the field strength. This, in turn, increases the voltage. The regulation of this type

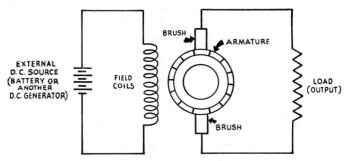

Fig. 199. Circuit of a separately excited DC generator.

of generator is, therefore, quite poor, since voltage variations occur continuously as the load requirements vary.

Since the field winding of a series generator must carry the full value of current developed by the armature, it must be wound of heavy wire and has relatively few turns.

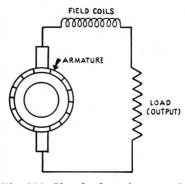

Fig. 200. Circuit of a series-wound DC generator.

c. *Shunt-wound Generators.* In the shunt-wound generator (Fig. 201), the field is connected in parallel to the armature. It (the field) is wound with smaller wire and has many turns. The resistance of the winding is, therefore, fairly high, and the field draws off but a small portion of the current developed by the armature. In other words, less of the power developed in the armature is wasted in exciting the field.

Variations in the load, however, will still affect the field. As more current is drawn from the armature, a lesser value is available to excite the field; this in turn decreases the voltage induced within the armature. To some extent, this poor regulation can be controlled by a field rheostat placed in series with

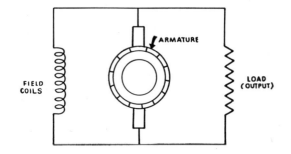

SHUNT-WOUND D. C. GENERATOR

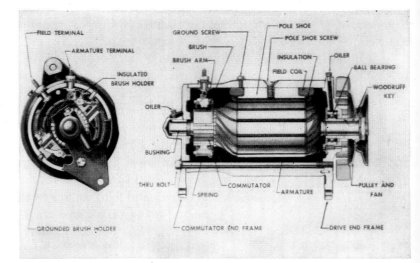

Fig. 201. Basic shunt-wound DC generator. (*Photograph courtesy of Oldsmobile Div. of General Motors Corp.*)

the field winding (Fig. 202). As the load is increased, the voltage drop across the field is lowered, owing to the lower value of current now available in the shunt winding. By *decreasing* the value of the resistance, the field current can be *increased*; this in turn increases the field strength and thus allows a higher voltage to be induced within the armature. The reverse action takes place as the load is decreased, and to offset the increased field strength, which would raise the output voltage, the resistance of the field rheostat is increased, thus cutting down the voltage across the field winding.

Field rheostats are used only on shunt- and compound-wound generators, the latter, as we shall shortly see, having both a

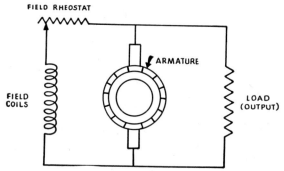

Fig. 202. In a shunt-wound generator circuit, the field rheostat is connected in series with the field coils.

series and a shunt winding. In compound generators also, the field rheostat is connected in series with the *shunt* winding. Instead of regular rheostats, some generators are equipped with automatic relays that place a resistance in series with the winding as the voltage increases and short the resistance out as the voltage drops. Such automatic operation avoids the use of manual control under certain conditions, such as those found in the use of automobile generators.

d. *Compound-wound Generators.* The shunt-wound generator does not, as we have seen, possess very good regulation, inasmuch as load variations affect its output to a large extent. We have seen, however, that the series-wound generator acts in contrary fashion to the shunt-wound device as the load is increased. When the load is increased, the series generator tended to increase its voltage output; the shunt generator dropped off.

By taking advantage of these opposite characteristics, the

compound-wound generator, which has *both* types of fields (Fig. 203), serves extremely well.

If the windings of the shunt and series fields are wound in the

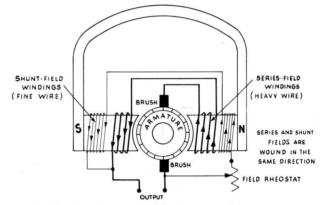

Fig. 203*a*. The circuit of a cumulatively wound compound generator. Note the direction of the windings.

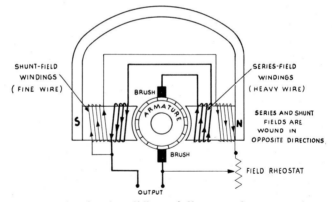

Fig. 203*b*. The circuit of a differentially wound compound generator. Note the direction of the windings.

same direction so that the effect of one field *adds* to the effect of the other, it is called a *cumulative* compound generator (Fig. 203*a*.)

A *differentially* wound compound generator has its separate fields *opposing* each other's actions (Fig. 203*b*). This type does not possess the good regulation of the cumulatively wound unit, but is expressly designed for use where very sudden and heavy loads (as in arc welding) are applied. When the heavy load occurs, the tremendous current drawn from the armature flows through the series winding, and the strong field thus developed neutralizes the effect of the shunt field, since one field opposes the other. The resultant weakened field causes the induced armature voltage to drop, and this, in turn, reduces the armature current. Such action protects the armature from overheating. We can, therefore, consider a differentially wound compound generator as incorporating an automatic overload control within its design.

The cumulative compound-wound generator finds general use where good regulation, that is, a steady voltage output under varying load conditions, is required. Its action should be clearly understood. Let us assume that a generator of this type is in operation and is delivering 100 volts to the load at 10 amp. The voltage across the shunt field is the same as that appearing across the load, 100 volts. The current drawn by the load is also passing through the series winding.

Now let us assume that the load drain is suddenly increased to 15 amp. This means that more current is being delivered by the armature, and since the resistance of the armature winding remains the same, the voltage developed by the armature decreases as the IR drop increases because of the heavier current. If we assume that the armature resistance is 2 ohms, the IR loss as the current is increased by 5 amp. is 10 volts.

$$E_{\text{drop}} = I_{\text{current increase}} \times R_{\text{armature}} = 5 \times 2 = 10$$

The voltage originally was 100, but with this increased load, it will drop to 90 volts $(100 - 10 = 90)$.

Since the shunt field is connected directly across (in parallel with) the armature, the voltage across the *shunt* field must also drop, thus *decreasing* the strength of its field.

Since the series field is connected in series with the armature, the current in the *series* field must increase as the current goes up from 10 to 15 amp., thus *increasing* the strength of the series field.

Decreasing the strength of the shunt field and increasing the strength of the series field to an equal degree leaves the *resultant* field exactly what it was originally. Hence, the generator output tends to maintain the same voltage it was originally delivering. It must be realized, of course, that this self-regulating action occurs quite rapidly, so that a voltmeter across the load would show but a slight change as the load varied.

Exactly the reverse situation occurs if the load is decreased. In this case, the series field is weakened as the shunt field is strengthened.

It would seem that self-regulation as described would allow *any* load variation to take place and yet maintain a steady output voltage, but, in fact, this action can take place only within specified limits. An excessively heavy load (for the particular machine) would still cause poor regulation, owing to a decrease of the machine's efficiency. The action described is simply intended to maintain a steady output voltage within defined limits.

The information describing the four types of DC generators can be classified as follows:

Type	*Advantages*	*Disadvantages*
1. Separately excited ...	Good regulation	1. Less economical 2. Requires more space
2. Series-wound........	....	Poor regulation (voltage rises as load current increases)
3. Shunt-wound	Can use field rheostat to regulate output to some extent	Poor regulation (voltage drops as load current increases)
4. Compound-wound *a.* Differential type...	Safety factor exists inasmuch as voltage automatically drops (thus reducing armature current) under very heavy load	Poor regulation
b. Cumulative type ..	1. Good regulation 2. Can use field rheostat to regulate output	

4. Armature Reaction

When no current is flowing in the armature of a generator (and in motors as well, as will be shown later), the magnetic flux between the field poles remains undistorted, that is, the lines of force seem to run in parallel lines from one pole to the other (Fig. 204).

If a line were drawn right down the center of the armature shown in Fig. 204 from top to bottom, that is, perpendicularly, this line would represent the *neutral plane* or position, where the

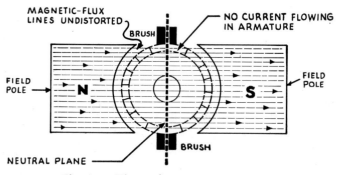

Fig. 204. The stationary neutral plane.

lines of force have the least effect, just as a line drawn from pole to pole in the direction of the lines of force would indicate the position where the flux has the greatest effect.

Now if a current appears in the armature, the armature itself becomes an electromagnet with a field of its own (Fig. 205). This field reacts with the one between the poles and *tends to shift the neutral plane in the direction of rotation* (Fig. 206).

This action, called *armature reaction*, has an important effect on the operation of motors and generators, because the brushes must be so mounted that they contact the commutator at the neutral plane under load. This is called the *running neutral plane*, and at this point sparkless commutation can best be obtained, owing to the fact that at this position the armature coil undergoing commutation is cutting a minimum flux.

In actual practice, the running neutral plane is somewhat farther advanced than so far indicated, owing to an additional factor that must be taken into account. We have already learned that a magnetic field once formed tends to oppose any change

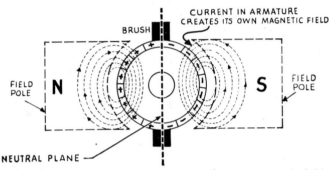

Fig. 205. The armature current creates its own magnetic field.

in the current originally inducing it. This opposition shows itself in the form of an induced current, which may reach a considerable value. As commutation takes place, the original current flow is being stopped, and as the result of the self-induction that occurs at that moment, the induced current that arises may cause considerable sparking at the brushes in the

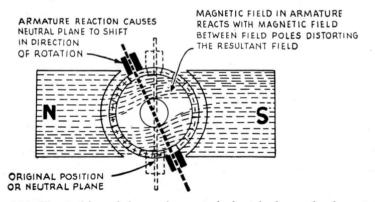

Fig. 206. The position of the *running* neutral plane is the result of *armature reaction*. The neutral plane has shifted in the direction of rotation.

same way that sparking occurs at a switch as a circuit is broken.

We can thus see that the brushes must be set at a point where the effects of armature reaction and self-induction are at a minimum in order that excessive sparking will not occur.

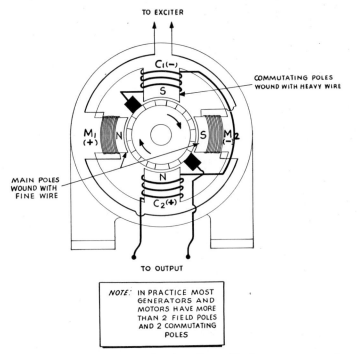

Fig. 207. By using *commutating poles*, the effects of both armature reaction and self-induction are greatly reduced.

However, since the changing value of current under varying loads has a definite effect on both armature reaction and self-induction, it is often difficult to determine the exact position of the running neutral plane, and a method has been developed by which sparking can be eliminated without great concern over the best running neutral plane.

This method calls for the use of *commutating poles* (Fig. 207), whose function is to set up a flux opposing and balancing out the flux at the normal neutral plane. Because of this action, the effects of armature reaction and self-induction at the neutral plane disappear for all practical purposes.

In other words, the original flux pattern is kept within bounds in a practically unchanged and undistorted position, allowing the brushes to be mounted on the neutral plane without incurring the possibility of heavy sparking as the armature undergoes the commutation process.

The field coils of the commutating poles are connected in series with the armature. They are wound with but a few turns of heavy wire so as to be able to carry the armature current without overheating. Variations in the value of the armature current strengthen or weaken their fields, and these fields, in turn, affect the regular field in increased or decreased strength. Since a heavy load would move the neutral plane more than a light load, the heavy current at such a time produces a stronger field to counteract that action. The reverse occurs under a light load.

The use of commutating poles also allows motors to be built that will reverse at full speed without heavy sparking at the brushes. Without such poles, the shift of the running neutral plane that occurs as the armature rotation reverses would necessitate either manual or automatic shifting of the brushes.

The polarity of a commutating pole is always the opposite of the main pole it follows when looking at the frame of the generator or motor *in the direction of the armature's rotation.* Thus, in Fig. 207, if the armature rotates clockwise, pole M_1 is positive (north), and the commutating pole C_1 is negative (south), while the next main pole M_2 is south and its commutating pole C_2 is north.

5. Other Forms of Alternator

1. *The Revolving-field Type.* The basic alternator previously studied is known as a *stationary-field* type since the armature rotates within a stationary or fixed field. Such alternators are used to advantage where the power to be developed is not too great. Where power requirements are greater, other types of alternators serve more satisfactorily.

In the *revolving-field* alternator, the armature remains in a *fixed* position and is called a *stator*, while the field coils are allowed to rotate and are called the *rotor*. This type of construction offers certain advantages:

1) The generated current can be taken from the stator without the use of slip rings and brushes.

2) Since the power generated in the stator is generally much higher than that used by the field coils, the stator coils can be built with greater insulation when occupying a stationary position. Similar insulation on a rotating armature is impractical owing to the excessive bulk and weight that would be necessary.

3) Since the field coils require comparatively low values of direct current, it is easier to feed them through brushes and collector rings of rather small size. Further, the reduced bulk of the field coils allows rotation with less friction and, therefore, less wear on the bearings.

The principle of operation of a revolving-field alternator is essentially similar to that of the revolving-armature type. In one case, the armature cut through fixed lines of force, whereas in the revolving-field type, the lines of force are changing their position, thus causing the armature to be cut by a varying number of lines of force as well as changing their direction of cutting. The effect is exactly the same, since a voltage can be induced within a coil either by moving the coil in and out of (or through) lines of force, or by having the lines of force expanding and contracting (as in the transformer) or varying their position (as when a field rotates).

Figure 208 shows a permanent magnet as the rotor for the sake of clarity. In its initial position, no voltage is induced within the stator (shown as a single loop), since the lines of force are moving parallel to the loop. As the magnet rotates clockwise, more lines of force begin to cut the *AB* part of the loop in an upward direction, and the *CD* part in a downward

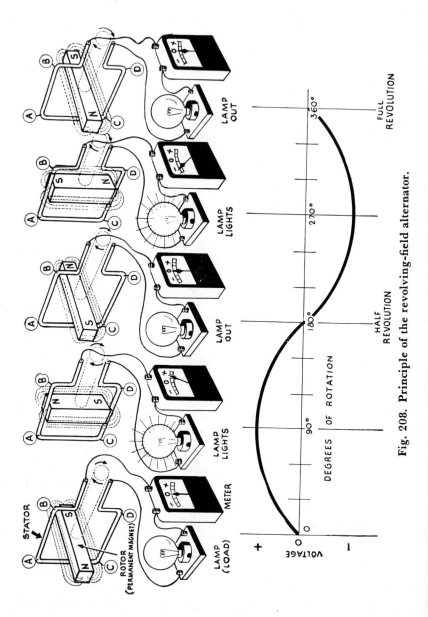

Fig. 208. Principle of the revolving-field alternator.

direction. The sine-curve cycle is now being formed, and as the magnet continues to rotate to the 90-degree position, the maximum point of the positive side of the cycle is formed. At the 180-degree position it drops to zero. Now, as the magnet continues to rotate, *the polarity of the field has been reversed*, since the south pole is moving upward, and the north pole downward.

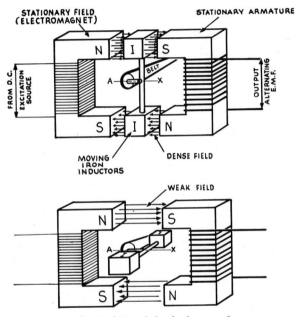

Fig. 209. Principle of the inductor alternator.

The induced current now flows in an opposite direction, completing the sine-curve cycle.

In this type of alternator, just as in the stationary-armature type, the voltage developed will depend upon the strength of the field and the speed of rotation, the speed governing the rate at which the lines of force cut through the stator. The rate of this cutting action affects both the voltage and the frequency. Frequency, of course, is also affected by the number of field poles used.

2. *Inductor Alternator.* Another type of alternator that is very efficient in operation, and is particularly advantageous where alternating current of high frequency is necessary, is known as the *inductor alternator.*

In this device, both the armature and field coils are stationary, entirely eliminating the need for brushes and collector rings. Its construction may be understood by referring to Fig. 209. The field magnet has its pole pieces separated from the armature poles by a considerable air gap. Within this gap, masses of iron (*I*), called *inductors*, are caused to revolve on an axis (*AX*) by an external source such as an electric motor.

When inductors are at the point between the field poles and the armature poles, there is a strong magnetic flux flowing between them due to the high permeability of the iron inductor. When the inductors move beyond this point, the air gap widens greatly. The low permeability of this gap reduces the magnetic flux considerably. This increase and decrease of magnetic flux (varying the density of concentration of the lines of force) surrounding the armature coil induces an alternating current within the armature, the current flowing in one direction as the flux increases, and in the opposite direction as the flux decreases.

In this type of alternator, a *complete cycle occurs each time an inductor mass passes the poles* since there is a complete cycle of flux expansion and contraction when this occurs.

$$\text{Frequency in cycles} = \frac{\text{number of poles} \times \text{RPM}}{60}$$

In other types of alternators, a cycle is completed only when two poles of opposite polarity are passed during rotation.

$$\text{Frequency in cycles} = \frac{\text{number of poles} \times \text{RPM}}{120}$$

Thus the same AC frequency can be obtained with half as many poles as with the revolving-armature or revolving-field alternators.

3. *Polyphase Alternators.* Suppose that the revolving-field alternator shown in Fig. 208 were reconstructed so that an additional armature winding (similar in construction, but completely separated electrically) were placed at right angles to it (Fig. 210). The rotation of the field magnet would induce an alternating current in the second loop exactly as it would in the first, the currents having the same frequency and the same values. The sole difference between them would be that they

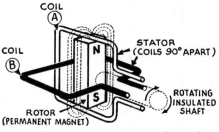

Fig. 210. Principle of the basic polyphase alternator.

would reach corresponding points in their cycles at different instants of time, since at the moment when the field magnet's poles were in line with the conductors of one loop (and thus producing a maximum e.m.f. within it), the other loop would be developing no e.m.f. whatsoever.

This can be illustrated by the sine curves in Fig. 211. The first sine curve (*A*) indicates the values recorded by one loop, and the second curve (*B*) the values of the second loop. Note that they are identical in shape, but, in relation to a given time interval, one has developed ahead of the other. If we now combine the curves (*C*), we have a picture of the sine curves of a *two-phase* alternator. This simply means that the individual e.m.f.s developed are 90 degrees apart. Another way to put it is to say that the flux of the field magnet is cutting the individual armature coils at intervals of 90 degrees.

In *three-phase* alternators, in which three separate armature windings are used, the interval is 120 degrees, as shown in Fig. 212.

A machine for simple alternating current is called a *single-phase* machine, and those alternators generating a two- or three-phase alternating current are called *polyphase*, which means *many-phase* or *more than one phase*. Polyphase generators

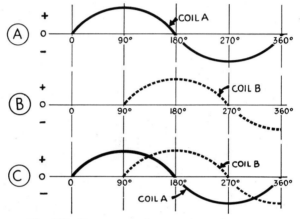

Fig. 211. Sine curves of a two-phase alternator.

offer certain advantages where used for power purposes, as in the operation of AC motors, the action of which will be studied later.

In the actual construction of polyphase armatures (as well as in the transformers used with them where it is necessary to raise or lower voltages for transmission purposes), the separate windings are combined in a manner that avoids the use of two leads for each individual phase. The three-phase devices (which

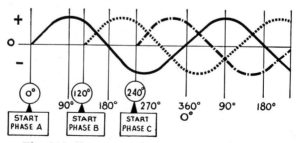

Fig. 212. Sine curves of a three-phase alternator.

are very common) are connected in *star* (also called Υ) and *delta* arrangements (Fig. 213), which require but three leads. The windings are so joined that, in effect, they are connected together at a common point, and the remaining leads furnish the output connections.

6. Regulation and Efficiency

Most electric generators are designed to operate at a fixed speed, except in special instances as in the automobile. If, under all circumstances, the field strength could be kept at a constant value, and if the output load did not change, the output voltage generated would also remain at a fixed value. A machine of this type would be called a *constant-potential* or a *constant-voltage* generator.

Most machines, however, do have some variation in the output voltage due to load variations, and the degree of such variation, as we have already noted, is termed the *regulation*. Regulation may be determined by the formula:

$$\% \text{ regulation of generator} = \frac{V_o - V_f}{V_f} \times 100$$

where V_o = voltage at no load
V_f = voltage at full load

Example: The output voltage of a generator varies from 110 volts at no load to 100 volts at full load. What is the percentage of regulation?

$$\% \text{ regulation} = \frac{V_o - V_f}{V_f} \times \frac{100}{1}$$

$$= \frac{110 - 100}{100} \times \frac{100}{1}$$

$$= \frac{10}{100} \times \frac{100}{1}$$

$$= 10\% \qquad \textit{Ans.}$$

The percentage of regulation should be as small as possible for best results where voltage variations are undesirable.

The ratio of the useful output of a device to its input is termed its *efficiency*. We have already seen how this was computed in the case of a transformer, and exactly the same formula will apply in the case of generators.

$$\text{Efficiency of generator} = \frac{\text{power output}}{\text{power input}} \times 100$$

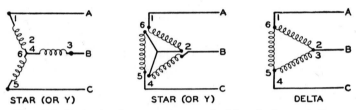

Fig. 213. Basic circuit connections used with polyphase windings.

The power input refers to *all* the energy used to *drive* and *excite* the generator. Thus, if a motor generator delivered 1,000 watts under load, and its motor drew 1,200 watts from the line, and the field excitation required 300 watts (assuming a separately excited field), the efficiency would be 66 per cent.

$$\text{Efficiency} = \frac{1,000}{1,500} \times \frac{100}{1} = 66\%$$

Generator efficiency varies with the load. It is usually lower for small machines than for large ones. Certain losses, such as mechanical losses, field-excitation losses, and core losses, are constant regardless of the load. Others, such as the armature (I^2R or copper) loss, increase rapidly with a load increase. Well-designed machines may have an efficiency ranging from 80 to 95 per cent.

Mechanical losses are those due to friction in the bearings, friction at the brush contacts, and friction between the moving parts of the machine and the air. Air-friction loss is called *windage*.

Copper or I²R loss is due to the resistance of the field and armature windings, and is often termed *field copper* and *armature copper* loss, respectively. The term *excitation loss* is also used to describe the field copper loss.

Core loss refers to losses in the magnetic circuit, just as in the case of a transformer. Here, too, they consist of *hysteresis* and *eddy-current* losses, which occur in the armature and field cores.

7. Maintenance

As will shortly be shown, the construction of motors and generators is fundamentally the same. Hence, many problems in the maintenance of such devices are also identical and will be mentioned in the chapter on motors. At this point, we shall simply refer to a few things that may particularly affect the operation of a generator with special reference to its main function of delivering a voltage to a load. We may roughly divide the problem into two categories:

1) The moving part (armature or rotor) is rotating, but the voltage available at the output terminals is either too high or too low, or absent entirely.

2) Output voltage is available, but excessive sparking at the brushes is occurring. When excessive voltage is apparent, it is usually due to excessive speed of rotation or excessive field excitation. The remedies, of course, are to reduce the speed or increase the value of the field rheostat, as the case requires. A reduced load will also increase the output voltage and allow the motor driving the generator to speed up since less work is being done. To offset the effect of a reduced load, the same operations as described apply. Usually the speed is not changed, but an adjustment of the field rheostat is sufficient. Generators and motors are designed to operate at certain speeds, and only under such operation is performance at the highest efficiency attainable. For the other conditions, that is, when the voltage

is too low or entirely absent, or where excessive sparking occurs, a trouble chart may be drawn as follows:

Chart 1. Reduced or No Output Voltage Available

Possible cause	Remedy
1. Open field circuit......	Locate open. Repair or replace coil. Open may be in the field rheostat, which should be checked first. Check fuses and replace if defective. Check for broken or shorted lead wires.
2. Loss of residual magnetism............	Insert a battery in series with the field. The polarity must be correct, that is, the positive side of the battery must be connected to the positive lead of the field; the negative side to the negative lead. After a few minutes, restore circuit and operate generator.
3. Shunt field coils reversed............	Reverse field-coil connections.
4. Armature rotating in wrong direction.....	Reverse direction of rotation.
5. Brushes not making contact to commutator or slip ring.........	If brushes are worn, replace. Be sure brush springs hold brushes firmly onto commutator or rings.
6. Open or shorted armature..............	Replace. Repair is ordinarily impossible except where special facilities are available.
7. Dirty commutator or slip rings..........	Remove excess soot, etc., with cloth dipped in carbona, gasoline, or other cleaning fluid. Then gently sandpaper with fine (00) sandpaper. Do not use emery cloth. Latter leaves metal particles, which may short out segments and also score them.

Chart 2. *Sparking at the Brushes*

Possible Cause	Remedy
1. Overloading..........	Reduce load to normal.
2. Brush springs too loose..	Increase tension so that brushes bear firmly on commutator or slip rings.
3. Brushes cracked, worn, or irregular.........	Replace. To smooth new brushes onto curved commutator or slip rings, place a piece of fine sandpaper around commutator or rings, allow brushes to rest on sandpaper, and rotate armature slowly by hand for a few revolutions.
4. Commutator or slip-ring surface worn or roughened..........	If condition not excessively bad, sandpapering gently may help. Otherwise, lathe must be used to "turn" the commutator or rings down to proper smoothness.
5. Armature coil or coils opened or shorted....	Replace armature.
6. Brushes not set at running neutral plane...	Move brushes to running neutral plane.
7. Commutating poles not functioning.........	Check commutating-pole field coils and their connections.

SUMMARY

1. The electric motor and the electric generator are both forms of the electric dynamo, a device that converts one form of energy into another.

2. A generator converts mechanical energy into electrical energy.

3. A motor converts electrical energy into mechanical energy.

4. The DC generator is distinguished from the alternator by its use of a commutator instead of slip rings. The commutator mechanically switches the AC output of the armature so that the output current will flow in a single direction.

5. The output of a DC generator is not pure direct current but a pulsating direct current. To reduce the pulsating effect, the armature is wound with a large number of coils so that the total voltage impulses developed blend more uniformly into a steady direct current. The pulsations (called *commutator ripple*) are further smoothed out by the use of a filter consisting of a parallel capacitor, or a combination of an inductor and a capacitor.

6. Direct-current generators are available in four forms:

a. Separately excited
b. Series-wound
c. Shunt-wound
d. Compound-wound

7. The separately excited and cumulative compound-wound types offer the best regulation, that is, a fairly steady output voltage under load variations.

8. Field rheostats are used in series with the shunt fields of shunt-wound and compound-wound generators to control the output voltage within given limits. Increasing the resistance of the rheostat decreases the strength of the field and the resultant output voltage.

9. Alternators (AC generators) are available in three forms:

a. Revolving-armature type
b. Revolving-field type
c. Inductor type

10. The revolving-field type is used where large values of power are to be generated, since the high voltage or current developed in the stator can be removed without the use of brushes and slip rings.

11. The inductor alternator is particularly used where high AC frequencies are to be generated. In this device, both the field magnets and armature remain stationary.

12. Polyphase alternators have additional armature windings so arranged that the voltages developed in each winding reach their full magnitudes at different time periods. A two-phase alternator has its phases 90 degrees apart; a three-phase alternator is arranged for 120-degree spacing.

13. Armature reaction (the result of the armature's field disturbing the regular field) and armature self-induction may produce sparking at the brushes unless the brushes are set at the running neutral plane or commutating poles are used.

Quiz: The Electric Generator

This quiz will help you review the material just studied. See the quiz directions on page 24 before answering the questions below.

1. The term *mechanical losses* in a generator does *not* include factors of: *a.* bearing friction; *b.* windage; *c.* eddy currents; *d.* brush friction.

2. The term *dynamo* is used to describe: *a.* only motors; *b.* only generators; *c.* only electric motor generators; *d.* all types of motors and generators.

3. The revolving-armature alternator may be physically distinguished from the DC generator by the fact that a DC generator is: *a.* physically larger; *b.* equipped with a commutator; *c.* equipped with collector rings; *d.* equipped with both a commutator and a single slip ring.

4. The indicator alternator has: *a.* stationary field magnets and a stationary armature; *b.* revolving field magnets and a revolving armature; *c.* stationary field magnets and a revolving armature; *d.* revolving field magnets and a stationary armature.

5. In order to produce three-phase alternating current, the dynamo used should be: *a.* a single-phase alternator; *b.* a polyphase alternator; *c.* an inductor alternator equipped with slip rings; *d.* a single-phase alternator equipped with a commutator.

6. The term *excitation loss* refers to: *a.* windage; *b.* bearing friction; *c.* armature copper loss; *d.* field copper loss.

7. The current *at the brushes* in a DC generator is: *a.* pure direct current equivalent to that obtained from a battery; *b.* pulsating direct current; *c.* alternating current and direct current combined; *d.* alternating current.

8. For best regulation, it is advisable to use a: *a.* cumulative compound-wound generator; *b.* differential compound-wound generator; *c.* shunt-wound generator; *d.* series-wound generator.

9. A generator converts: *a.* electrical energy into mechanical energy; *b.* electrical energy into thermodynamic energy; *c.* mechanical energy into electrical energy; *d.* mechanical energy into thermodynamic energy.

10. Commutator ripple may be reduced by the use of: *a.* a filter; *b.* a heavier load; *c.* broader commutator segments; *d.* larger brushes.

11. A field rheostat, used with a compound-wound generator, should be connected in: *a.* parallel with the series field; *b.* parallel with the shunt field; *c.* series with the series field; *d.* series with the shunt field.

12. A DC generator is described as having 5 per cent regulation. This means that the voltage output: *a.* does not vary at all; *b.* varies slightly; *c.* varies greatly; *d.* varies only under a light load.

13. Decreasing the resistance of a field rheostat: *a.* decreases the field strength and output voltage; *b.* decreases the field strength and increases the output voltage; *c.* increases the field strength and output voltage; *d.* increases the field strength and decreases the output voltage.

14. A motor generator draws 2 kw. from the line and delivers 1.5 kw. to the load. The efficiency is: *a.* 25 per cent; *b.* 50 per cent; *c.* 75 per cent; *d.* 95 per cent.

15. Excessive sparking at the brushes may be due to: *a.* overloading; *b.* underloading; *c.* excessive spring tension; *d.* excessive armature bearing resistance.

16. Emery cloth should *not* be used to clean a commutator because it: *a.* is expensive and not readily available; *b.* leaves metallic particles that may short out the segments; *c.* causes the commutator to become oily; *d.* prevents the brushes from contacting the commutator.

17. In the *revolving-field alternator*, direct current must be used to excite the: *a.* rotor; *b.* stator; *c.* inductor; *d.* armature.

18. The current *in the armature* of a DC generator is: *a.* pure direct current equivalent to that obtained from a battery; *b.* pulsating direct current; *c.* alternating current and direct current combined; *d.* alternating current.

19. Should a commutator become dirty with grit or residue from the wearing of the carbon brushes, it may be cleaned with a cloth soaked in: *a.* water or sulfuric acid; *b.* lubricating or vegetable oil; *c.* graphite or linseed oil; *d.* carbona or gasoline.

20. In a DC generator, sparking at the brushes *cannot* be due to: *a.* overloading; *b.* an open field; *c.* cracked or irregular brushes; *d.* loose brush springs.

21. If there is excessive voltage output from a generator, it may be caused by: *a.* decreased line voltage; *b.* decreased speed of rotation; *c.* excessive speed of rotation; *d.* excessive load.

22. In a DC generator, a *complete absence* of voltage output is ordinarily *not* due to: *a.* an open field; *b.* an open field rheostat; *c.* a blown fuse; *d.* overloading.

23. An *inductor* alternator equipped with 24 poles is operating at 1,000 r.p.m. The AC frequency is: *a.* 200 cycles; *b.* 400 cycles; *c.* 600 cycles; *d.* 800 cycles.

24. *Commutator ripple* means most nearly the: *a.* pulsating current appearing at the output of an unfiltered DC generator; *b.* appearance of 60-cycle AC current at the generator output terminals; *c.* variations in the AC voltage exciting the field coils; *d.* mechanical up and down movement of the brushes contacting the commutator.

25. To prevent the effects of armature reaction and armature self-induction, the brushes must be set in the: *a.* positive plane; *b.* negative plane; *c.* highest plane; *d.* neutral plane.

Chapter 10. The Electric Motor

1. General

The electric motor is a device that converts electrical energy into mechanical energy. Its basic construction, as well as the basic principles applicable to its operation, are similar to those of the electric generator. Just as generators have field coils and armatures, so do motors. Just as a generator develops a counter-e.m.f. as a result of self-induction, when its armature is rotating, so does a motor. Just as generators are of various types such as series-wound, compound-wound, and the like, so are motors. The essential difference lies in the fact that a generator is caused to rotate by mechanical means and is used to produce an electric current; a motor is caused to rotate by the application of an electric current and is used to produce a mechanical force.

2. The Basic DC Motor

Let us assume that we have a group of permanent magnets arranged as in Fig. 214a. Magnet 1 is in a fixed position and acts as the field magnet, but magnet 2 is mounted on a pivot and can therefore be rotated. We can call this latter magnet the *armature.* Since like poles repel each other, the armature tends to swing away from the original position shown. As it reaches the halfway position shown in Fig. 214b, the south pole of the armature tends to be attracted by the north pole of the field magnet.

The armature therefore can continue to rotate till it reaches the position shown in Fig. 214c. At this point, since unlike poles face each other, the armature comes to rest as no repulsion force exists that would cause it to move on. We can now theoretically do either of two things to repeat the condition originally existing, that is, a situation where like poles face each other and tend to repel one another: (1) the polarity of the *field magnet* can be

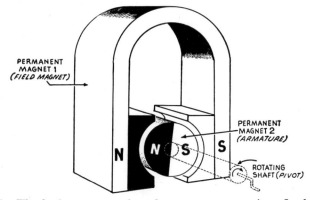

Fig. 214a. The basic motor consists of two magnets, one in a fixed position (the field magnet in this case) and the other (the armature) capable of rotating.

reversed or (2) the polarity of the armature can be reversed. If either is done quickly so that the rotating force developed by the armature does not drop to zero, the armature will continue to

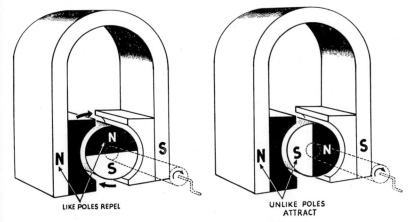

Fig. 214b. Since like poles repel, the north pole of the armature tends to move away from the north pole of the field.

Fig. 214c. When the armature reaches the position shown, it cannot rotate further since unlike poles face each other.

rotate in the same direction. In practice, it is convenient to reverse the polarity of the armature rather than the field magnet, and this is what is done in the basic DC motor shown in Fig. 215. In order to change the armature polarity easily, an electromagnet is used as an armature. The construction of this motor is identical

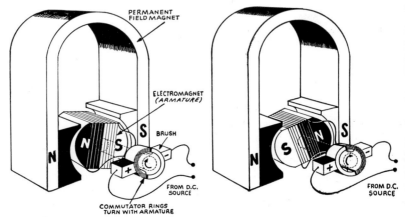

Fig. 215a. By using a wound armature with a commutator, it is possible to reverse the polarity as soon as unlike poles face each other. Above, the like north poles are repelling each other.

Fig. 215b. As the unlike poles line up with each other, they tend to lock the rotor into place but just before this occurs the commutator action reverses the polarity of the armature.

to that of the DC generator. Whereas in the generator, a current was taken *from* the armature winding, in the motor, a current is fed *into* the armature, and by the action of the commutator, the direction of current flow through the armature winding is so maintained that an *unlike* pole is always produced as that part of the armature reaches the field pole.

In Fig. 215a, the current entering the armature through the commutator produces a north pole opposite the north pole of the field magnet. The repulsion that occurs causes the armature to rotate, and when it reaches the point shown in Fig. 215b, the south pole of the armature comes under the influence of the north pole of the field magnet. The rotation does not halt because just as the armature reaches the point shown in Fig.

215*b*, the current in it is reversed by action of the commutator and this reverses the polarity of the armature (Fig. 215*c*). The armature pole that was formerly the south pole becomes a north pole and is now repelled by the north pole of the field magnet till it reaches the position shown in Fig. 215*d*. Here

Fig. 215*c*. The polarity of the armature is reversed by the action of the commutator. *Like* poles again face each other.

Fig. 215*d*. The newly created (and reversed) poles of the armature tend to be repelled by the fixed field poles, causing continued rotation. The momentum of the rotating armature maintains rotation in the same direction at the instant the commutator is acting to reverse the poles.

it comes under the attracting power of the south field pole and moves toward it. Just as it reaches this point, the commutator again reverses the direction of the current flow, causing the armature polarity to be reversed once again. This allows the process of rotation to continue.

The tendency of a motor armature to rotate under the conditions described is called the *torque*, and the degree of torque is dependent upon two factors:

a. The strength of the field (flux)

b. The armature current.

This may be expressed in a formula:

$$\text{Torque} = \text{flux} \times \text{armature current } (I)$$

In the basic motor just described, the flux strength could not be changed, since a permanent magnet was used as the field magnet, but the strength of the armature current could be varied. Thus, in this type of motor, the value of the armature current alone would affect the speed; the higher the value of the current, the greater the torque and, consequently, the higher the speed of rotation.

3. Armature Current and Counter-e.m.f.

The actual value of armature current when rotation occurs is quite different from the value of current that would be measured when the armature is stationary. In the latter condition, the resistance of the armature would be the sole governing factor. Suppose this resistance measured 1 ohm and the motor were connected to a 100-volt DC source. By Ohm's Law ($I = \dfrac{E}{R}$), we could determine that the current would be 100 amp. It is because of this low armature resistance (and the consequent high value of current that will flow before the normal speed of rotation is attained) that special *starting boxes* composed of automatically or manually controlled resistors must be used when starting a motor initially. Their operation will be described later.

The armature of a motor is similar to an armature used in a generator. Thus, as rotation occurs, a voltage is developed in the armature (just as a voltage is produced in the armature of a generator), and the current thus produced as a result of this voltage or e.m.f. tends to oppose the flow of current fed into the armature from the external line. This opposing voltage is called the *counter-e.m.f.* or *back-e.m.f.* The strength of the counter-e.m.f. increases as the speed of rotation increases (just as the output voltage of a generator increases with the speed of rotation). Thus, at the start of rotation practically no counter-e.m.f. exists, but it steadily increases as the motor gains speed. When the normal speed of rotation is reached, the actual value of armature current is, comparatively speaking, quite low, as this value represents the *difference* between the incoming current fed through the commutator and the opposing current due to the counter-e.m.f. This may perhaps be made clearer if we consider some arbitrary values:

	Armature at rest	Rotation, r.p.m.				
		100	500	1,000	1,500	*Normal speed*
Armature current, amp.	100	100	100	100	100	100
Current due to counter-e.m.f.	−0	−10	−30	−50	−70	−80
Resultant actual current	100	90	70	50	30	20

This chart shows how with increased speed, the actual current in the armature drops owing to the opposing current set up by the counter-e.m.f.

The value of the counter-e.m.f. is also affected by the strength of the field. If the field strength is increased, the counter-e.m.f. is increased. If the field strength is decreased, the counter-e.m.f. is decreased. This brings us to a most interesting situation in the operation of a motor. In the generator, it will be recalled, *we increased the field strength to increase the output*, but in a motor, *increasing the field strength decreases the speed of rotation*. This is due to the fact that an increased field strength increases the counter-e.m.f. The increased counter-e.m.f. increases the value of the opposing current in the armature. This causes the actual armature current to drop further, and since this current value is one of the factors controlling the torque, the speed decreases as the torque decreases.

In reverse fashion, decreasing the field strength decreases the counter-e.m.f., allowing the actual armature current value to rise and resulting in increased torque and speed.

Here, too, this may be shown clearly by the use of arbitrary figures, following the formula:

$$\text{Flux} \times I \text{ (armature)} = \text{torque}$$

CHART 1

Flux strength	100 (normal)	120	150	200
Actual arm. current	×5	×4	×3	×2
Torque	500	480	450	400

CHART 2

Flux strength	100 (normal)	80	60	50
Actual arm. current	×5	×7	×10	×15
Torque	500	560	600	750

Chart 1 shows how an increased flux decreased the actual armature current (by increasing the counter-e.m.f.) and thus reduced the torque.

Chart 2 shows how a decreased flux, in reverse fashion, increased the torque.

The increase or decrease of armature current is much greater in *proportion* than the decrease or increase in the field strength that caused it. Hence the resultant torque increases when the armature current rises even though the field flux has been decreased. The reverse holds true when the field strength is increased, that is, the decrease in armature current plays a *proportionately* greater part in affecting the produced torque than does the increase in field strength.

4. DC Motors

Direct-current motors are similar in most respects to DC generators. In fact, they can be used interchangeably. A DC motor, if caused to rotate by external means, will act as a generator. Similarly a DC generator will rotate as a motor if DC current is fed into its armature.

Direct-current motors, just like DC generators, are classified into three main types:

   a. Series

   b. Shunt

   c. Compound

Each type has distinct operating characteristics. Each has some advantages and some disadvantages.

1. *The DC Series Motor.* In a series motor (Fig. 216), the line current goes through the armature winding into the field coils

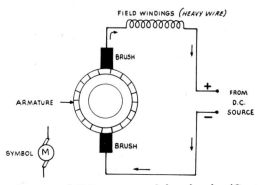

Fig. 216. A series-wound DC motor and its circuit. (*Courtesy of Alliance Manufacturing Co.*)

and then back to the line. Thus the current value in both the field and the armature is always the same, and since these values may be comparatively high, the field coils must be wound of heavier wire than is used in other types of motors.

A series motor is capable of developing very high starting torque, since the high current in the field coils develops a strong flux almost instantly as the voltage is applied. This high starting torque allows the motor to develop speed and power very quickly.

Use is made of this characteristic in such devices as electrically driven trolley cars and trains where tremendous loads must be moved quickly.

A series motor must always be connected to its load; otherwise it will "run away" (speed up to an abnormally high degree) until centrifugal force destroys the armature. This can be understood when we realize that it is the counter-e.m.f. developed by the motor that acts to control its speed. If the load is removed, the speed builds up tremendously and in turn builds up an extremely high counter-e.m.f. This high counter-e.m.f. cuts down the line current entering the motor, and since this current also flows directly through the field coils, the magnetic flux drops very low. We have already seen how weakening the magnetic field increases motor speed, and in the series motor, this continued weakening of the field, as the armature speed increases when the load is removed, causes the runaway action.

A series motor must never be started without its load nor should the load be removed at any time while the motor is running.

The speed of a series motor is determined by

a. The load
b. The applied voltage

Assuming a constant voltage, an increase in the load reduces the speed. Contrariwise, a decrease in the load increases the speed. This varying speed as the load value changes is one of the disadvantages of the series motor.

If we assume a constant load, then an increase in the applied voltage will increase speed, and the speed will decrease as the applied voltage is reduced. A rheostat in series with the motor and the voltage source may be used to control the speed. It should be noted here that the rheostat is in series with *both* the armature and the field coils, thus reducing or increasing the current in *both* units simultaneously. In a series motor, increasing the value of the resistance decreases the applied voltage, thus decreasing the current flowing through the series-connected armature and field. This results in lowered torque and reduced speed.

It is possible to operate a DC series motor on alternating current. In fact, so-called *universal motors* designed to operate on both alternating current and direct current are series-wound. Universal operation is possible since both field poles and armature reverse their polarity simultaneously as the AC current reverses its direction. Thus, if at a given instant, the north pole of the field coil opposite the north pole of the armature reverses to become a south pole, so does the armature pole. The repulsion (or attraction if opposite poles are involved at that instant) continues to take effect, thus producing rotation.

Further, this action is made possible owing to the low inductance of the field, which is wound with comparatively few turns of heavy wire. Owing to the low inductance, the rapid current reversals can nevertheless build up the field to sufficient strength to function properly. In other DC motors (such as the shunt-wound type to be studied shortly) where the inductance of the field is very high, the flux cannot build up rapidly enough when alternating current is used.

For efficient operation, universal motors are constructed using laminated cores. (This is also the case, it will be recalled, in the construction of transformers.) Thus the rapid current reversals when alternating current is used will not produce excessive losses, as would be the case if a solid core were used.

Reversing the current in the line to which a series DC motor is connected will not reverse the direction of rotation. To reverse the direction of rotation, the current must be reversed in *either* the field coils or in the armature. This rule also applies to other types of motors using wire-wound armatures.

2. *The DC Shunt Motor.* In the DC shunt motor (Fig. 217), the field coils are connected in parallel to the armature and thence both are connected across the line. The shunt field has comparatively high resistance and is composed of a large number of turns of fairly small wire. The current flowing through this winding is quite small, and this permits the field strength to remain quite constant even when the line voltage fluctuates.

Because of this fairly constant field, the speed of the motor

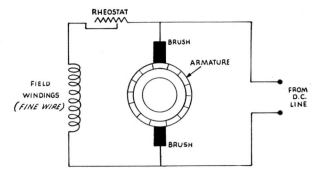

Fig. 217. A shunt-wound DC motor and its circuit. (*Courtesy of Alliance Manufacturing Co.*)

under load variations does not change as greatly as does the speed of a series motor. In the latter, both armature current and flux density increase simultaneously; this allows the counter-e.m.f. to develop to high values and thus causes the speed to fall off rapidly. In the shunt motor, additional torque to handle an increased load is produced by an increase in the armature current alone, the field flux remaining practically constant and not producing, in turn, a greater counter-e.m.f. Thus the speed does not drop to the extent it does in the series motor. This action explains why the shunt motor is often referred to as a *constant-speed* motor.

Shunt motors are used where loads do not vary excessively and where constant speed is important. Most machine tools, such as lathes, require this type of motor.

The speed of a shunt motor is generally controlled by a rheostat placed in series with the field coils. To increase the speed, the rheostat's resistance is increased, thus lowering the field flux. A lowered flux decreases the counter-e.m.f., which in turn allows the armature current to rise. The increase in the actual armature current is much greater proportionately than the decrease in field current. This rise in armature current increases the torque and speed.

Though the speed could also be regulated by using a rheostat in series with the armature, this procedure is not advisable because of the heavier current that appears there. This would necessitate a physically bulky rheostat wound with very heavy wire so that it would carry the high current.

Similarly, control of speed by varying the line voltage (as was done in the case of the series motor) is inadvisable since voltage variations would have to be fairly great to affect the field flux. This would not only require a large rheostat capable of carrying the total current drawn by the field coils and the armature together, but would reduce the over-all efficiency of the motor, which is designed to operate on full voltage.

In the operation of the shunt motor, care must be taken to avoid a *loss of field excitation*. If this occurs, the speed becomes so great that the armature may be damaged. The residual magnetism in the pole pieces is insufficient to allow the building up of a sufficient counter-e.m.f. Loss of line voltage, or an open in the armature, does *not* affect the motor in this manner. In the former case, the motor comes to a stop quickly (though not as quickly as a series motor, since the larger field winding prevents the field from collapsing as quickly). In the case of an open circuit in one of the armature coils, rotation will continue accompanied by heavy sparking at the brushes, but if the main lead to the entire armature opens, rotation soon ceases, since without armature current no torque can be created. Heavy sparking also occurs due to the higher counter-e.m.f. that is developed.

A number of devices are used to prevent injury to a shunt motor should the field be lost. These are generally part of the starting arrangement used with the motors and will be studied shortly.

Loss of load does not affect a shunt motor in the same way as it does a series motor. The motor will tend to speed up somewhat until the counter-e.m.f. developed equals the applied voltage. Since the field remains almost constant, this equality is attained and maintained at a certain speed that is slightly higher than the normal speed of rotation.

3. *The DC Compound Motor.* The DC compound motor, like the DC compound generator, is available in both the differential and cumulative types. These motors accentuate the characteristics of the shunt and series types, combining in one unit the advantages of both.

The differential compound motor (Fig. 218) has two sets of field coils, one in shunt and the other in series with the armature. The series and shunt coils are so mounted that their respective fields oppose or "buck" each other. When the load on the motor increases, the increased current in the armature also flows through the series field, and since this field bucks the fairly constant shunt field, the total effect is to reduce the flux. Weakening the resultant field in this manner allows the motor to pick up speed. This action takes place quite rapidly, thus allowing the motor to rotate at an even pace.

The speed regulation of this type of motor is very high, that is, the variation in speed as the load varies is slight. In fact, it is considerably better than the ordinary shunt motor and this explains its wide use.

Even though the differential compound motor has a series

field, it does not, like the simple series motor, have a high starting torque. This is due to the fact that the series field is quite small and, in addition, acts to oppose the shunt field.

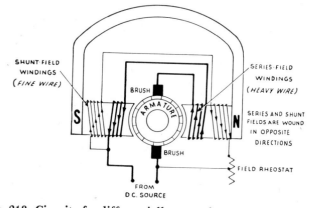

Fig. 218. Circuit of a differentially wound compound DC motor.

Where higher starting torques are required and yet a series motor will not serve, the cumulative compound motor (Fig. 219) is used. In this device, the series and shunt fields are so mounted that they aid (instead of opposing) each other. Thus large starting torque is obtained owing to the heavy flux created by the series

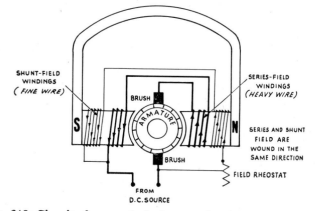

Fig. 219. Circuit of a cumulatively wound compound DC motor.

field when the current is first applied, and since the shunt field maintains a steady flux, the motor cannot run away (as is the case with a series motor) if the load is removed.

The speed regulation of the cumulative compound motor is much lower than that of the type previously mentioned. It changes speed considerably as the load varies, but it is used extensively where high starting torque is required. Some motors of this type are so designed that the series field is automatically cut out of the circuit after it is started. This gives the advantage of high torque when starting and then leaves the motor to run as a shunt type once it is actually operating.

The following chart compares the characteristics of the three types of DC motors:

Type	*Advantages*	*Disadvantages*
1. Series...............	1. High torque 2. No injury if field or armature opens	1. Poor speed regulation 2. Runs away without load
2. Shunt...............	1. Fairly constant speed (good speed regulation) 2. Field rheostat can be used to control speed 3. Does not run away if load is removed	1. Runs away if field opens 2. Low torque
3. Compound *a.* Differential type.....	1. Very good speed regulation 2. Field rheostat can be used to control speed 3. Does not run away when load is removed	1. More expensive 2. Low torque
b. Cumulative type....	1. High starting torque 2. Does not run away if load is removed 3. Field rheostat can be used to control speed	1. Speed regulation only fair 2. More expensive

5. Starting Boxes

1. *Purpose of the Starting Box.* At normal running speed, the current in the armature is comparatively low, being the difference between the applied current and the current produced by the counter-e.m.f. At rest, however, the current is very high owing to the armature's low resistance. If the armature were to be wound with sufficiently heavy wire to carry this high current, it would be an extremely bulky affair and the efficiency of the motor would be reduced. All armatures are therefore built to accom-

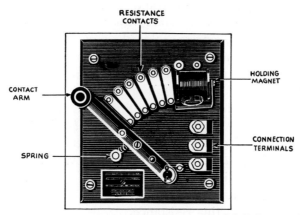

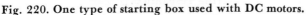

Fig. 220. One type of starting box used with DC motors.

modate the current *normally appearing during rotation.* To protect the armature when the motor is first started, some form of starting box is always used except on very small motors.

The starting box (Fig. 220), or motor starter, is basically a variable resistance placed in series with the armature. It allows the line to be connected to the shunt field directly, so that the field can build up immediately, but limits the flow of current through the armature until normal speed is reached. In operation, as the contact arm is moved from the open position, it first allows the line current to enter the field directly; then, in progressive steps, as the arm is gradually passed over the other contacts, allows current to enter the armature. At the first step, all the resistance is in the circuit, and the amount of resistance is successively reduced thereafter. The idea is to keep the armature current low until the motor has gradually built up its normal counter-e.m.f., which then automatically limits the armature current. As the speed is built up, more resistance is removed from the circuit until, at normal speed, the external resistance is cut out entirely.

The starting box is usually so constructed that other safety features are included. For example, if the line voltage were to drop out entirely, the motor would stop. If the power were then turned on, the motor would start without any resistance in series with the armature. To prevent this, the moving arm of the starter is controlled by a heavy spring that automatically returns it to the starting position if released. When it reaches its maximum position, and the motor is in full operation, it is held there by a holding magnet as long as there is line current.

2. *No-field Release Box.* The *no-field release box* is also known as the *three-point* starting box, since it has three connection terminals (*points* or *binding posts*) through which the device is connected to the motor and the line.

This box serves a triple function:

1) It acts as a starting resistance.

2) If the main line voltage fails, it opens the circuit to the motor, preventing the motor from starting without a resistance in the armature circuit should the line voltage come on again.

3) It opens the main line circuit if any open occurs in the field circuit, thus preventing a shunt-field motor from running away owing to the loss of field flux.

The diagram in Fig. 221 shows how the no-field release box is connected. When the line switch is closed, no current can enter either the armature or the field coils, but as the movable arm touches the first contact point, the full line voltage is applied to the field (allowing the field to develop at once), but only a limited amount of current can flow through the resistance and thence through the armature. As the armature begins to rotate, the contact arm is moved toward the second point, and this procedure is followed until the final contact is reached and the motor is operating at normal speed. As each contact point is passed, less resistance is allowed to remain in the armature circuit until at the final contact point, the resistance is entirely cut out and the full line voltage appears across the armature (as it already does across the field). The holding magnet is con-

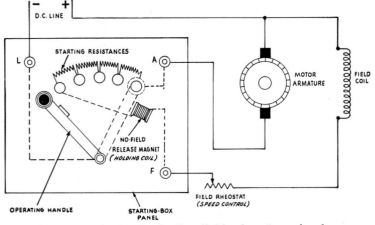

Fig. 221. Basic circuit of a "no-field release" starting box.

nected in series with the field, and since full current is flowing through the circuit, its magnetic action holds the contact arm at its final running position. If anything occurs to break the field circuit (such as the line voltage failing or a break in the field coil that opens the circuit), the holding magnet is demagnetized and releases the contact arm. The arm is pulled back by its spring to the starting position, and the motor stops. To restart, it is necessary to repeat the procedure described, *after* the trouble is remedied.

In operating the starting box, the contact arm must be moved across the points at a fairly slow rate. If it is moved too fast, an excessive current will flow through the armature, thus possibly causing the very trouble it is intended to prevent. If it is moved too slowly, the large values of current flowing through the starting resistance may burn out sections of the resistance due to overheating.

3. *No-voltage Release Box.* The *no-voltage release box* (Fig. 222) is often called a *four-point* box since it has four terminals. The

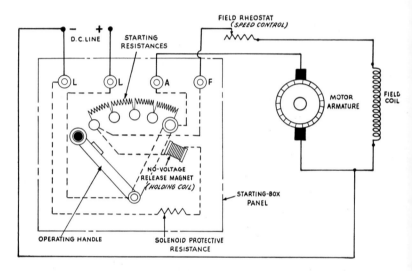

Fig. 222. Basic circuit of a "no-voltage release" starting box.

essential difference between this box and the three-point type is that the holding magnet is connected *across the line* instead of in series with the field. Thus it need not be designed to carry the current flowing through the field and draws only a small amount from the line directly. If the line voltage fails, it releases the contact arm and the motor will stop.

4. *Overload Release Devices.* Some starting boxes are equipped with overload release devices that automatically break the circuit should an excessive current be drawn by the motor. Figure 223 shows one type as part of a starting box. The plunger is normally in the down position and is held there by its own weight and by an adjustment spring. The contacts X and Y are thus open. If the motor draws a current value in excess of a predetermined amount, the plunger is drawn upward by the heavier magnetic field set up by the coil and shorts contacts X and Y. Shorting these contacts also shorts out the holding magnet coil, which then loses its magnetism and releases the contact arm. This stops

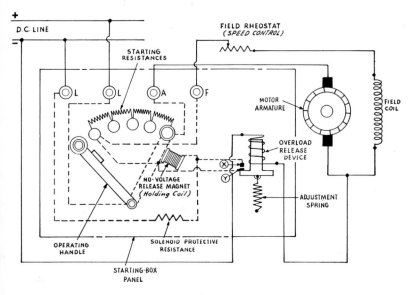

Fig. 223. Basic circuit of a starting box equipped with an overload release device.

the motor by opening the circuit. By adjustment of the plunger, it can be made to rise at any predetermined current value.

5. *Automatic Starter.* There are many types of automatic motor starters differing in details of construction and mode of operation. However, they all are designed to serve a similar purpose, that is, to regulate the flow of current into the armature at the proper rate.

One such device (Fig. 224) is shown for the purpose of illustration. This is called a counter-e.m.f. type of starter, as its operation depends upon the counter-e.m.f. developed as the armature gains speed. A plunger P is mounted below the solenoid S into which it can be drawn. The solenoid is *polarized*, that is, so connected across the armature *that its magnetic attraction depends upon the direction of flow of current set up by the counter-e.m.f.* and not upon that set up by the armature current produced by the line voltage. The counter-e.m.f. current, it will be recalled, flows in the opposite direction to that of the armature current. Thus the

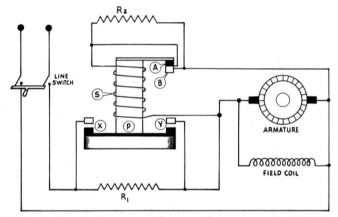

Fig. 224. Basic circuit of one type of automatic starter used with DC motors.

armature current produces a magnetic repulsion effect, forcing the plunger to remain outside the solenoid, while the current induced by the counter-e.m.f. causes the solenoid to attract the plunger upward.

The resistance R_1 is in series with the armature. When the line switch is thrown, this resistance limits the amount of current that can flow through the armature. As the motor gains speed, it builds up its counter-e.m.f. and since the solenoid S is polarized to accept magnetization by the counter-e.m.f., it draws up the plunger as soon as the counter-e.m.f. reaches a predetermined value. Contacts XY are thus closed, shorting out resistor R_1 and allowing the line to be directly connected to the armature. At the same time, the rising plunger opens contacts AB which allows R_2 to be connected in series with the solenoid coil, thus limiting current through the coil. This prevents its overheating but allows sufficient magnetization to hold the plunger in place.

Some devices use a series of resistors and contacts that are shorted out as the plunger rises. Others use a series of plungers, also. The effect is a more gradual adjustment of the current flow.

6. The Motor Generator

So far, we have discussed motors and generators as single units but, as has been stated, they are used together in many instances. A generator, for example, must be rotated by an external source and an electric motor serves in this manner in many applications. The connection between the two devices may be made in a number of ways, such as by the use of a chain or pulley drive, or by direct contact between their shafts through a suitable coupling device. When they are so connected, they are called *motor generators*. Sometimes one motor may drive two or more generators depending upon the design of the equipment (Fig. 225).

Some motor generators have but a single shaft and a single frame in which both motor and generator are housed. The armatures for the motor and the generator are mounted on the common shaft and have their separate commutators. Slip rings, of course, are used for an AC generator. Thus, a motor generator may be equipped with a commutator for use with the motor, and a set of slip rings for the AC-generator section of the combined device.

The separate field coils are also mounted on the common frame, the motor field coils surrounding the motor armature and the generator's field coils similarly surrounding its armature. This type of construction allows for compactness and is prevalent for units that are not overlarge.

7. The Rotary Converter and the Dynamotor

Under some conditions, it is necessary to produce alternating current where direct current alone is available. This is accomplished by the use of a motor generator or rotary converter. In

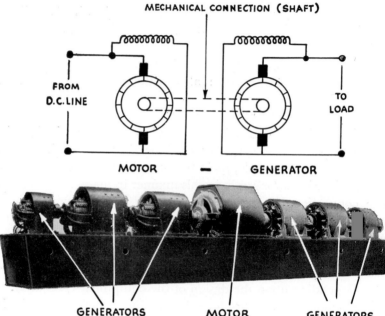

MECHANICAL CONNECTION (SHAFT)

FROM
D.C. LINE

TO
LOAD

MOTOR   —   GENERATOR

GENERATORS   MOTOR   GENERATORS

**Fig. 225. A special motor generator in which one motor is used to drive
six DC generators.** The diagram above the illustration shows a single generator
only in the circuit and is the one ordinarily used to identify a single-motor
generator set. In multi-unit devices, such as the General Electric set shown
above, the circuit diagram is extended to show the additional generators.
(*Courtesy of General Electric Co.*)

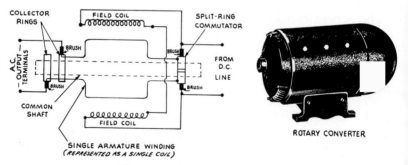

COLLECTOR
RINGS

FIELD COIL

SPLIT-RING
COMMUTATOR

BRUSH

A.C. OUTPUT TERMINALS

BRUSH

FROM
D.C.
LINE

BRUSH

BRUSH

COMMON
SHAFT

FIELD COIL

SINGLE ARMATURE WINDING
(*REPRESENTED AS A SINGLE COIL*)

ROTARY CONVERTER

Fig. 226. The rotary converter.

the former device, the motor operates on direct current and rotates (drives) an AC generator. The *rotary converter* (Fig. 226) is a special type of motor generator and is constructed with a special

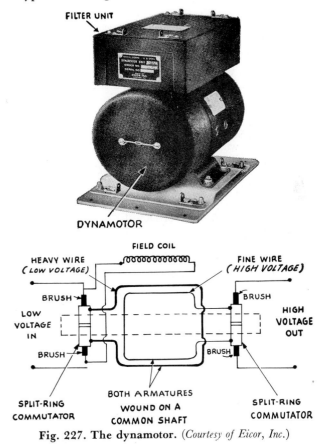

Fig. 227. The dynamotor. (*Courtesy of Eicor, Inc.*)

armature, having, on one end, a set of slip rings, and on the other end, a regular commutator. A *common* set of field coils surrounds the armature. The direct current from the line is fed into the armature via the commutator and also excites the field coils, thus allowing the device to act as a DC motor. Alternating current can then be drawn from the slip rings. It will be recalled that alternating current is always being produced when a coil rotates within a magnetic field. The armature in the rotary converter thus serves a dual purpose.

    a. It acts as a *motor* armature.

    b. It serves as an *AC-generator* armature.

In brief, a rotary converter accomplishes with *one* armature and one set of field coils what the regular motor generator does with

Device	*Identification*	*Use*
Motor generator..	1. Separate field coils 2. Separate armature windings 3. Commutator on motor side if DC 4. Slip rings or commutator on generator side, depending on whether AC or DC	1. AC to DC of different values 2. DC to AC of different values 3. DC to DC of different values
Rotary converter.	1. Common field coils 2. Common armature winding 3. One commutator (motor side) 4. One set of slip rings (generator side)	Generally DC to AC of slightly lower voltage
Dynamotor......	1. Common field coils 2. Separate armature windings 3. Two commutators	DC to DC of higher voltage

two. The disadvantage is that the generated voltage is somewhat less than the input voltage.

The dynamotor (Fig. 227) is a compact motor generator used where it is necessary to convert one value of direct current to another value of direct current (the rotary converter was used to convert direct current into alternating current). Two *separate* armatures are wound on a common shaft, and each has its own commutator. A *common* set of field coils is used. One armature is usually wound with fairly heavy wire and is used as the motor armature. The other armature is wound with smaller wire but has many more turns. This allows it to develop a high voltage output, though the amount of current developed is usually fairly low.

Dynamotors are generally used where operation from batteries is the only source of power available. Thus, it is possible to operate a dynamotor on a 6- or 12-volt storage battery and produce a higher DC voltage as required.

8. AC Motors

1. *The Universal Motor.* As has been stated previously, the universal motor is a series-wound device. To assure effective operation, its constructional details differ slightly from the DC series motor in that the field cores are laminated and the windings of both the field and the armature coils are designed to have a minimum of inductance. Such motors find general use in many household appliances such as vacuum cleaners, electric mixers, and the like. In some instances, they are used in large commercial devices since, like all series motors, they possess a high degree of starting torque. The speed regulation, however, is similarly poor.

2. *The Induction Motor.* When an alternating current is fed into a coil, the field that is created expands and contracts at a rate equivalent to the frequency. If two such coils are placed so as to form the stator of a motor and each is excited by a separate AC phase, a peculiar phenomenon results. The separate fields that are developed react upon each other, and the resultant field appears to revolve or rotate continuously. If a compass is placed within this rotating field, the compass needle will begin to spin just as if it were being attracted by a magnet sliding around the inner face of the stator (Fig. 228).

Now, if a rotor made up with a laminated core is placed within this rotating field, exactly the same thing will occur as when the compass needle was used. This is due to the induced currents set up in the rotor. These currents produce their own magnetic fields and these newly created fields tend to cause rotation in exactly the same way an ordinary armature (magnetized by an external source of current) tends to rotate. Note, however, that there is no connection between the rotor and the line. We are dealing here with induced currents entirely, just as if the device were a transformer. In fact, an *induction motor*, as

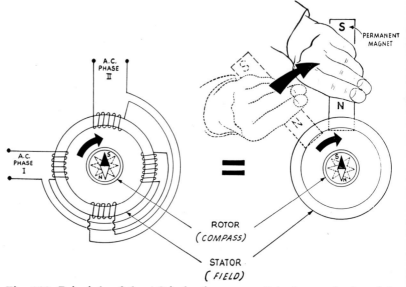

Fig. 228. Principle of the AC induction motor. Polyphase excitation of the stator (field) windings produces the effect of a rotating field. The compass needle (serving as a rotor) keeps turning clockwise as if attracted by a magnet sliding around the inner face of the stator.

this device is termed, is actually a form of transformer, the secondary winding of which (the rotor) is capable of turning on its axis.

The action of an induction motor may be further explained by reference to the diagrams in Fig. 229. Let us assume phase 1 of the AC input is exciting poles A and B, and phase 2 is connected to poles C and D.

At the moment when phase 1 is at maximum, phase 2 is at minimum. Hence the flux between poles A and B is at maximum, while no flux appears between poles *C* and *D*. A compass needle placed within the field will therefore take up a position in line with poles *A* and *B*. As phase 2 begins to rise and phase 1 to decline, all poles are equally excited, and the needle moves 45 degrees to the right. As phase 1 drops to zero, phase 2

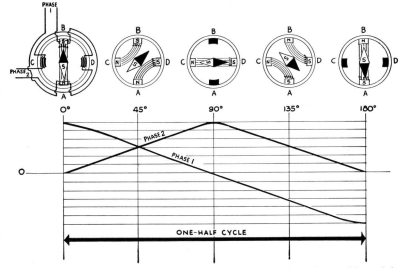

Fig. 229. Principle of the AC induction motor. The changing position of the flux (lines of force) between the poles of the polyphase stator produces the effect of a rotating field. The compass needle will move in a clockwise direction as the phases shift their relative positions.

reaches its maximum, and now the maximum flux exists between poles *C* and *D*. The needle is thus forced to move into line with *C* and *D*. This action will continue as the phases again shift.

Though two-phase excitation has been shown for the sake of simplicity, in practice, three-phase excitation is generally used, but the theory of operation is the same.

Once a polyphase induction motor is started, it will continue to run even if one of the phases is opened. It is thus operating on a single-phase supply. However, this type of motor will not start on a single-phase supply, since there is no rotating field under this condition.

To allow automatic starting on a single-phase supply, a number of methods are in use, since many induction motors are used on such power-supply systems.

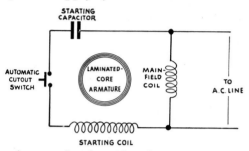

Fig. 230a. Use of a capacitor in conjunction with a starting coil to allow automatic starting of a single-phase induction motor.

a. *Split-phase Starting.* A special starting coil may be used to allow automatic starting, this coil being connected in series with a capacitor or inductance (Figs. 230a, b, and c). The effect of this capacitor or inductor is to throw the current and flux in the starter coil out of phase with the main field. The resultant field is thus caused to rotate, producing the necessary torque. Once the motor is running, the accessory starter circuit is switched out, either manually or automatically.

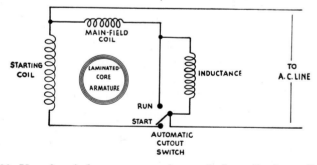

Fig. 230b. Use of an inductance to produce a similar split-phase effect as in Fig. 230a.

In the ordinary capacitor-start motor, the capacitor is used only to *start* the motor. During the starting period, the capacitor supplies large values of current that are out of phase with the current in the regular winding. Hence, the capacitance of the unit is usually very high—from 70 to 450 μf, depending upon the motor's rating. Such capacitors are usually of the nonpolarized electrolytic type designed for intermittent use only. Thus, if the time required for the motor to reach its normal speed is excessive because of improper load, the capacitor may fail and need replacement. The value of the capacitor for maximum torque is not too critical, but if it is too great (or too small), it will cause a decreased starting torque. It is, therefore, important to replace a defective unit with the exact (or nearly exact) capacitance called for by the manufacturer.

Permanent split-phase capacitor motors are also in common use (Fig. 230c). Such motors have a relatively low starting torque in contrast to the capacitor-start motors in which the starting torque is several times greater than running torque. Their design allows multiple-speed operation (with accessory speed regulating devices). The capacitor is a unit in which oil and paper form the dielectric since voltages appearing across the unit may be quite high compared to the line voltage. Such capacitors may have capacitance values of between 2 to 20 μf. Voltage ratings are generally higher than in electrolytic units. These capacitators are capable of operating continuously.

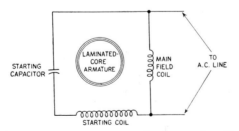

Fig. 230c. The permanent split-phase capacitor motor in which the capacitor functions both upon initial starting and while the motor is running.

b. *Shaded Poles.* In *shaded-pole* motors, a section of each regular pole is modified as shown in Fig. 231. A solid ring of copper or a loop of wire is placed around this modified pole section. When a flux change occurs, an induced current is formed in these rings

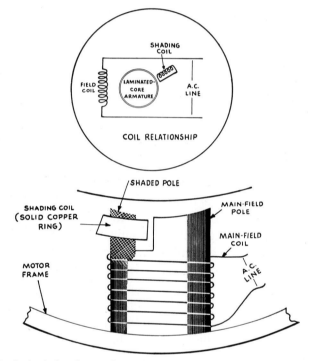

Fig. 231. A shaded pole can be used to allow automatic starting of a single-phase induction motor.

or windings, and this current tends to oppose the change. As a result, flux variations around the regular pole will be out of step with those occurring around the *shaded pole.* This difference of behavior produces a rotating flux as the two separate fields interact upon each other.

The rotors of induction motors may be either the *squirrel-cage* or *wire-wound* type. The squirrel-cage rotor, so called because of its resemblance to a type of cage that can be rotated by its squirrel occupant, is constructed of conductors that are simply plain bars of metal (Fig. 232). There are no wire-wound coils, nor are any slip rings used. There is no connection from the rotor to the line.

Fig. 232. Wagner squirrel-cage rotor. (*Courtesy of Wagner Electric Corp.*)

The wound type, on the other hand, has armature coils and slip rings, but in this case also there is no connection to the power line. Instead it is connected to an external resistance, which is used to improve the starting efficiency. The resistance is cut out automatically when the rotor attains full speed.

The induction motor has characteristics that are quite similar to the DC shunt motor, and is used in similar applications.

The induction motor, like most AC motors except those of very large size, does not require a manual or automatic starting box such as is used with DC motors. Some motors, however, do use a form of speed control, and this is particularly true of very large devices. This *starting* or *speed control* generally consists of a variable transformer, which allows a lower voltage to be used when starting or when a slower speed is required. The full voltage can then be applied when normal running speed is desired.

It is also possible to "dynamically brake" an AC line-operated induction motor by removing the alternating current from the stator and applying direct current instead (Fig. 232a). The DC voltage necessary for the purpose is obtained by rectifying the alternating current (changing the alternating current to direct current). Rectifiers are studied in Chap. 11.

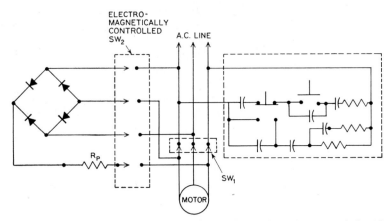

Fig. 232a. Circuit illustrating the use of metallic rectifiers for dynamic braking of an AC motor.

3. *The Repulsion Motor.* In the AC repulsion motor, the armature is similar in construction to the type used in the DC motor. However, instead of having the brushes connected to the line, they are actually short-circuited together. When current is applied to the field coils of the stator, the currents induced in the armature set up magnetic poles of their own, much as such poles appeared in the rotor of the induction motor. The brushes are so placed that these poles are slightly out of line with the stator poles. The repulsion that exists between these stator and rotor poles produces the rotation.

A repulsion motor acts like a DC series motor. It has high starting torque, and the speed increases greatly if the load is removed or reduced.

Some single-phase induction motors using wire-wound armatures are actually started as repulsion motors. As the full running speed is reached, the armature is shorted automatically, and the brushes are lifted from the commutator in order to reduce friction.

4. *The AC Synchronous Motor.* When soldiers are marching in formation, each man keeps in step with the entire group who, in turn, follow a pace set by their commander. Each soldier is thus synchronizing his pace with that of the others. In other words, he is keeping in time.

An AC motor designed to "keep time" with the frequency of the AC supply is called a *synchronous motor.* Such motors possess the advantage of running at a constant speed regardless of the load, provided that the load does not exceed the capacity of the motor. Variation in the AC frequency will, of course, affect the speed.

Any of the alternators previously described will act as a synchronous motor when alternating current is applied to their fields. Polyphase motors of this type are self-starting but single-phase units, just as single-phase induction motors, are not self-starting unless specially adapted for the purpose in the same way induction motors are adapted to the purpose.

The synchronous motor used in electric clocks is a good example of a simple motor of this type. Its rotor is made up of soft iron and has a predetermined number of toothlike projections around the edge (Fig. 233). When alternating current is applied to the field, and the rotor started by turning it manually, it will continue to rotate at a fixed speed. The flux between the poles is changing from zero to maximum constantly. At a moment when it is maximum, it attracts the rotor tooth nearest to the pole and just as the tooth reaches it, the field disappears. Owing to the momentum gained by the rotor, it continues to move beyond the pole. At that moment, the field again reaches maximum, attracting the next tooth and continuing the process just described.

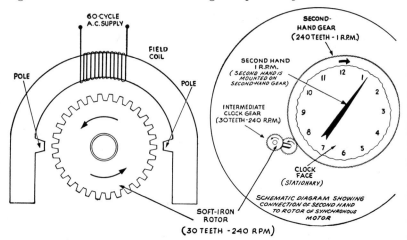

Fig. 233. A type of synchronous motor used in electric clocks.

The number of revolutions in 60 seconds will be determined by the number of teeth and the AC frequency. On a 60-cycle AC supply, which represents 120 current reversals per minute, the speed would be computed by the following formula:

$$\frac{120 \times 60}{X}$$

where X = number of teeth of rotor

Thus, if the rotor had 30 teeth, it would revolve at a speed of 240 revolutions per minute (240 r.p.m.). By the use of proper gears, the second hand on the clock can then be made to complete one rotation per minute as the rotor actually is turning at 240 r.p.m.

Automatic-starting synchronous motors are in common use. They are generally of the shaded-pole type (Figs. 233a and b).

It is of interest to note that synchronous motors are often used on direct current along with ordinary types of DC motors where smooth operation of variable-speed equipment is essential.

In order to obtain the direct current, rectification of the alternating current is obtained in a manner similar to the dynamic braking of the AC motors previously mentioned.

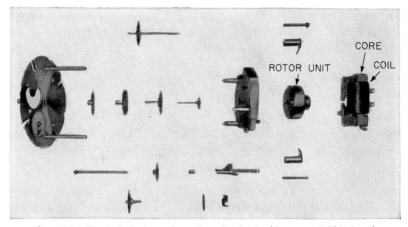

Fig. 233a. Exploded view of an electric clock. (*Courtesy of Telechron.*)

Fig. 233b. Modern electric clock using a synchronous motor. (*Courtesy of Westclox.*)

5. *Efficiency and Horsepower Ratings.* The output of a motor is commonly rated in *horsepower*, 1 horsepower (1 hp.) being the equivalent of 746 watts.

The efficiency of a motor is a figure measured in terms of percentage and compares the actual input in watts to the actual output.

Thus, if a motor rated at 1 hp. is drawing 1,000 watts from the line, the efficiency would be

$$\frac{746}{1,000} \times \frac{100}{1} = 74.6\%$$

where 746 represents the 1 hp. output (in watts), and 1,000 represents the watts drawn from the line, that is, the input to the motor. The formula, therefore, may be stated as follows:

$$\text{Efficiency} = \frac{\text{watts output}}{\text{watts input}} \times \frac{100}{1}$$

The general efficiency of motors is quite high, ranging between 60 and 95 per cent depending upon their design and construction as well as the use to which they are put.

6. *Maintenance of Motors and Generators.* Like all mechanical devices, motors and generators require a certain amount of routine care to assure their proper operation.

The rotors of these machines revolve at high speeds, and proper lubrication of the bearings (the part of the machine upon which the rotor rests) must always be assured. Though many motors are equipped with sealed bearings requiring no lubrication over lengthy periods, oil wells or grease cups are provided on most machines, and these must be checked regularly. The grease cups should be kept filled and should be screwed down slightly as the grease is used up. They should be refilled when approximately half the grease has been dissipated.

With oil wells, the cover should be lifted to examine the oil level, and they should be refilled when the level drops to about half depth. To avoid soiling the machine by excessive oil dripping out of the wells, only small amounts should be added, as required to maintain the proper level.

The machine should be kept dusted and dry. A soft cloth will serve well for this purpose. Occasionally, a "blower" can be used to blow out the accumulated dust from the inside of the machine.

The brushes and commutator should be checked periodically. Worn brushes should be replaced to avoid having the brush spring scrape the commutator. The spring pressure should always be firm to maintain the brushes securely on the commutator. This assures good electrical contact. Loose brushes will cause sparking, overheating, and voltage variations. Excessively tight brushes may scratch and overheat the commutator and may increase the friction to such an extent that the speed may be affected.

The commutator (or slip rings) should be kept clean and polished. A piece of cloth (such as canvas) can be used to clean it while it is actually rotating, but care must be used that the machine is running at low speed (if the speed is adjustable) to avoid injury. *Never wear loose articles of clothing (like a tie) when working on rotating machinery. If the device is a high-voltage generator, be certain the field excitation is turned off before cleaning the commutator.*

A badly scoured (scratched) or tarnished commutator should first be sandpapered with very fine sandpaper and then polished with a piece of cloth. Emery paper, which is made of a metal abrasive, should never be used on a commutator. Not only will the soft copper segments of the commutator be scratched still more if emery cloth is used, but the metallic particles may create a short circuit between adjacent segments.

If a motor or generator becomes overheated, it is not advisable to stop rotation immediately as it may *freeze*, that is, bind into its bearings so tightly (due to expansion of the metal) that it cannot be rotated again without great difficulty. It is best to slow it down over a period of time, feeding quantities of oil into the bearing oil wells. The continuous flow of fresh oil will aid in cooling the bearings, and this cooling process may be further aided by having a fan blow on the equipment. When the machine is finally turned off, the cause of overheating should be carefully investigated.

On many machines, the pressure on the bearings is adjustable, and this adjustment should be such that rotation is smooth and noiseless. *Wobbling* (a side-to-side or up-and-down movement of the shaft), *hunting* (a variation in speed occurring rather irregularly), or *knocking* (a pronounced noise) may indicate defective or worn bearings or a sprung shaft (a shaft that is out of line or bent). Inadequate lubrication may also be the cause of noisy or erratic rotation. Sometimes the small pipe leading from the oil well to the bearing becomes clogged with sediment, preventing the oil from actually lubricating the bearing. A wire should be inserted down into the well and then into the pipe to clear it. The well should then be flushed out with fresh oil.

Motors that are coupled to generators through external means have some form of coupling between the units. If this coupling becomes too loose, considerable noise may develop. Some couplings are designed to have a certain amount of *play* (looseness), but this should never be excessive.

Reduced speed in a motor may be due to low line voltage, overloading, a shorted field, low field or field-rheostat resistance, or excessive brush friction. Excessive speed may be caused by an open or high-resistance field coil or field rheostat, high line voltage, underloading, or a shorted armature.

If a motor fails to start, it may be due to lack of line voltage, blown fuses, excessive overloading, or an open circuit in the motor itself.

SUMMARY

1. An electric motor is a device that converts electrical energy into mechanical energy.

2. Like a generator, to which it is structurally and electrically very similar, the motor has two basic parts, the stationary part, called a *stator*, and the rotating part, called the *rotor*. The rotor may consist of a wire-wound armature equipped with a commutator or slip rings or may be of solid metal construction.

3. Wire-wound armatures are commonly used in universal and DC motors and in some cases are also used in induction, repulsion, and synchronous motors, which operate on alternating current exclusively.

4. Torque may be defined as the tendency to rotate. Its strength is the product of the field flux and the armature current.

5. The counter-e.m.f. developed by a rotating armature limits the speed of rotation. Its value is determined by the strength of the field and the speed of armature rotation. It acts to decrease the actual value of armature current. No counter-e.m.f. can exist unless rotation takes place. Hence, when starting a DC motor, it is necessary to limit the current through the armature by use of a starting-box resistance until the counter-e.m.f. is developed.

6. Weakening the field of a motor will increase the speed since the counter-e.m.f. is thus decreased. The lowered counter-e.m.f. allows an increase in armature current that, in turn, increases the torque.

7. To reverse the direction of rotation, the direction of current flow in *either* the armature or field must be reversed but not in both.

8. Direct-current motors are classified like DC generators.

9. The series-wound DC motor has high starting torque but poor speed regulation. It must never be run without its load nor must the load ever be removed while it is rotating.

10. The shunt-wound DC motor has low starting torque but a fairly constant speed under varying loads. Loss of field excitation will cause this type of motor to "run away," just as loss of the load will cause a series motor to act similarly.

11. The compound-wound DC motors are designed to have exaggerated characteristics of both the series and shunt types. The cumulative compound type has high starting torque but, unlike the series motor, will not run away if the load is removed. The differential compound motor has excellent speed regulation.

12. Starting boxes for DC motors may be manually or automatically operated. Their function is to limit the armature current until normal speed is reached and the counter-e.m.f. is developed. They may be equipped with safety devices such as *no-voltage release*, *no-field release*, and an *overload circuit breaker*.

13. The *motor generator* is a combined motor and generator having either the separate units coupled together or a common shaft on which both armatures are wound. Separate field coils and separate armature windings are used.

14. The rotary converter has a common set of field coils and a common armature. It acts as both DC motor and AC generator. The armature is equipped with both a commutator and a set of slip rings.

15. The dynamotor has a common set of field coils, but the armature windings are separate. It acts as a combined DC motor and DC generator. The armature has two commutators, one for the motor and one for the generator. It is generally used on a low-voltage direct current supply such as a battery, where it is necessary to produce higher DC voltages as required.

16. The *universal* motor is designed for operation on either alternating current or direct current. It is a series-wound device with low-inductance field and armature coils. The cores are laminated to reduce losses.

17. The induction, repulsion, and synchronous motors are intended for AC operation exclusively.

18. The induction motor usually has a *squirrel-cage* (all metal) rotor in which currents are induced by the field. Polyphase motors of this type are self-starting, but single-phase units require a shaded pole or split-phase arrangement to allow automatic starting.

19. The repulsion motor has a wire-wound armature and brushes so mounted that the current flow through the armature allows a torque to be created due to the relative positions assumed by the rotor and stator.

20. The synchronous motor is essentially similar to any alternator, and its main characteristic is its constant speed under all loads within its capacity, provided the AC frequency does not vary.

Quiz: The Electric Motor

This quiz will help you review the material just studied. See the quiz directions on page 24 before answering the questions below.

1. The rotary converter, which is generally used to convert direct current to alternating current, may be recognized by the fact that it is equipped with: *a.* two sets of field coils and one armature winding; *b.* a single armature winding having both a commutator and a set of slip rings; *c.* an armature having two sets of slip rings; *d.* two armature windings and one set of field coils.

2. The universal motor may be distinguished from the ordinary series motor by the: *a.* laminated field and armature cores; *b.* heavier field windings; *c.* size of the brushes; *d.* position of the commutator poles.

3. An increased value of counter-e.m.f. in a motor will: *a.* reverse the direction of rotation; *b.* decrease the field flux; *c.* affect the output voltage; *d.* affect the speed of rotation.

4. The best method of controlling the speed of a series motor is to: *a.* increase the load; *b.* decrease the load; *c.* vary the voltage across the motor; *d.* vary the position of the brushes.

5. A starting box or similar device must be used with DC motors. It is required when starting a motor in order to limit the current in the: *a.* series field; *b.* shunt field; *c.* armature; *d.* line.

6. All other factors remaining unchanged, increased torque will result if the: *a.* line voltage is decreased; *b.* armature current is increased; *c.* field current is decreased; *d.* armature current is decreased.

7. A single-phase synchronous motor is: *a.* self-starting regardless of design; *b.* incapable of being made self-starting; *c.* self-starting if designed with a shaded-pole arrangement; *d.* self-starting if used on direct current and then on alternating current.

8. Speed regulation is *poorest* in the: *a.* AC synchronous motor; *b.* DC series motor; *c.* DC differentially wound compound motor; *d.* DC shunt motor.

9. The squirrel-cage type of rotor is used in the: *a.* DC series motor; *b.* AC induction motor; *c.* AC repulsion motor; *d.* universal motor.

10. The dynamotor, generally used on a low-voltage DC source to furnish higher DC voltages, is equipped with: *a.* two sets of field coils and two armature windings; *b.* two sets of field coils and one armature winding; *c.* one set of field coils and one armature winding; *d.* one set of field coils and two armature windings.

11. A *permanent split-phase capacitor* motor utilizes: *a.* electrolytic capacitors of high capacitance when in a running position; *b.* electrolytic capacitors of low capacitance when stopping; *c.* oil-impregnated paper capacitors of low value when in a running position; *d.* oil-impregnated paper capacitors of very high value when stopping.

12. A motor is said to be *hunting* when it tends to: *a.* increase its speed after a warming-up period; *b.* decrease its speed as the load decreases; *c.* vary its speed when adjustments are made to the field rheostat; *d.* vary its speed when it should be running steadily.

13. To "dynamically brake" an induction motor, it is necessary to: *a.* reverse the AC line; *b.* apply direct current to the stator; *c.* apply direct current to the squirrel-cage rotor; *d.* apply alternating current to the squirrel-cage rotor.

14. To allow a single-phase AC induction motor to start automatically in a split-phase starting arrangement, the starter coil may be placed in series with the capacitor. The effect of this capacitor is to: *a.* produce a rotating flux by shifting the phase relationship between the starter coil and regular field coils; *b.* create a counter-e.m.f. capable of increasing the torque to a point where the motor will start; *c.* develop the armature current to a point where the torque is sufficiently high to overcome the inertia of the armature; *d.* reverse the flow of the alternating current in the field coils so that opposite poles appear on the armature and field pole pieces simultaneously.

15. A DC *series* motor will run away if the load is removed while the power is still being applied. This is the result of the: *a.* loss of counter-e.m.f.; *b.* low input voltage to the armature; *c.* increased counter-e.m.f. acting to weaken the field; *d.* high voltage developed across the field.

16. In a synchronous motor, speed regulation is mainly dependent upon the: *a.* voltage across the field; *b.* current in the field; *c.* current in the armature; *d.* frequency of the AC supply.

17. Emery cloth should *not* be used to clean a commutator because it is: *a.* likely to increase the resistance of the commutator segments; *b.* likely to short the segments; *c.* too oily, whereas sandpaper is dry; *d.* too smooth and hence will not remove the carbon deposited by the brushes.

18. A shaded pole is used to: *a.* allow automatic starting of single-phase AC motors; *b.* reduce sparking at the brushes; *c.* prevent a DC series motor from running away if the load is removed; *d.* prevent a DC shunt motor from running away if the field opens.

19. The *capacitor-start motor* differs from the permanent split-phase capacitor motor in that the capacitor-start motor uses capacitors: *a.* for starting only; *b.* both for starting and for stopping; *c.* only for starting and for running; *d.* on polyphase AC circuits only.

20. In case there are signs that a motor bearing is beginning to "freeze," it is advisable to: *a.* speed up the motor gradually while adding fresh oil continuously; *b.* slow down the motor gradually while adding fresh oil continuously; *c.* stop the motor suddenly and place the bearing in a bath of warm oil; *d.* increase the room temperature gradually while removing the oil from the bearing wells.

21. To reverse the direction of rotation of a DC shunt motor, it is necessary to: *a.* reverse the line voltage; *b.* reverse the direction of current flow in both the armature and field windings; *c.* reverse the direction of current flow in either the armature or field winding; *d.* move the brushes out of the neutral position in the direction of rotation desired.

22. Decreasing the amount of resistance of the field rheostat in series with the field of a DC shunt motor will cause the motor to: *a.* reverse its rotation; *b.* stop entirely; *c.* slow down; *d.* speed up.

23. If a DC *shunt* motor is connected across an AC supply, the motor will: *a.* reverse its normal direction of rotation; *b.* oscillate back and forth as the frequency varies; *c.* operate normally; *d.* not revolve.

24. A motor is rated at $\frac{1}{4}$ hp. It is drawing 250 watts from the line. Its efficiency is, therefore: *a.* $87\frac{1}{2}$ per cent; *b.* 91 per cent; *c.* 94 per cent; *d.* 100 per cent.

25. In a capacitor-start motor, the capacitor is designed for: *a.* continuous operation since it is an electrolytic capacitor; *b.* continuous operation since it is an oil-impregnated paper capacitor; *c.* intermittent operation since it is an oil-impregnated paper capacitor; *d.* intermittent operation because of the high starting current.

Chapter 11. Rectification of Alternating Current

1. General

Alternating current has come into general use owing to a number of advantages it offers. For one thing, it can be transmitted from the power plant to the point where it is to be used more economically and more efficiently. By the use of transformers, it can be stepped up or stepped down as required. In contrast, a DC supply can be transmitted only at its generated voltage and is thus subject to high losses caused by the resistance of the line. To reduce this resistance loss, and to carry the full current load, large-sized wire must be used, and this leads to greater expense in the construction of the DC wiring system. Alternating current, on the other hand, may be stepped up from the generated voltage to a very high voltage, and this high voltage can be transmitted over smaller wires over greater distances, owing to the proportional decrease in current values when the voltage is increased by the action of the transformer. For example, a 220-volt AC generator delivering 100 amp. at the powerhouse can, by the use of transformers, furnish 2,200 volts at 10 amp. (the power being the same). Since a 10-amp. current can be handled by wire of much smaller diameter, it can be seen that a considerable saving will result in the construction of the line. Further, the voltage drop in the line when a current of 10 amp. is flowing is only one-tenth as great as when one of 100 amp. appears in the line (Fig. 234). The need for transformers, of course, increases the expense of construction, but this is amply made up by the fact that the power can be transmitted over vastly greater distances with a minimum of loss, and also by the fact that the use of transformers allows any desired voltage (either higher or lower than the transmitted value) to be obtained at the point of delivery.

With the prevalence of AC power, it is often necessary to

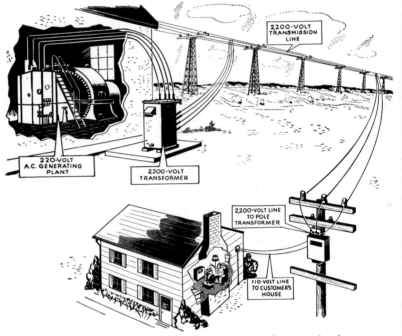

Fig. 234. The principle of how alternating current is transmitted over great distances. In actual practice, transmission voltages are much higher when great distances are being covered.

convert alternating current into direct current for specific purposes such as battery charging and electroplating, as well as for other needs. The process of converting alternating current to direct current is known as *rectification*, and the device that performs this function is generally called a *rectifier*. A special device, similar in construction to a rotary converter (which is used to convert direct current into alternating current), called a *synchronous converter* is also available. It is, of course, also possible to use an AC motor driving a DC generator. Rectifiers, however, are simpler and more compact in construction, cost less to purchase, maintain, and operate, and are equally efficient for most purposes. Further, most rectifiers are absolutely quiet in operation, or develop a minimum of noise, as contrasted to the noise and vibration necessarily developed by rotating mechanical devices such as the synchronous converter or motor generator set.

2. The Synchronous Converter

The synchronous converter, like the rotary converter, has one set of field coils and one armature winding. Similarly, the armature is equipped with both slip rings and a commutator but, in this case, the alternating current is fed into the field and slip rings to produce rotation, thus causing the device to act like an AC motor. The DC output, taken from the commutator, is delivered to the load.

Synchronous converters are ordinarily used only where large amounts of DC power must be supplied. For lighter loads, rectifiers are commonly preferred.

3. Vacuum-tube Rectification

1. *Electronic Emission.* We already know that all substances are composed of atoms, which in turn are made up of a positively charged nucleus and a varying number of negatively charged electrons, depending upon the character of the atom. These electrons are normally revolving around the nucleus continuously but, under certain circumstances, may be caused to leave their orbits. The resultant movement from their own atom to another produces the phenomenon of an electric current.

The movement of the electrons in any substance may be speeded up by the application of heat. Thus, when an electric current passes through a filament of wire (the word *filament* denotes a thin, threadlike piece of wire), the wire tends to heat up, and electron movement increases greatly. If the wire be-comes hot enough to glow, some electrons acquire such high speeds that they tend to break away from the wire and emerge into the surrounding area in the form of an electronic stream. When this occurs, it is known as an *electronic emission* (Fig. 235).

A filament such as has just been described would disintegrate (break up) quickly if exposed to the air. Therefore, it is enclosed

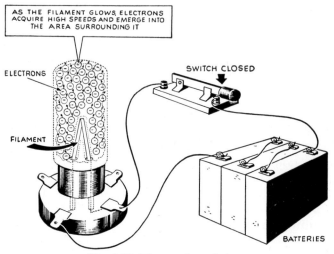

Fig. 235. Electronic emission.

in a glass envelope from which the air has been removed to a large degree, producing a near vacuum. In this condition, disintegration occurs far more slowly. The ordinary electric bulb is an example of this construction, though in this case the function of incandescence (lighting effect) alone is sought.

In the vacuum-tube rectifier, incandescence plays a secondary part entirely, and the function of electronic emission is the primary factor.

2. *Utilization of the Electronic Stream.* Electronic emission would be of little consequence in the operation of a vacuum tube if it could not be controlled and utilized for practical purposes. One method of controlling the emission is to vary the amount of current flowing through the filament, which, in turn, affects the degree of emission (Fig. 236).

Another method is to take advantage of the fact that electrons bear a negative charge and will be attracted to a positively

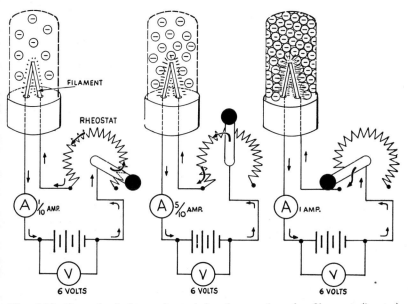

Fig. 236. Control of electronic emission by varying the filament (heater) current.

charged body. Contrariwise, a negatively charged body will repel them. Thus, by placing a charged body in close proximity to the filament, the electron stream can be directly affected. It is this action that plays an important part in the process of rectification (Fig. 237).

3. *The Rectifier Tube.* The practical rectifier tube (Fig. 238) consists of two main parts called *elements* or *electrodes*:

    a. The *filament*, or *cathode*, whose function is to emit electrons
    b. The *plate*, or *anode*, whose function is to *attract* or *repel* electrons depending upon the polarity of the charge placed upon it

Anode and *cathode* are the preferred terms in industrial electronics, whereas *plate* and *filament* are commonly used in the radio field. Therefore, in this book, *anode* and *plate* are purposely used interchangeably, as are *filament* and *cathode*.

The two electrodes are housed in a glass or metal envelope from which air has been evacuated as completely as possible. This is done to prevent disintegration of the cathode and also

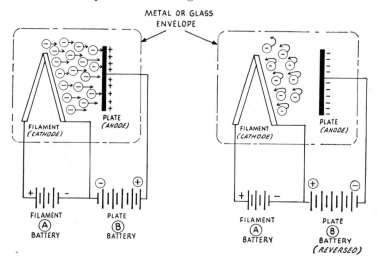

Fig. 237. Control of electronic emission by varying the polarity of the plate (anode).

to allow free movement of the electrons. In some tubes, a special gas is purposely placed inside the envelope to perform a specific function. Such gas-filled tubes using argon or mercury vapor will be studied later. The presence of any gas, even air, in an *ordinary* tube is harmful to the tube's life and performance. Such a tube is said to be *gassy* or *soft* and can be recognized by overheating of the plate and by the appearance of a violet-colored glow between the plate and the cathode. This should not be confused with the bluish glow that appears in mercury-vapor tubes or the yellowish glow that appears in argon-filled tubes. In some radio tubes, too, a violet-blue glow normally is present near the glass envelope. This is quite different from the rich violet color appearing in the space between the plate and cathode of a soft tube of other than a gas-filled type.

Two types of cathodes are used (Fig. 238). A *directly heated* cathode consists of a filament of tungsten, a metal that stands up exceptionally well when heated by an electric current. To increase the electronic emission, the tungsten itself is generally

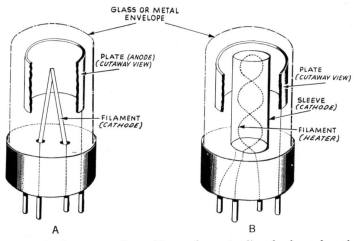

Fig. 238. Basic types of rectifier tubes. *A,* directly heated cathode; *B,* indirectly heated cathode.

impregnated or coated with some other substance, such as thorium or special oxides. The use of such materials allows the filament to be operated at lower temperature while maintaining the same degree of emission. This aids in prolonging tube life.

An *indirectly heated* cathode consists of a thin metal sleeve coated with electron-emitting material. Within the sleeve is a heater that corresponds to a filament, but, in this case, the filament is *not* used to emit electrons directly. Its sole purpose is to heat the cathode sleeve surrounding it, the sleeve in turn emitting the electrons.

The anode of a rectifier tube is constructed of any of several types of materials such as tantalum, graphite, carbon, and the like.

Connections to the anode and cathode are made to *pins* (elongated metal terminals) on an insulated tube base, and, in some tubes, one or more connections may be right on the glass envelope (Fig. 239).

A tube consisting of a single anode and a cathode is called a

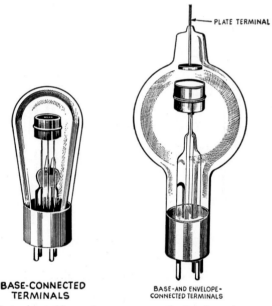

PLATE TERMINAL

BASE-CONNECTED
TERMINALS

BASE-AND ENVELOPE-
CONNECTED TERMINALS

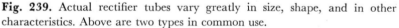

Fig. 239. Actual rectifier tubes vary greatly in size, shape, and in other characteristics. Above are two types in common use.

diode (two-electrode tube), but it should be noted that even a diode has more than two contact terminals to which external connections are made. Thus in a diode with a directly heated cathode, there would be two contacts for the filament and one for the anode, making a total of three contacts in all. An indirectly heated type of diode would have four contacts, two for the filament (heater), one for the cathode, and one for the anode (Fig. 240).

Some rectifier tubes have two anodes rather than one. Such tubes serve a dual purpose (as we shall see when studying full-wave rectification), and they are therefore called *duo-diodes,* that is, two diodes in one envelope.

4. *Diode Action.* Figure 241 shows a diode connected to two batteries, with a milliammeter and load resistor in series with the plate. The battery across the filament is used to heat it to incandescence. Instead of a battery, a transformer could be used since the polarity of the voltage supply across the filament

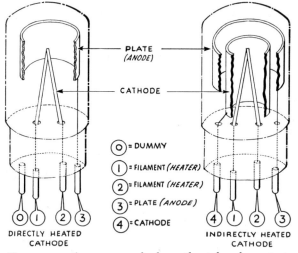

PLATE
(ANODE)

CATHODE

($\bigcirc$) = DUMMY

($\mathbf{I}$) = FILAMENT *(HEATER)*

($\mathbf{2}$) = FILAMENT *(HEATER)*

($\mathbf{3}$) = PLATE *(ANODE)*

($\mathbf{4}$) = CATHODE

DIRECTLY HEATED
CATHODE

INDIRECTLY HEATED
CATHODE

Fig. 240. How connections are made from the tube elements to the outer contact terminals.

will not affect electronic emission. The battery in series with the plate, however, is shown with its positive side connected to the plate, which therefore bears a positive charge. This battery is commonly called a *plate battery* and, in trade language, is said to furnish *plate voltage.* It should be remembered, however, that the term *voltage* actually represents a difference in potential between at least two points in a circuit. Thus, the more exact expressions would be *plate-to-cathode voltage* or *anode-to-cathode voltage,* rather than *plate voltage* alone, since it is the difference of potential between the anode (plate) and the cathode that is one of the determining factors that affect the tube's operation.

When the filament is heated, *thermionic emission* occurs, that is, electrons are shot away from the cathode and travel toward the plate, whose positive charge tends to attract them. In effect, the stream of electrons produces a path between the cathode and

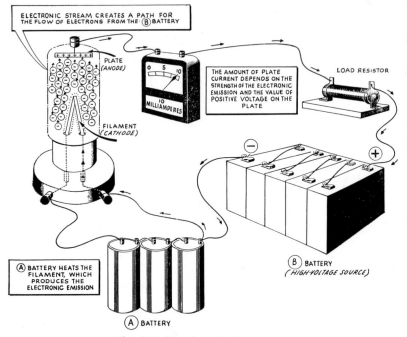

Fig. 241. The flow of plate current.

plate, thus closing an electric circuit running from the cathode to the plate and from the plate through the load resistor and plate battery, returning once again to the cathode. The current that then flows through this complete electric circuit is called the *plate current* and will be shown by a deflection on the meter scale.

If the plate voltage is decreased, the plate current will drop. Thus, it can be seen that control of the electronic stream in a diode is dependent upon the plate voltage when the cathode potential remains at a fixed value. The greater the positive charge on the plate (which is increased by an increase in plate voltage), the more electrons that will be attracted. For every type of tube, however, there is a certain plate voltage beyond which no additional voltage value will produce an increased current. The reason is that all the electrons are already being drawn to the plate. This maximum current that a tube can pass is called the *saturation current* or, sometimes, the *emission current*. The point at which no current increase occurs when the plate voltage is increased is known as the *saturation point* (Fig. 242).

5. *Diode as a Rectifier.* In the example just given, a constant

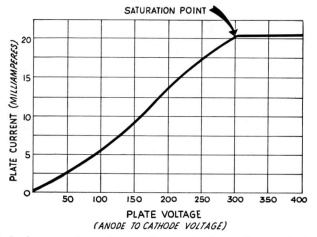

Fig. 242. At the saturation point, any increase in the anode-to-cathode voltage (plate voltage) will not produce an increase in plate current.

positive potential appeared on the plate, and as long as this positive potential was there, a flow of plate current was observed. If the plate battery connections were now reversed (Fig. 243), and a negative potential put on the plate, the electrons would be repelled and no plate current would flow. *It therefore follows that a voltage of changing polarity placed on the plate would allow current to flow only when the plate was at positive potential.* This is the basis of rectification of alternating current, sometimes referred to as the *unilateral conductivity* of a rectifier.

If the plate battery shown in Fig. 241 were replaced by an AC supply, such as an alternator or the secondary of a trans-

former (Fig. 244), the diode would pass current *only* when the
AC cycle imposed a positive potential on the plate. Thus, if an
AC sine wave, shown in Fig. 245, represents the alternating
current supplied to the plate, at point 1 on the curve the alternating current is beginning its cycle on the positive side. At
point 2 it has reached its maximum potential, dropping to zero

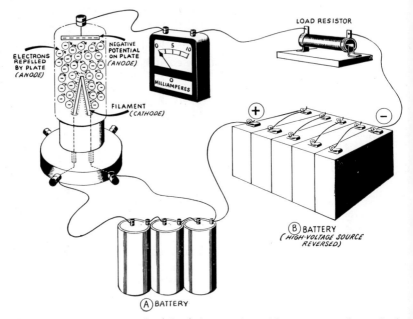

Fig. 243. When the anode (plate) is negative with respect to the cathode
(filament), the electrons cannot reach the anode and no plate current will flow.

at point 3. During this portion of the cycle, a positive potential
appears on the plate of the tube, and plate current flows.

At point 3, the sine curve begins to drop below zero, and the
alternating current is now on the negative portion of its cycle.
It reaches a maximum negative potential at point 4 and returns
to zero at point 5. During this portion of the cycle, a negative
potential is on the plate, and no plate current can flow. The
process is again repeated as the sine wave forms again and
continues as long as the AC supply remains uninterrupted.

The curve in Fig. 245 can now be shown as in Fig. 246. Only the positive half of each cycle has allowed plate current to flow. Hence, the original alternating current is now said to

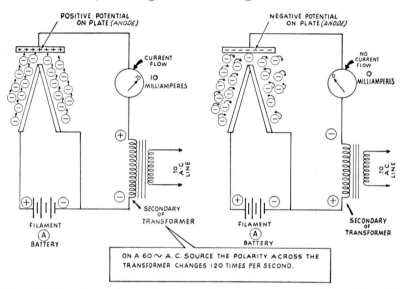

Fig. 244. No plate current will flow on the negative portion of the AC cycle. The electrons cannot reach the plate when this condition exists.

be *rectified*, that is, a form of direct current now appears in the output circuit. The process is known as *half-wave* rectification, as only half of the AC cycle has been used to produce the desired DC output.

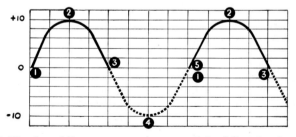

Fig. 245. The dotted line represents that part of the AC cycle when a negative potential is on the plate of the rectifier tube shown in Fig. 244.

6. *Half-wave Rectification.* Figure 247*a* shows a basic half-wave rectifier circuit operated from a transformer. Note that the transformer has two secondary windings in this case, one winding furnishing the AC voltage to be rectified (this may be at a value higher or lower than the line voltage depending upon the purpose the rectifier will serve), and the other winding furnishing the voltage to activate the filament of the rectifier tube. In Fig. 247*b*, a rectifier tube with an indirectly heated cathode is

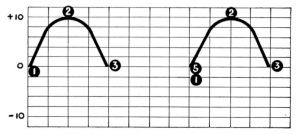

Fig. 246. When rectification occurs, the negative portions of the AC cycle fail to appear in the output circuit. In Fig. 245, the dotted line represented the negative part of the cycle. Note its absence here.

shown, while in Fig. 247*a*, a directly heated cathode is being used.

It would be well to note the following facts about the half-wave rectifiers:

1) The section of the transformer secondary furnishing the voltage to be rectified is not *center-tapped*, that is, connections are required only on the ends of the winding. One connection of this winding goes to the plate and the other becomes the *negative* output connection.

2) The *positive* output connection may be made in one of the following ways:

a) To either side of the filament.

b) To the *center-tap* of the filament winding on the transformer if a center tap is available. (Use of a center-tapped filament or heater winding allows the strain on the filament due to electronic emission to be somewhat equalized rather than having one side used up faster than the other.)

c) To the cathode in the type of tube with an indirectly heated cathode.

3) Only *one* rectifier tube (that is, a tube having a single plate and one cathode) is required.

In a half-wave rectifier, owing to the spaced intervals between

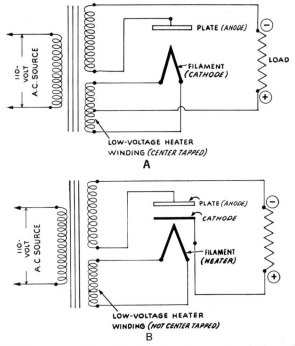

Fig. 247. Half-wave rectifier circuits. *A*, using a directly heated cathode; *B*, using an indirecty heated cathode.

the crests of the AC sine curve, the output is not uniform. The rectified alternating current is a pulsating direct current, and because of this spacing, it is somewhat more difficult to filter (smooth out).

7. *Full-wave Rectification.* To overcome the disadvantage of half-wave rectification, another form of rectification may be used. This is known as *full-wave rectification*. In this type of circuit, both sides of the AC cycles are rectified, and therefore the spacing between the crests of the AC cycle is reduced. This allows the pulsating direct current produced to be filtered more efficiently. Figure 248 shows a full-wave rectifier circuit and the resulting action.

The following facts should be noted about a full-wave rectifier:

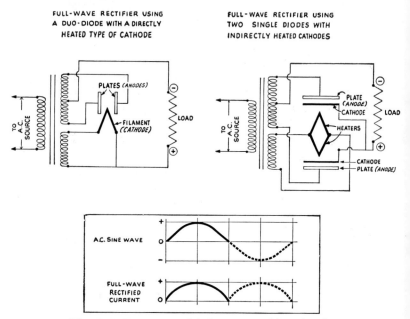

Fig. 248. Two types of full-wave rectifier circuits.

1) *The section of the transformer secondary furnishing the voltage to be rectified is center-tapped.* The outer connections are connected to the plates of the rectifier tube or tubes. The *center-tap* is used as the *negative* output connection.

2) The *positive* output connection is made

a) To either side of the filament.

b) To the center-tap of the filament winding on the trans-former if a center-tap is available.

c) To the cathodes in tubes with indirectly heated cathodes.

3) Either one tube having a double plate (that is, two plates) or two separate single tubes must be used.

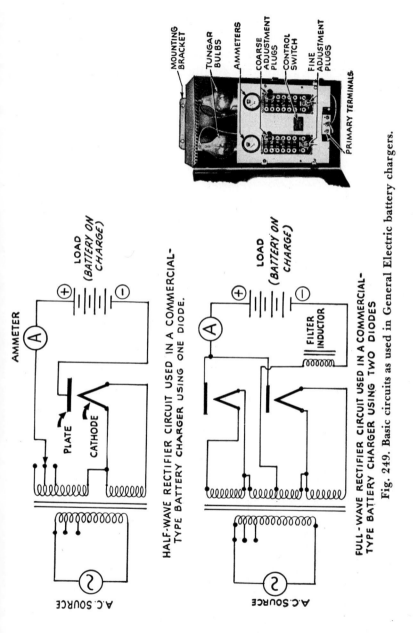

Fig. 249. Basic circuits as used in General Electric battery chargers.

In some commercial battery chargers, the circuits used differ from those just studied. These are shown in Fig. 249. The basic principle of operation, however, is the same.

If one tube in a full-wave rectifier (using two separate single-plate tubes) burns out, the device will continue to operate as a half-wave rectifier.

Another point of interest in a full-wave rectifier is the fact

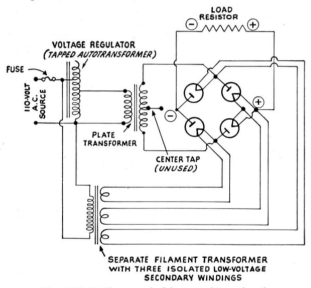

Fig. 250. Full-wave bridge rectifier circuit.

that the center-tapped secondary winding furnishing the voltage to be rectified must deliver *twice* the voltage that a half-wave device would require. This is due to the fact that only half the winding is functioning at one time, that is, when its respective tube is conducting. The sole exception to this rule occurs when a full-wave *bridge rectifier* is used. In this case, full-wave rectification is obtained without the use of a center-tapped winding, the full secondary voltage being available for rectification. In this circuit, requiring four diodes, two are conducting on one part of the cycle, and the other two conduct on the other half of the cycle (Fig. 250).

8. *Voltage Doubler.* Under certain circumstances, higher voltages than may be available from an AC line are required. Advantage of certain rectifier tubes (either two sets of elements within a single envelope or separate diodes) may be taken in this regard as shown in Fig. 250*a*. If regular diodes are used, separate heater transformers (or a single transformer with separate windings for each heater) are preferred. Higher output voltages are obtainable by using the high-voltage secondary winding of a transformer so equipped, and this unit may have the needed heater windings wound on it as well.

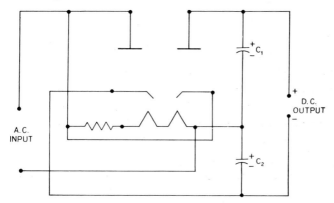

Fig. 250*a*. Basic full-wave voltage-doubler rectifier circuit.

The capacitors C_1 and C_2 may be of the electrolytic type. Connections must be made with their proper polarities in mind. The two capacitors may be contained in one case *but must have separate negative leads*.

Operation of the circuit is dependent upon the fact that during one part of the AC cycle, capacitor C_1 is charged whereas, in the remaining part of the cycle, capacitor C_2 is charged. It is the potential difference across these capacitors that determines the available output voltage and is usually somewhat less than twice the AC input voltage.

Using additional rectifier elements and capacitors allows further multiplication of existing voltages.

9. *Gas-filled Rectifier Tubes.* In all types of rectifiers, it is possible to use special, gas-filled tubes instead of vacuum types.

The *mercury-vapor* tube, which is most common, contains a small amount of mercury, which is partially vaporized when the filament is heated. The vapor consists of mercury atoms, and when these atoms are bombarded by the electrons emitted by the cathode, they tend to lose some of their own electrons. This process is called *ionization*. When the atoms have lost some of their negative electrons, they act as positive bodies and draw to themselves many of the electrons that are lost in the space between the plate and the cathode. These "lost" electrons (those that have failed to reach the plate) form a *space charge* that hinders the flow of other electrons. Thus, by removing these lost electrons, the mercury atoms reduce the space charge, and this, in turn, has the effect of reducing the resistance of the electric path formed between the cathode and plate by the electronic stream. Because of this lower resistance, the voltage drop within the tube is reduced considerably, being very much lower than in the vacuum type of tube rectifier. This low resistance also improves voltage regulation.

In operation, such tubes are characterized by a bluish glow within the tube. In order to safeguard the filaments while the mercury is vaporizing, the voltage (in high-voltage rectifiers) should not be applied to the plates for at least 30 sec. or more after the filaments are turned on.

In low-voltage rectifiers (such as battery chargers), argon gas may be used in the tubes. The principle of operation is quite similar. In operation, the tubes give off a yellowish light with a bluish glow sometimes visible near the cathode.

4. Metallic Rectifiers

A type of rectifier in common use is the *copper-oxide* type. The actual rectifying element is constructed of discs of copper on which *barrier* layers of copper oxide have been formed (Fig. 251). Such a combination offers a very low resistance to current flowing from the copper oxide to the copper but very high resistance to a current flow in the opposite direction. This peculiar characteristic, called *semiconduction*, causes the element to act just as a rectifier tube does, that is, it will pass current only in one direction.

The discs forming each element are firmly bolted together, and a number of these elements are ordinarily used together to form a *bank* or group. The size of the bank will depend upon the

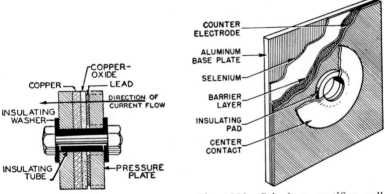

Fig. 251. The basic copper-oxide rectifier element.

Fig. 252. Selenium rectifier cell. (*Courtesy of Bradley Laboratories, Inc.*)

voltage and current to be handled. To dissipate the heat produced in operation, metallic *fins* or plates placed alongside the discs are used. This allows the device to work at highest efficiency, since heat increases the resistance of the elements and thus decreases the output.

After the elements are placed in service, it will be found that the amount of current that can be passed will gradually decrease as aging takes place. The amount of such aging will be determined by the degree of use, the amount of current that is being handled, and, to a large extent, the degree of nonuse as well. Aging continues to some extent even when the elements are not in operation, owing to chemical action.

Metallic, semiconductor rectifiers can be used in half-wave, full-wave, bridge, and voltage-doubler rectifier circuits just as

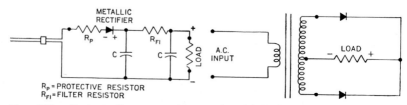

Fig. 253a. Basic half-wave rectifier using the metallic type of rectifier unit instead of a diode.

Fig. 253b. Basic full-wave rectifier circuit using metallic rectifiers.

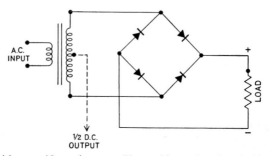

Fig. 253c. Bridge rectifier using metallic-rectifier units. One-half available output voltage may be obtained by using connection to center-tap of transformer.

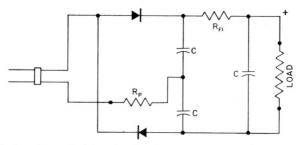

Fig. 253d. A voltage-doubler circuit with the metallic-rectifier elements. R_p is a protective resistor to limit the input surge when the device is first connected to the line and the operation started. R_{fi} is a filtering resistor. A choke may be used here for more effective results in eliminating ripple voltage.

tube rectifiers are (Figs. 253a to d). They are quiet in operation and require a minimum of attention.

Another type of metallic rectifier that observes a similar

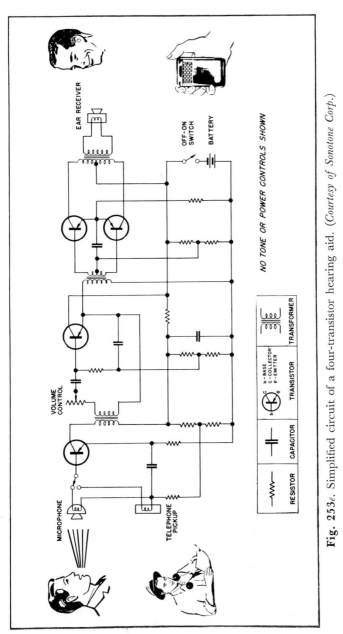

Fig. 253e. Simplified circuit of a four-transistor hearing aid. (*Courtesy of Sonotone Corp.*)

principle and is usable in similar circuits is the *selenium unit* (Fig. 252). Such rectifiers are very popular and of increasing industrial importance because of their great versatility.

A third type, using combinations of *germanium* alloy, is commonly utilized in the *transistor,* a device that rivals the multi-element vacuum tube in many ways. A typical circuit using transistors is shown in Fig. 253e.

5. Voltage Control

Most rectifiers use some form of tapped transformer (with either or both primary and secondary windings tapped) to control the voltage output of the device. Switches, plugs, or other means of varying the connections to the taps are used. Some equipment of this type utilizes rheostats for the same purpose, but a tapped transformer is the preferable method of voltage control (Figs. 253a to d).

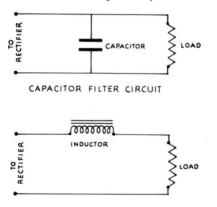

CAPACITOR FILTER CIRCUIT

INDUCTOR FILTER CIRCUIT

Fig. 254. Basic filter circuits using a single capacitor or a single inductor.

6. Filters

Since the output of any type of rectifier system is not a pure or steady direct current, *filters* are used to smooth out current variations.

A filter consists of a capacitor, an inductor, or a combination of both capacitors and inductors. The inductors are always placed in *series* with the load and offer a high impedance to the ripple (varying) voltage. The capacitors are placed in *parallel* to the load and thus store energy on the voltage peaks, releasing such energy on voltage dips. Thus the voltage output tends to be equalized to a great extent.

Simple capacitor and inductor filters used with rectifiers are shown in Fig. 254. In selecting the capacitors, it must be borne in mind that they must be capable of withstanding the full AC peak voltage surge across the secondary winding of the transformer. If the rectifier is designed to furnish 100 volts DC, the capacitor must be capable of withstanding at least 141 volts AC. Usually, even higher ratings are desirable.

The inductor (also called a *reactor* or *choke*) must be capable of passing the full current to be drawn by the load. Its insulation

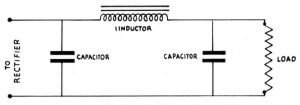

Fig. 255. Circuit of a brute-force filter.

should also be sufficient to withstand the voltages developed to prevent a breakdown, that is, a rupture of the insulation with a consequent shorting of the turns between themselves or to ground. The term *ground*, as used in this case, also refers to the core and metal housing of the inductor, which, in turn, are usually grounded. More complex filters are shown in Figs. 255 and 256.

Figure 255 shows a *brute-force* filter, which has the advantage of producing a higher output voltage than the choke-input filter shown in Fig. 256, owing to the fact that the *input* capac-

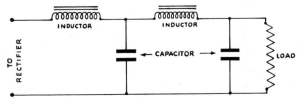

Fig. 256. Circuit of a choke-input filter. "Input" refers to the rectifier side of the circuit.

itor charges up to the peak value of the input voltage (1.4 times the voltage as measured by an AC voltmeter). In such a filter, therefore, the input capacitor must be selected so as to allow for such peak voltages, just as was the case where a simple

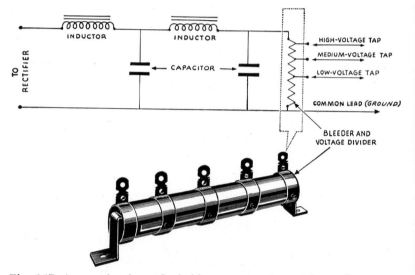

Fig. 257. A tapped resistor of suitable wattage rating can be used as a combination bleeder and voltage divider. The ohmic resistance must also be high enough so as not to act as an excessive load across the circuit.

capacitor filter is used. The *choke-input* filter shown in Fig. 256 gives somewhat lower voltages, but regulation is distinctly improved.

7. Bleeder

In high-voltage rectifiers, in order to prevent injury should an individual come into contact with the terminals of the charged filter capacitor even after the line voltage has been turned off, a *bleeder* is placed across the output of the filter. The bleeder is simply a resistor of fairly large value that acts as a constant light load on the rectifier (thus aiding voltage regulation) and serves to discharge the filter capacitors when the voltage is turned off. The bleeder is called a *voltage divider* when it is equipped with *taps*, which allow use of the voltage drop across any part of it to supply lower voltages than the maximum available (Fig. 257).

8. Operation and Maintenance

When a new rectifier is placed in operation, it is advisable to age it by using it at lower outputs for a period of about 8 hr. This also applies when a new tube or copper-oxide disc is put in after the original unit has failed. This is particularly advisable with tube rectifiers in order to avoid tube destruction by a flashover (a momentary or continuing spark or flow of current between the electrodes). In high-voltage tube rectifiers, it will be recalled, the filaments should be turned on for a minimum of 30 sec. before the voltage is applied to the plates. This precaution is usually not necessary in low-voltage devices.

The rectifier should not be turned on until the load is connected. Without a load, the peak voltages may be high enough to damage the tubes and capacitors. Contrariwise, the load should never be removed without first turning off the line voltage. Thus, in battery charging, the line voltage should be turned off *before* removing the battery.

Maintenance of rectifiers is a very simple procedure compared to the maintenance involved when motor generators are used. It consists mainly of keeping the equipment clean. Rectifier tubes and copper-oxide banks should be replaced when necessary and, whenever possible, before they actually become entirely defective. A poor tube, for example, may still have a good filament but will deliver a lowered output. This lowered output is made apparent when the ammeter or voltmeter used with the equipment, either as an integral part or as a test accessory, shows a low reading under otherwise normal conditions.

9. Trouble Chart

The following chart lists some of the troubles that may be found in a rectifier and the probable cause. The remedy in each case will depend upon the cause of the trouble:

Trouble	*Cause*
No AC input voltage.........	1. Failure of power source 2. Open power cord 3. Short-circuited power cord 4. Poor plug contact 5. Burnt-out fuse 6. Fuse loose in clip 7. Loose connection between transformer and line 8. Transformer primary open 9. Defective line switch
No DC output voltage........	1. Any of the causes above 2. Transformer secondary open 3. Defective tube (tube may light and still be bad) 4. Loose, broken, or high-resistance connection in output circuit 5. Defective filter (open choke or shorted capacitor) 6. Dirty or corroded contacts on tubes 7. Defective metallic rectifier bank
Excessive output voltage......	1. Improper voltage-control setting 2. High line voltage 3. Low load value
Low output voltage..........	1. Defective tube or metallic rectifier bank 2. Low line voltage 3. Improper voltage-control setting 4. Partially shorted (leaking) capacitor 5. Excessive load value 6. High-resistance connections in wiring or on tube contact pins or sockets
Excessive ripple in DC output..	1. Defective filter unit 2. Defective tube or metallic rectifier bank

SUMMARY

1. A rectifier is a device that converts alternating current into direct current.

2. A synchronous converter also is used to convert alternating current into direct current where large quantities of power must be made available. Its construction is similar to that of a rotary converter (used to convert direct current into alternating current) having one set of field coils and a single armature equipped with both a commutator and slip rings.

3. Rectifiers are of *two* main types:

a. Vacuum or gas-filled tube types
b. Metallic or semiconductor types, including the copper-oxide, selenium, and germanium devices

Both types allow current to pass only in a single direction. Thus, currents may pass only on the positive part of AC cycle.

4. The vacuum tube utilizes the phenomenon of electronic emission. Electrons leaving the cathode (thermionic emission) are attracted to the anode when the latter is positively charged and are repelled when the anode is negatively charged. Plate current will flow only when the anode is at a positive potential.

5. Ionization occurs in a gas-filled tube when the electrons bombard the gas atoms. Electrons are driven off the atoms. The atoms are thus left with a positive charge. This action reduces the space charge, and, in turn, also reduces the tube's resistance. This allows a lesser voltage drop to occur when the tube is conducting.

6. A copper-oxide rectifier element is constructed of copper discs on which a layer of copper oxide is formed. Electrons can flow most readily from a copper disc to a copper-oxide barrier layer, but not as easily in the reverse direction. (However, industry still uses the concept of *current flow* from copper oxide to copper on the old idea of the current flowing from a point of high to one of low potential.) Other semiconductor types of metallic rectifiers operate on similar principles and use similar circuits.

7. A half-wave rectifier allows current to pass only on one-half of the AC cycle.

8. A full-wave rectifier passes current on both halves of the AC cycle. The output is, therefore, more uniform.

9. A bridge rectifier acts like a full-wave rectifier but does not require a center-tapped transformer.

10. A filter is used to smooth out the pulsating direct current produced by a rectifier. It consists of either a capacitor, an inductor, or a combination of both.

11. A bleeder is a resistor placed across the output side of a filter to discharge the filter capacitors. When tapped, so as to furnish different voltage values, it is called a *voltage divider*.

12. A voltage-doubler rectifier circuit allows rectification of alternating current and increased DC voltage to be simultaneously obtained.

Quiz: Rectification of Alternating Current

This quiz will help you review the material just studied. See the quiz directions on page 24 before answering the questions below.

1. As aging of a copper-oxide rectifier occurs, the output is: *a.* unaffected; *b.* decreased; *c.* increased; *d.* subject to constant variation.

2. A transformer with a *center-tapped* secondary winding is required for a: *a.* synchronous converter; *b.* half-wave rectifier; *c.* bridge rectifier; *d.* full-wave rectifier.

3. *Choke-input* filters are used because of: *a.* higher output voltages; *b.* economy; *c.* better regulation; *d.* higher current-carrying capacity.

4. In operating a battery charger, it is best practice to: *a.* remove battery before turning off power; *b.* disconnect line voltage before removing battery; *c.* decrease output before removing battery; *d.* increase output before removing battery.

5. The *main* function of a filter is to: *a.* step up the voltage output; *b.* smooth out the DC voltage; *c.* provide various voltages; *d.* protect the rectifier from an overload.

6. The *voltage divider* in a rectifier is used to: *a.* provide different voltages at the output of the rectifier; *b.* increase the output voltage; *c.* act solely as a filter; *d.* rectify the AC input.

7. *Mercury-vapor* tubes have: *a.* no voltage drop and good regulation; *b.* medium voltage drop and poor regulation; *c.* low voltage drop and good regulation; *d.* high voltage drop and good regulation.

8. *Brute-force* filters are used because of: *a.* higher output voltages; *b.* better regulation; *c.* greater compactness; *d.* ease of servicing.

9. The capacitance used in a voltage-doubler circuit is critical in that its value affects the: *a.* input voltage; *b.* heater voltage; *c.* plate voltage; *d.* output voltage.

10. The resistor used to discharge filter capacitors and to improve voltage regulation is called a: *a.* voltage control; *b.* reactor; *c.* bleeder; *d.* filter.

11. Should one tube of a full-wave rectifier burn out, continued operation would: *a.* be impossible; *b.* burn out power transformer; *c.* only be possible by replacing tube; *d.* be possible.

12. Electrically, the AC synchronous converter is closest in its constructional features to: *a.* a synchronous motor of the solid-iron-rotor type; *b.* a rotary converter; *c.* a dynamotor; *d.* an alternator.

13. Electronic emission in a vacuum tube takes place when the: *a.* filament is heated; *b.* space charge within the tube is reduced; *c.* plate voltage is applied; *d.* load is connected from the plate to the cathode.

14. The copper-oxide rectifier and the selenium rectifier are alike in that they both represent the characteristic of: *a.* semiconduction;   *b.* toto-conduction;   *c.* toto-deduction; *d.* semideduction.

15. When an alternating current is applied to the rectifier tube in a half-wave rectifier circuit, a direct current appears in the output side of the half-wave rectifier circuit only when the: *a.* anode is negatively charged by the negative part of the AC cycle; *b.* anode is positively charged by the positive side of the AC cycle; *c.* cathode is indirectly heated; *d.* cathode is directly heated.

16. The aging of a copper-oxide rectifier takes place: *a.* only when the rectifier is first used; *b.* only when the current is at a minimum; *c.* at all times; *d.* only when the temperature is very low.

17. In a *full-wave* tube rectifier arranged in a *bridge circuit* and *using individual tubes of the diode type*, it is necessary to have at least: *a.* one tube; *b.* two tubes; *c.* three tubes; *d.* four tubes.

18. In a *half-wave* rectifier, it is necessary to have at least: *a.* one tube; *b.* two tubes; *c.* three tubes; *d.* four tubes.

19. In operation, a mercury-vapor tube may be distinguished from an argon rectifier tube by the fact that it gives off a glow having a: *a.* green color; *b.* yellow color; *c.* blue color; *d.* violet color.

20. In a *half-wave* rectifier circuit using a selenium rectifier, the latter can be replaced by a copper-oxide unit provided that it is similar in: *a.* physical dimensions; *b.* electrical characteristics; *c.* thermoreactive characteristics; *d.* thermodynamic characteristics.

21. In a *brute-force* filter that has been placed across a rectifier designed to deliver 500 volts DC, the capacitor which is closest to the rectifier side should be capable of withstanding a minimum of: *a.* 500 volts; *b.* 705 volts; *c.* 915 volts; *d.* 1,000 volts.

22. Excessive output voltage from a rectifier will *not* be caused by: *a.* high line voltage; *b.* heavy loads; *c.* high plate voltage; *d.* tubes that have lost their emission.

23. "In a full-wave rectifier circuit using tube rectifiers (diodes), *separate* filament transformers (or windings) must be used." This statement is: *a.* incorrect; *b.* correct; *c.* correct only if the filament transformers are poorly insulated; *d.* incorrect since a bridge rectifier is of the same type.

24. A transformer with a center-tapped secondary delivering 500 volts across the *full* winding is available. If it is used with a full-wave bridge rectifier, the maximum voltage obtainable will be: *a.* 125 volts; *b.* 250 volts; *c.* 500 volts; *d.* 1,000 volts.

25. *Thermionic emission* refers to the escape of electrons: *a.* due to voltage breakdown; *b.* when the cathode is heated; *c.* upon application of a negative potential on the plate; *d.* when the heater burns out.

Chapter 12. The Electric Meter

1. General

Even the most skilled electrician in any of the branches of
electricity cannot perform his duties properly without suitable
equipment that includes his basic tools and various electric
meters. An electric meter is an instrument that measures one or
more of the electric quantities, such as the volt, the watt, or the
ampere. Basically, the meter is a form of electric motor whose
degree of rotation is limited. It is available in a number of
forms, modifications in its design and appearance being determined mainly by such factors as the intended use and the
manufacturer's particular idea as to what is most suitable from
the viewpoint of appearance and utility.

2. The Basic DC Meter

In the chapter on magnetism, we have previously studied the
construction of the basic DC meter. Figure 104 showed its
construction, and it will be recalled that it actually consisted of
two magnets:

   a. A fixed, permanent magnet, and
   b. An electromagnet mounted on a pivot and free to rotate to a
   limited degree

The electromagnet, when connected to a DC source, tended to
move from its original position, the degree of movement being
proportional to the amount of current flowing through the coil.
A pointer mounted on the coil was thus caused to move across a
calibrated scale marked in volts or amperes, as the case might be.

A *voltmeter* is always connected *across* (in parallel to) a circuit
of which the voltage is being measured.

An *ammeter* is always connected *in series* with a circuit in which the rate of current flow is being measured. A milliammeter is simply an ammeter measuring in terms of 1/1000 amp., and therefore, it, too, is always connected in series.

Direct-current meters can be used on direct current only, and correct polarity of connections must be carefully observed to avoid damage. Incorrect connections may damage the meter beyond repair. In any case, if the polarity is reversed, the pointer will read below zero. Good-quality meters are regularly provided with a *zero adjustment screw* mounted on the face of the case. This is used to return the pointer to the zero setting should it be moved away by an overload, jarring, or a temperature change.

3. Extending Meter Ranges

By the use of *multipliers* (series resistors) with voltmeters, and *shunts* (parallel resistors) with ammeters and milliammeters, the ranges of the meters can be greatly extended. Some meters have the multipliers, or shunts, or both, housed within the meter case and controlled by a switch. This allows use of the meter as a multi-range voltmeter, ammeter, or both, as the design allows. Such meters can usually be recognized by the dial scale, which is calibrated in different sections.

It is sometimes desirable or even necessary to extend the range of a voltmeter or an ammeter when larger values of voltage or current than the meter will handle must be measured.

This can be done quite easily when the resistance of the meter is known. Most modern voltmeters are so marked directly on the dial that the internal resistance can be determined at a glance. Suppose it were necessary, for example, to extend the range of a 0 to 10 DC voltmeter to read up to 20 volts, and, on the dial, the following statement is made: "1,000 ohms per volt." This means that the internal resistance of the meter is 10,000 ohms. Therefore, in order to read values up to twice the voltage ($2 \times 10 = 20$) for which the meter is designed, an *external* resistance measuring 10,000 ohms can be connected in series with the meter. *It should be carefully noted that the internal resistance of the meter itself must always be considered in arriving at the final value of the multiplier.* This may be expressed by a formula:

$$R_{\text{mult.}} = \left(\frac{V_2}{V_1} - 1\right) \times R_m$$

where $R_{\text{mult.}}$ = unknown resistance of the multiplier
R_m = internal resistance of the meter
V_1 = original range of meter in volts
V_2 = desired range in volts

Example: To illustrate the use of this formula, let us assume we would like to increase the range of the same 0 to 10 DC voltmeter up to 50 volts.

Step 1. $R_{\text{mult.}} = \left(\dfrac{V_2}{V_1} - 1\right) + R_m$ *First, write down the formula.*

Step 2. $R_{\text{mult.}} =$
$\left(\dfrac{50}{10} - 1\right) + 10{,}000$ *Substitute the known quantities.*

Step 3. $R_{\text{mult.}} =$
$\left(\dfrac{\overset{5}{\cancel{50}}}{\underset{1}{\cancel{10}}} - \dfrac{1}{1}\right) \times 10{,}000$ *Cancel the fractions within the parenthesis.*

Step 4. $R_{\text{mult}} = 4 \times 10{,}000$ *Solve and remove the parenthesis.*

Step 5. $R_{\text{mult.}} = 40{,}000$ ohms   *Ans.*

If the meter scale is not recalibrated for use with the multiplier, it will be necessary to compute the correct value by multiplying the scale reading by a number representing the degree by which the range has been increased. In the example just given, the range has been increased from 10 volts to 50 volts, or *five times* the original range. This figure is automatically obtained by comparing V_2 and V_1 of the formula and is called the *scale multiplying factor*:

$$\text{Scale multiplying factor} = \frac{V_2}{V_1} = \frac{50}{10} = 5$$

If the user of such a converted meter forgets to use the scale multiplying factor, the values recorded will be grossly in error.

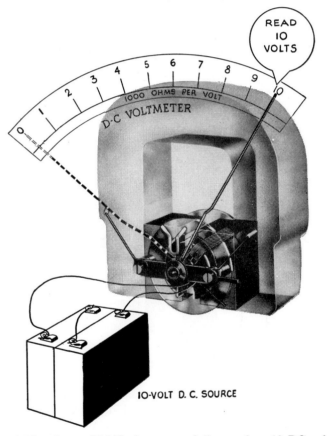

Fig. 258a. The phrase, "1,000 ohms per volt," on a 0 to 10 DC voltmeter indicates that the full meter resistance is 10,000 ohms. This data obviates the necessity of determining this factor when it is necessary to increase the range of the meter.

Thus, in the first case described using a 0 to 10 DC voltmeter with a multiplier that doubled its range to 20 volts, each reading on the original scale would indicate only one-half of the

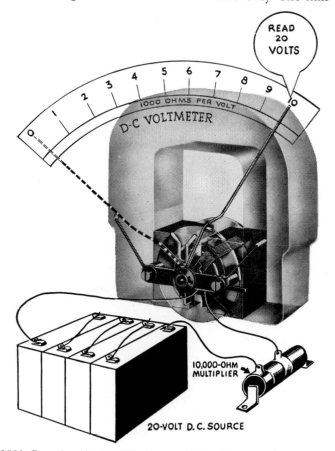

Fig. 258b. By using the 10,000-ohm multiplier in series with the 1,000 ohm per volt 0 to 10 DC Weston meter, the range is doubled.

true value. Hence, with the unconverted meter, a reading of 10 volts on the scale would mean that 10 volts were being measured, while a similar reading with the converted meter, that is, with the multiplier in the circuit, would indicate an actual value of 20 volts, and it should be so read (Figs. 258 *a* and *b*). The scale multiplying factor in this case is 2:

$$\left(\frac{V_2}{V_1} = \frac{20}{10} = 2\right).$$

If the internal resistance of the meter is unknown, it would then be necessary to determine what it is by the use of suitable

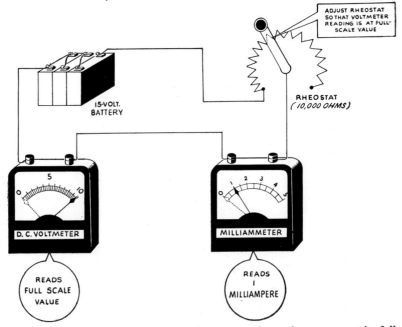

Fig. 259. A method of determining the current drawn by a meter at its full-scale reading.

resistance-measuring equipment or by finding out what current is drawn by the meter when it is reading full scale. A milliammeter would be required for this purpose and should be connected in series with the voltmeter and the voltage supply. The voltage should be controlled by a rheostat and set at a point where the voltmeter reads its full-scale value. A recording of the milliammeter reading is then made, and Ohm's Law applied (Fig. 259).

As an example, suppose the method described is being used to determine the resistance of a 0 to 10 DC voltmeter. The milliammeter shows a reading of 1 ma. $\left(\dfrac{1}{1000} \text{ amp.}\right)$. Using Ohm's Law $\left(R = \dfrac{E}{I}\right)$, the meter's resistance is found to be 10,000 ohms $\left(R = \dfrac{10}{0.001} = 10,000\right)$.

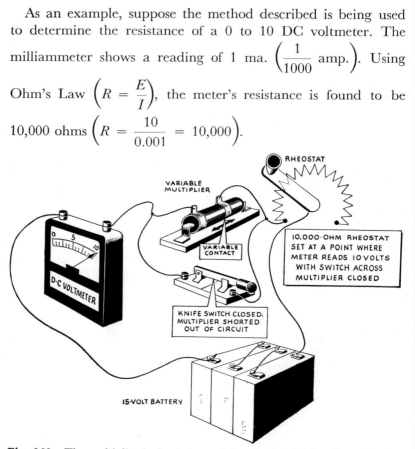

Fig. 260a. The multiplier is shorted out of the circuit initially when adjusting the voltage values so that a full-scale reading is obtained.

Still another method can be used. This method requires that an external multiplier whose resistance can be changed readily is available.

The multiplier is connected in series with the voltmeter and, at first, is shorted out of the circuit (it may, of course, be left out entirely during the preliminary adjustments) (Fig. 260a). The voltage across the meter is then adjusted by any means available (a rheostat can be used) until a full-scale reading is obtained. Then, the short from the external multiplier is removed, and its value adjusted until the meter reads one-half the value originally observed. If the multiplier is left at that setting and is used as

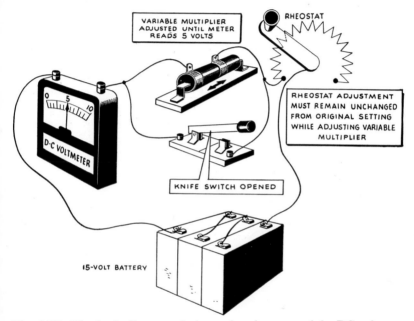

Fig. 260*b*. The final adjustment in increasing the range of the DC voltmeter is made with the multiplier connected in series with the meter.

a series resistance with the meter, the meter range will have been doubled (Fig. 260*b*). This is just another way of determining a resistance value that equals the resistance of the meter when its range is to be doubled.

In extending the range of milliammeters and ammeters, the method just described can also be used, but in this case the adjustable shunt would be connected directly in parallel to the meter connection (Fig. 261*a*). If a 0 to 10 DC ammeter were being used, the current through the meter would be adjusted until a full-scale reading is obtained. The shunt should then be adjusted until the meter reads 5 amp. (Fig. 261*b*). Use of the shunt will then allow the meter range to be doubled. A shunt usually has very low resistance, and its value may be a very odd

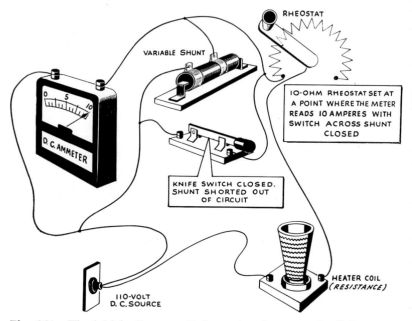

Fig. 261*a***.** The initial adjustment in increasing the range of a DC ammeter is made with the variable shunt shorted out of the circuit.

amount. For this reason, it is usually difficult to obtain accurate shunts of one's own manufacture.

Suppose it were necessary to extend the range of a milliammeter with a maximum scale reading of 5 ma. to cover a range up to 1 amp. Assume further that the meter's internal resistance is 10 ohms. The meter movement itself will continue to handle a maximum of 0.005 amp. (5 ma. or "mills"). The shunt will have to pass the balance or 0.995 amp. (both together would then be handling the 1 amp. required). To solve this problem, the following formula would be used:

$$\frac{R_m \times I_m}{1 \; - I_m}$$

where R_m = internal resistance of meter
$\quad I_m$ = full-scale current of meter
$\quad I$ = current reading desired

Substituting actual values in the formula gives

$$\frac{10 \times 0.005}{1 \; - 0.005} = \frac{0.05}{0.995} = 0.0502 \text{ ohm}$$

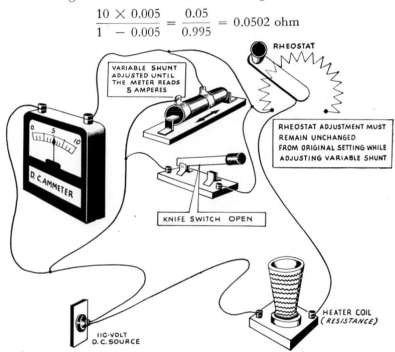

Fig. 261b. The final adjustment in increasing the range of the DC ammeter shown in Fig. 261a.

4. The Ohmmeter

A DC meter can be used to test for circuit continuity or resistance by using it with a suitable battery. *Continuity* is a term applied to a circuit when it is electrically complete, allowing a current to flow. A meter used to test for circuit continuity is called an *ohmmeter*, since the scale is generally calibrated to read the ohmic resistance directly. Sometimes, the term *continuity meter* is used.

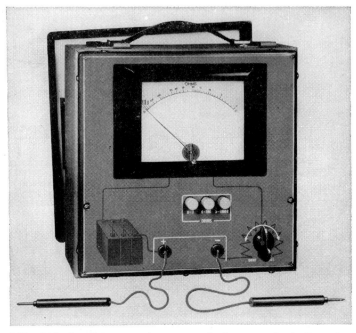

Fig. 262. A basic ohmmeter (exaggerated phantom view). By using the push buttons (not shown connected), the scale readings are either direct (*X*-1), 100 times the reading (*X*-100), or 10,000 times the reading (*X*-10,000).

An ohmmeter is commonly equipped with a rheostat and battery that are housed in the same case as the meter itself (Fig. 262). The use of a rheostat rather than a fixed resistor allows adjustments to be made to obtain full-scale deflection as the battery voltage decreases. When the battery is new, as a matter of fact, it also allows adjustment to avoid overloading the meter.

Full scale on the ohmmeter is marked *zero ohms*, because that is the value of resistance when the test prods used with the ohmmeter are shorted together. The other side of the scale (the zero point on an ordinary voltmeter or ammeter) is marked as the point of "infinite" resistance, that is, resistance so high

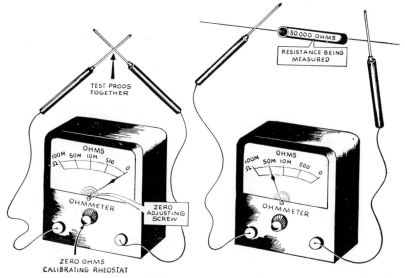

Fig. 263. The zero-ohms adjustment is made by turning the calibrating rheostat to a point where, *with the prods shorted*, a zero-ohms reading at the extreme right of the scale is obtained. The zero adjustment screw is *only* used when necessary to set the meter pointer at the extreme *left* of the scale *with the prods disconnected*. The position of the pointer at the left of the scale is the normal position when the prods remain apart and corresponds to the zero reading position of any other type of meter.

that it cannot be measured by the instrument. This condition exists when the test prods are apart.

Before the ohmmeter is used to test for continuity or to measure the resistance of a particular device, the lead terminals (the contact points on the test prods) are shorted (usually by holding the ends of the prods together), and the calibrating rheostat is adjusted so that the meter reads *zero ohms* (Fig. 263).

The meter pointer, of course, should be accurately set at the extreme left of the scale (corresponding to the zero point if the meter were an ammeter or voltmeter) before this zero-ohms adjustment is made. The former adjustment is made, when necessary, with the zero adjustment screw alone, and it is not desirable to compensate for any variation from that zero point by varying the setting of the zero-ohms calibrating rheostat. The latter is used only to adjust the battery voltage so that the meter reads zero ohms when the leads are shorted. After the described adjustment has been made, if the prods are touched to the device whose resistance is to be measured, the scale will indicate its ohmic value.

The range of an ohmmeter will depend upon the sensitivity of the meter (the value of current required for full-scale deflection) and the voltage used. Some ohmmeters are equipped with a number of ranges, selection of which is controlled by a switch.

5. Meter Sensitivity

The term *sensitivity* as applied to meters indicates whether the meter will respond to small or large values of current. A sensitive ammeter, for example, will respond to very small values, whereas a less sensitive meter would require larger values to move the pointer a similar distance across the scale. Where ammeters and milliammeters are concerned, it is customary to say that the instrument has a sensitivity of a given value, such as 1 ma. This means that a current value of 1/1000 amp. *flowing through the meter coil* will cause full deflection.

In the case of a voltmeter, the term *sensitivity* means not that the instrument will respond to low values of *voltage* but that it will draw only a small value of *current* in making the measurement. This avoids putting an additional load on the source of voltage and thus automatically reducing it proportionately. The meter actually reads the net voltage across the measured points.

A sensitive voltmeter, therefore, is constructed so that its coils will respond to a small value of current and act as a light load. Hence, its resistance is very high and is measured in ohms per volt. Thus a 0 to 10 DC voltmeter may have the same sensitivity as a 0 to 1,000 DC voltmeter if their resistance, in both cases, is 1,000 ohms per volt. *The current drawn by each will be the same.* The only difference will be in their full internal resistance, one being 10,000 ohms and the other 1,000,000 ohms. The 10,000-ohm unit will act as a very light load on voltages up to 10, while the 1,000,000-ohm unit will act similarly on voltages up to 1,000. In each case, at full scale, the meter will be drawing a maximum of only 1 ma.

In selecting a meter for use, it is best to select one that will handle slightly more than the maximum voltage or current normally to be found in the circuit. Use of an excessively large scale meter will make it difficult to read small values or variations thereof. Thus, if the maximum voltage in a circuit is 100 volts, use of a 0 to 1,000 voltmeter will crowd the zero and 100 points to the extreme left on the scale. Small variations of voltage, then, would be barely noticeable. On the other hand, the use of a 0 to 150 voltmeter in this case would allow the scale to be spread out, and small voltage variations could be read easily. Note that a 0 to 150 voltmeter was selected rather than a 0 to 100 voltmeter even though the normal maximum voltage was only 100 volts. This is also a safety precaution, as it allows a reasonable margin of safety should a possible overload occur through some unforeseen accident.

6. AC Meters

Alternating-current meters, like DC meters, are used with shunts or multipliers, depending upon whether they are used as ammeters or voltmeters. All AC meters will operate on direct current as well as on alternating current. The polarity of the connections when AC meters are used on either alternating or direct current, has, of course, no bearing on their operation.

It is often possible to identify AC meters by their irregular scale calibration. Direct-current meters have scales that are evenly graduated since they indicate a movement that is *proportional* to the applied voltage or current. *Alternating-current*

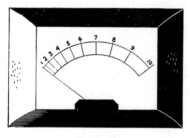

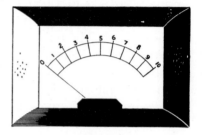

A.C. SCALE   **D. C. SCALE**

Fig. 264. Alternating-current meters may often be distinguished from DC meters by the appearance of their scale graduations. In DC meters, the graduations are generally quite uniform; in AC meters, they are often nonuniform.

meters, on the other hand, record values corresponding to the square of the current flowing in the circuit. This causes the scale to be nonuniform, with the scale graduations for lower values crowding the lower end of the scale while the graduations toward the higher end are spaced a considerable distance apart (Fig. 264).

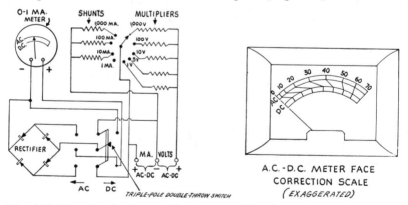

Fig. 265. The circuit of a rectifier-type combination AC-DC volt-milliammeter.

1. *Rectifier Type of AC Meter.* One of the reasons that a DC meter cannot be used to read alternating current is the fact that the current reversals occur so rapidly that the pointer cannot follow the changes of polarity. Therefore, if alternating current is applied, the pointer will simply vibrate at the zero point.

It is, however, possible to use a metallic rectifier with a sensitive DC meter to allow it to read AC voltages. A bridge rectifier circuit is ordinarily used (Fig. 265), and the rectifier is housed within the meter case along with the proper multipliers. The combined device is known

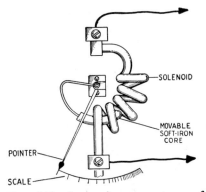

Fig. 266. A moving-vane type of meter that uses a soft-iron plunger instead of a regular vane. (*Courtesy Weston Electrical Instrument Corporation.*)

as a *rectifier type of AC meter*, and is equipped with a non-uniform, "square-law," scale. If an ordinary DC scale were used, each reading would have to be multiplied by the factor 1.11, which represents the ratio between the effective and average AC values. It is the effective AC value, it will be recalled, that produces an effect similar to a DC value.

Though the rectifier type of AC meter will operate on direct current, the scale readings will be distorted for the reason described above. All readings will actually be greater than the real value. Meters of this type designed for both AC and DC operation are, therefore, equipped with a correction scale on the dial face.

2. *Moving-vane AC Meters.* There are three main types of moving-vane AC meters:

1) In one device, a soft-iron plunger, to which a pointer is connected, is drawn into a solenoid as current passes through the winding (Fig. 266).

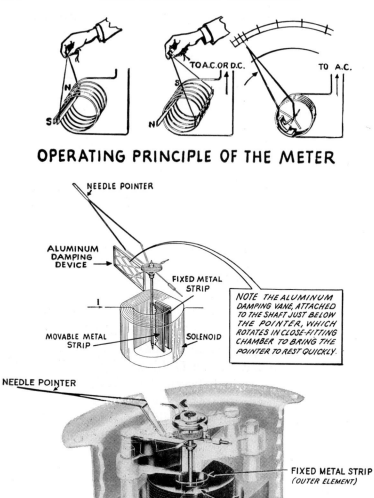

Fig. 267. The basic Weston moving iron vane mechanism used in meters of their manufacture.

2) In another type, a metal strip is attached to the inner side of the coil and another metal strip, to which the pointer is attached, is mounted on a suitable pivot and placed alongside the first strip. When current passes through the coil, both strips are similarly magnetized. This causes the fixed piece of metal to repel the movable piece, the degree of repulsion depending upon the strength of the current in the coil (Fig. 267).

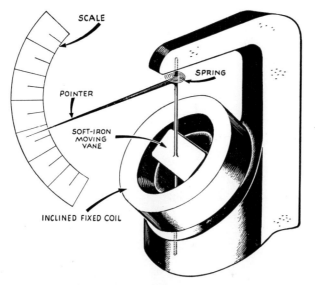

Fig. 268. The inclined-coil type of moving-vane AC meter.

3) In the inclined-coil type of moving-vane meter (Fig. 268), the current in the coil affects a single metal vane mounted on a shaft. When current is passing through the coil, the vane will rotate to a position where it will allow the maximum number of lines of force to pass through it. The degree of rotation is determined by the amount of current flowing through the coil.

3. *The Electrodynamometer AC Meter.* With the exception of the rectifier type of AC meter, which is capable of being used on AC frequencies as high as 25,000 cycles with good efficiency, the other AC meters so far discussed are generally limited to the lower AC frequencies such as are used for lighting, heating, and power. Such frequencies may range from 25 to 60 cycles with the latter being standard in most sections of the United States.

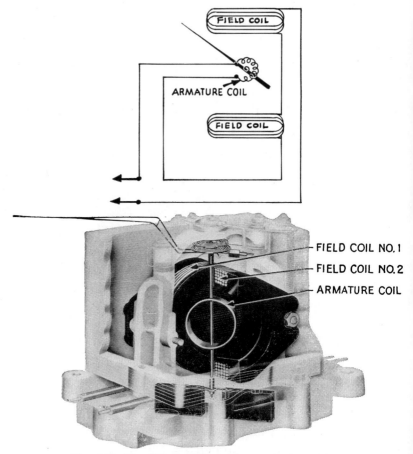

Fig. 269. The Weston Electrodynamometer meter.

In other countries, frequencies such as 25, 40, or 50 cycles are prevalent. If these meters are used on very high frequencies, losses due to the heat developed become too high to allow efficient operation.

Perhaps the most efficient meter used for low-frequency AC measurements is the *electrodynamometer* type (Fig. 269). In this instrument both the fixed field coils and the rotating armature coil are electromagnets, whereas the DC meter uses a permanent field magnet. There are three solenoids in all, two acting as the field coils and the third acting as the armature. All the solenoids

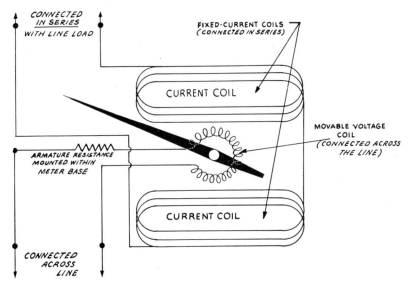

Fig. 270. The circuit of the basic wattmeter.

are connected in series. When current flows through the circuit, the armature will be forced to rotate out of its normal position in exactly the same fashion as in a meter using a permanent magnet. As in other meters, the degree of rotation will be dependent upon the strength of the current.

4. *Wattmeter.* When it is desirable to measure the electric power consumed in a circuit, as measured in watts, without resort to the use of a voltmeter and ammeter, it is possible to use a *wattmeter*, which will indicate watts directly. This device is quite similar to an electrodynamometer, but instead of having the field and armature coils connected in series, they are brought out to separate connections (Fig. 270). The armature is called a *voltage coil* and is connected across the line, while the fixed coils are called *current coils* and are connected in series with each other and with the line.

Since the voltage coil is directly across the line, its field is of constant value. The current coils, in series with the line, have a field of varying strength, depending upon the amount of power the line is furnishing, the current being greater when the power is greater. Hence, the degree of repulsion between the coils, and the resultant movement of the scale pointer, depends upon the power drawn by the circuit under test. The scale is calibrated directly in watts so that no computation is required.

The wattmeter measures the true power in both AC and DC circuits. No power-factor correction is required in use on alternating current, owing to the construction of the instrument, which automatically makes the necessary correction.

5. *Hot-wire Meter*. The *hot-wire meter* (Fig. 271) is used mainly where very high AC frequencies are in use, primarily in the field of radio, where frequencies up to 300 million cycles and higher are found. This meter will, however, also operate on lower frequencies.

Its operation depends upon the expansion of a wire when it is heated by a current of electricity. As the wire expands, its length increases, and this causes the wire to sag. A spring, attached to a silk thread that is drawn through a pulley and fastened to the wire, tends to pull the thread as the tension of the wire decreases. The movement of the thread thus causes the pulley to revolve, and since the pointer is pivoted on the pulley, it also moves. The degree of movement across the scale is proportional to the square of the current. Hence, the scale, as on other AC meters, is not evenly graduated.

Hot-wire meters are neither accurate nor stable in operation. Further, due to the very nature of their construction, they are easily burned out if forced to carry an overload even momentarily. Further, the wire tends to stretch after use, thus making frequent adjustments necessary.

6. *The Thermocouple Type of Meter.* Far more sensitive, accurate, and reliable than the hot-wire ammeter is the *thermocouple* type of AC meter (Fig. 272), also primarily designed for high-

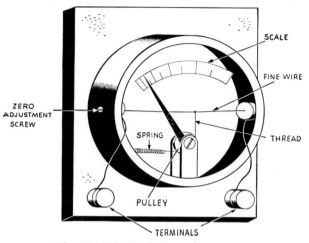

Fig. 271. The basic hot-wire meter.

frequency measurements. Though these instruments can be used on low-frequency alternating current and direct current too, their cost does not ordinarily warrant such action.

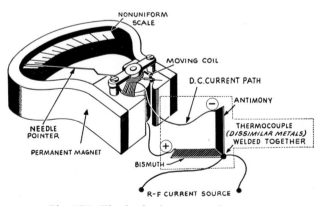

Fig. 272. The basic thermocouple meter.

The meter itself is a sensitive DC meter across which a thermocouple is placed. Heat created by the passage of an electric current at the juncture of the two metals forming the thermocouple will cause a DC voltage to be developed across the device. This voltage is then recorded on the scale of the DC meter, which, like the scale of an AC meter, is calibrated with nonuniform graduation, since heating of the thermocouple is proportional to the square of the current flowing through the circuit at the point where the thermocouple is connected.

Both the thermocouple type of meter and hot-wire meters are used as ammeters or milliammeters, exclusively. They are not used as voltmeters. Hence, they are usually described as *thermoammeters*, *thermocoupled ammeters*, and *hot-wire ammeters*.

Thermocouple meters are frequently used to measure temperatures directly. An instrument of this type is called a *pyrometer* (heat meter). The scale is calibrated in degrees of temperature, like that of a thermometer. Since the thermocouple unit can be placed at a point remote from the meter itself, the heat acting on the thermocouple will not affect the meter. Thus extremely high temperatures can be measured without fear of damaging the meter or causing injury to the observer.

7. *Combination Meters.* For purposes of economy, convenience in operation, and compactness of construction, *combination meters* (Fig. 273) are available. Such meters, using a single movement of sensitive design, are equipped with the necessary multipliers and shunts as well as with a rectifier, if they are intended for AC operation in addition to DC operation. By means of switches, the desired range and selection for use as an AC or DC device is obtained. In some cases, the selection is obtained by the use of contact pins (*plugs*) placed into proper receptacles (*jacks*) on the panel of the meter.

A combination meter is often included as an integral part of a complete *test set*, which, in addition, is generally equipped with suitable tools, test prods, and accessory equipment as needed in a particular trade.

In using a multi-range meter, it is advisable to set the range switch initially at the highest reading for which the meter is designed, adjusting it to the required range after the meter is in actual use. This prevents overloading the meter should a higher voltage or current value be present than was anticipated.

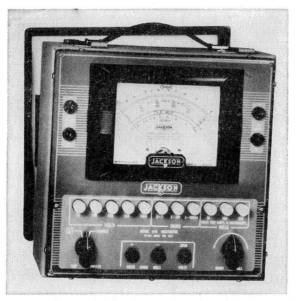

Fig. 273. A modern combination meter, the Jackson Multimeter.

7. Testing without Meters

For most efficient results, the use of electric meters in any type of electrical testing is desirable. Occasionally, however, if they are not available, resort may be made to other devices.

As an example, it is sometimes necessary to determine whether the available voltage supply is alternating current or direct current, and in the case of direct current, the polarity may have to be determined as well. By using a peeled raw potato or a glass of salt water, this can be done very easily (Fig. 274).

If the two leads from the line are held slightly apart (to prevent a short circuit) and touched to the potato, both the spots touched will turn dark and begin bubbling in a few moments if the line supply is alternating current. Only one spot (that in contact with the negative lead) will turn dark if it is direct current.

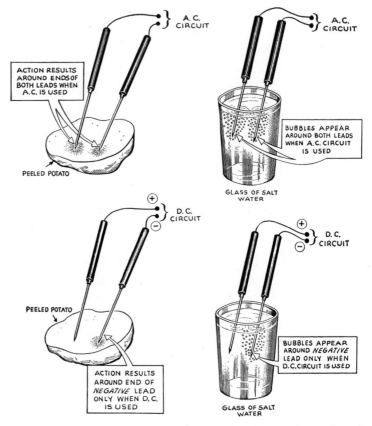

Fig. 274. A peeled, raw potato or a glass of salt water can be used to check for voltage and to indicate polarities.

Similarly, if the wires are immersed in a glass of salt water, bubbles will form around both leads if alternating current is present, and around only one (the negative lead) if direct current is present.

These tests can also be used to see if any line voltage is available, though the use of an ordinary light bulb or neon lamp is rather easier. A neon lamp shows polarity as well, since a glow around both terminals will indicate the presence of alternating current, while a glow around only one (the negative side) will indicate direct current (Fig. 275). Neon bulbs, however, will

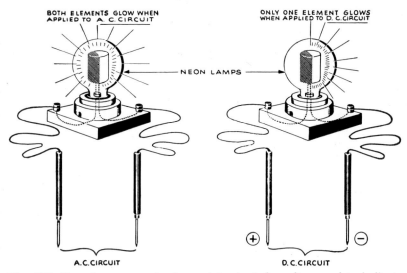

BOTH ELEMENTS GLOW WHEN APPLIED TO A. C. CIRCUIT

ONLY ONE ELEMENT GLOWS WHEN APPLIED TO D. C. CIRCUIT

NEON LAMPS

A.C. CIRCUIT

D.C. CIRCUIT

$(+)$ $(-)$

Fig. 275. Neon lamps can also be used to check for voltage and to indicate polarities.

not light if the voltage is too low, and electric-light bulbs will light only very dimly, or not at all, if the voltage is considerably lower than normally required. This must be borne in mind—otherwise it may be believed that no voltage at all exists when actually there is some voltage available.

8. Maintenance of Meters

Meters require no attention in operation on proper circuits. The important thing is that they be used only at their proper ratings. Overloading a meter by using it on an excessive voltage or current, as the case may be, usually results in its destruction, either by its burning out or by having the pointer flung to one side with such violence that it is broken or bent. Direct-current meters, of course, should only be used on direct current, and the polarity of connections must be carefully observed. Alternating-current meters will serve for DC use if necessary, though this is not a recommended procedure if accuracy is paramount. It is also important to remember that AC meters should only be used on the AC frequencies for which they are intended. Most AC meters, with the exception of the thermoammeter and hot-wire ammeter, are used for low-frequency AC measurements, while the rectifier type of AC meter can serve well up to 25,000 cycles.

Portable meters should be handled carefully to avoid breakage and loss of accuracy. A meter that has received rough handling, like being dropped, may become inaccurate owing to loss of magnetism (if fixed permanent magnets are used) or to a bent armature shaft or broken pivot bearing.

Accuracy will also be affected if the meters are placed in the vicinity of strong magnetic fields. This should be avoided.

SUMMARY

1. An electric meter is an instrument that measures one or more electric quantities. Basically, it is a form of electric motor with a limited degree of rotation.

2. The basic DC meter consists of a fixed permanent magnet and an electromagnet that is capable of rotating when excited by an electric current. The electromagnet is called a *coil* or an *armature*. The polarity of the connections on a DC meter must be observed, and it cannot be used on alternating current unless used in conjunction with a suitable copper-oxide rectifier (it is then termed a *rectifier type of AC meter*) or with a thermocouple (when it becomes a *thermoammeter*).

3. Alternating-current meters may be used on direct current without damage, but the accuracy of some types is impaired when this is done.

4. The moving-vane group of AC meters is designed for low-frequency AC operation, as is the electrodynamometer type, which is the most efficient device for such use. The electro-dynamometer AC meter has a set of fixed coils and a movable coil (the armature), all of the coils being in series. The coils become electromagnets when a current passes through the windings, and repulsion between the armature and the fixed coils occurs in accordance with the rules of magnetism.

5. The wattmeter is a special type of electrodynamometer with a scale recorded in watts. The armature is known as the *voltage coil* and is connected in parallel to the line. The field coils are called *current coils* and are connected in series with the line. Variations in the current strength increases or decreases the degree of repulsion between the fixed coil and the armature. A wattmeter can be used on either direct current or alternating current and in both cases will measure the true power.

6. Thermocouple AC meters and hot-wire meters are generally used on high-frequency AC current.

7. Shunts and multipliers are used to extend the range of ammeters and voltmeters, respectively. To determine their values, it is necessary to know the internal resistance of the meter and the current drawn by the meter at maximum deflection.

8. The ohmmeter is a sensitive DC meter calibrated in ohmic resistance and is used in conjunction with a suitable battery and adjustable rheostat. It measures ohmic resistance directly without the necessity of first determining the voltage and current in a circuit.

9. The term *sensitivity* refers to the amount of current required for full-scale deflection of the pointer on a meter. Sensitive meters require smaller values of current.

Quiz: The Electric Meter

This quiz will help you review the material just studied. See the quiz directions on page 24 before answering the questions below.

1. The graduations of the calibrated scale on a DC meter are uniform. This is because the degree of armature rotation is: *a.* inversely proportional to the current; *b.* directly proportional to the current; *c.* proportional to the square of the current; *d.* proportional to the cube of the current.

2. A zero adjustment screw is provided on most meters in order to adjust the: *a.* range of the meter; *b.* sensitivity of the meter; *c.* pointer to the zero setting should it be off that point; *d.* meter so that it can be used both as an ammeter and as a voltmeter.

3. In an AC electrodynamometer, the two field coils and single armature coil are so connected that: *a.* All coils are in parallel. *b.* All coils are in series. *c.* The armature coil is in parallel to the field coils. *d.* One field coil is in parallel to, and the other in series with, the armature coil.

4. An electric meter may be compared to an electric: *a.* motor; *b.* generator; *c.* rectifier; *d.* battery.

5. The polarity of the connections is important when using: *a.* a thermoammeter; *b.* an electrodynamometer; *c.* a hot-wire meter; *d.* a DC voltmeter.

6. If a DC meter is used on alternating current of the proper voltage, the meter will: *a.* burn out immediately; *b.* record higher incorrect readings; *c.* record lower incorrect readings; *d.* not record at all.

7. A DC voltmeter has an internal resistance of 1,000 ohms and at maximum deflection records a value of 10 volts. To increase the range to 100 volts, the multiplier used must measure: *a.* 5,000 ohms; *b.* 7,000 ohms; *c.* 9,000 ohms; *d.* 10,000 ohms.

8. A thermoammeter used as a thermometer is commonly called a: *a.* hygrometer; *b.* hydrometer; *c.* barometer; *d.* pyrometer.

9. Before using an ohmmeter, the test prods should be shorted together and the calibrating rheostat adjusted so that the meter reads: *a.* infinity; *b.* zero ohms; *c.* at a point midway between zero and infinity; *d.* 1,000 ohms, which is the base reading.

10. The term *continuity* refers to a circuit that is: *a.* electrically complete; *b.* electrically incomplete; *c.* physically complete; *d.* physically incomplete.

11. In a wattmeter, the two field coils and single armature coil are so connected that: *a.* All coils are in parallel. *b.* All coils are in series. *c.* The armature coil is in parallel to the line, and the field coils are in series with each other and the line. *d.* The armature coil is in series with the line, and the field coils are in parallel with each other and the line.

12. "Voltmeters of greatly different ranges may be of equal sensitivity." This statement is: *a.* untrue since high-range meters have greater resistance; *b.* untrue because a higher current is always drawn when the voltage is greater; *c.* true because the meters may draw the same current at maximum deflection; *d.* true because the increased weight of the armature in higher range meters is compensated for the increased current.

13. A *continuity meter* is another name for: *a.* a voltmeter; *b.* an ammeter; *c.* an ohmmeter; *d.* a wattmeter.

14. A rectifier-type AC meter should not ordinarily be used on an AC supply of: *a.* 25 cycles; *b.* 60 cycles; *c.* 5,000 cycles; *d.* 100,000 cycles.

15. The "full-scale" mark on an ohmmeter always is: *a.* 1,000 ohms per volt; *b.* zero volts; *c.* zero amperes; *d.* zero ohms.

16. A moving-vane type of AC meter should not ordinarily be used on an AC supply of: *a.* 25 cycles; *b.* 40 cycles; *c.* 60 cycles; *d.* 5,000 cycles.

17. Heating of the thermocouple in a thermoammeter produces: *a.* an alternating current that is recorded on an AC meter; *b.* an alternating current that is rectified and read on a DC meter; *c.* a direct current that is recorded on a DC meter; *d.* a direct current that is recorded on an AC meter.

18. Meters of high sensitivity draw: *a.* more current than cheap meters; *b.* less current than less sensitive meters; *c.* more current than less sensitive meters; *d.* less current than meters of even higher sensitivity.

19. The graduations of the calibrated scale on a thermocouple AC meter are nonuniform. This is because the degree of heat exciting the thermocouple is: *a.* inversely proportional to the current; *b.* directly proportional to the current; *c.* proportional to the square of the current; *d.* proportional to the cube of the current.

20. When a wattmeter is used on alternating current, the: *a.* voltage (armature) coil must be connected in series with the line; *b.* current (field) coils must be connected in series with the line and the voltage coil in parallel to the line; *c.* current coils must be connected in parallel to the line and the voltage coil in series with the line; *d.* current coils must be connected in parallel to the line to compensate for power factor.

21. Four voltmeters rated, respectively, at 100, 1,000, 2,000, and 100,000 ohms per volt are available. For highest sensitivity, it is best to use the voltmeter rated at: *a.* 100,000 ohms per volt; *b.* 2,000 ohms per volt; *c.* 1,000 ohms per volt; *d.* 100 ohms per volt.

22. The maximum current *normally* found in a particular circuit is 60 amp. The ammeter that is best adapted to this circuit, from the standpoint of efficient and safe operation, should have a range of: *a.* 0 to 50 amp.; *b.* 0 to 60 amp.; *c.* 0 to 75 amp.; *d.* 0 to 500 amp.

23. In the absence of a suitable meter, the use of a neon bulb will allow the user to determine: *a.* only whether the normal voltage is available; *b.* only whether the supply is alternating current, provided the available voltage will ignite the lamp; *c.* whether the supply is alternating current or direct current, providing the available voltage will ignite the lamp; *d.* only whether direct current is available.

24. In first using a multi-range combination meter on a circuit of unknown voltage, one should set the range selector at: *a.* the point midway between the lowest and highest voltage range, since it is the average voltage range that is normally encountered; *b.* any point, as the meter adjusts itself automatically to the correct voltage; *c.* the highest point and work downward till the proper range is determined; *d.* the lowest point and work upward to the proper range.

25. In the absence of a suitable meter, one can determine whether a line is alternating current by immersing two leads therefrom in salt water. Alternating current is known to exist if bubbles: *a.* fail to form around either lead; *b.* form around one lead only; *c.* fail to form around both leads; *d.* form around both leads.

Appendix 1. Square Root

---

1. The Meaning of the Term Square Root

The square root of a particular number is a number that when multiplied by itself equals the particular number.

Thus, the square root of the number 4 is the number 2, since 2 multiplied by itself (2 × 2) equals the original number 4. This is the equivalent of saying that the square root of a number is a number that, when squared, equals the original number. Thus, the square root of 4 is 2, since the square of 2 (written 2^2 and meaning that the number 2 is to be multiplied by itself) equals 4. In similar fashion, the following can be computed:

$$4^2 = 4 \times 4 = 16$$
$$8^2 = 8 \times 8 = 64$$
$$10^2 = 10 \times 10 = 100$$
$$500^2 = 500 \times 500 = 250,000$$

If we want to find the square root of a number, we indicate that fact by putting a *radical* sign around the number in the following manner:

$$\sqrt{16} \qquad \sqrt{64} \qquad \sqrt{100} \qquad \sqrt{250,000}$$

In each case, this simply means that we are to determine a particular number, the square of which equals the number under the radical sign.

Thus, the square root of 16 ($\sqrt{16}$) = 4 since 4^2 (4 × 4) = 16.

2. Finding the Square Root

Suppose we want to find the square root of 25 ($\sqrt{25}$). First we write this figure down:

$$\sqrt{25}$$

Below this figure and slightly to the left place a number that, mentally computed, is believed to be that number which, when squared, would equal 25. This number is 5.

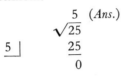

$$\sqrt{25}$$

5 |

We know that $5^2 = 25$, so we write the number 25 below the 25 covered by the radical.

$$\begin{array}{r} 5 \quad (Ans.) \\ \sqrt{25} \\ 5 \mid \quad \underline{25} \\ 0 \end{array}$$

Subtracting these two figures leaves zero and this indicates that $5^2 = 25$. The square root of 25 ($\sqrt{25}$) is therefore 5. We then place the figure 5 above the radical, indicating that it is the answer.

Suppose we now try another example and find the square root of 81 ($\sqrt{81}$).

Step 1. $\sqrt{81}$ *The number is written under the radical sign.*

Step 2. $\sqrt{81}$ *We try the number 10 to see if it works but find that the square of 10 is 100. 100 is greater than 81 and is, therefore, wrong.*

10 | 100

Step 3. $\overset{9}{\sqrt{81}}$ *We now try 9, which squared equals 81. Since this equals the figure under the radical sign, and thus leaves zero, we know it is correct. We therefore place the 9 above the radical indicating that 9 is the square root of 81.*

9 | $\underline{81}$ 0

The examples so far given have been comparatively simple as they dealt with numbers that had an answer in one figure and did not involve fractions.

In finding the square root of more involved numbers, it is easier if we mark off the numbers in groups of two figures, counting from right to left of the decimal point for whole numbers, and from left to right of the decimal point for the fractional amounts. The marking consists of drawing a short line above each group as follows:

$$\sqrt{\overline{7}\ \overline{83}\ \overline{15}.\ \overline{14}\ \overline{17}}$$

$$\sqrt{\overline{65}\ \overline{87}.\ \overline{10}}$$

Where there is an *odd* number of figures to the *left* of the decimal point, the single figure on the extreme left is considered as a group by itself.

$$\overline{4}\ \overline{87}\ \overline{96}.$$

$$\overline{8}\ \overline{43}\ \overline{16}.$$

Where there is an *odd* number of figures to the *right* of the decimal point, a zero is added in order to make an even group. *Adding zeros to the right* of a group of numbers in a decimal does not change the value of the number they represent.

$$0.6 = 0.60 = 0.600 = 0.6000, \text{ etc.}$$

Thus, 78.461 and 382.154 would be marked off as follows:

$$\overline{78}.\overline{46}\overline{10}$$

$$\overline{382}.\overline{15}\overline{40}$$

In addition to marking the numbers off in groups of two figures, it often helps actually to separate the groups in the following way:

$$\overline{78}.\ \overline{46}\ \overline{10}$$

$$\overline{3}\ \overline{82}.\ \overline{15}\ \overline{40}$$

To find the square root of a complex number, we work from left to right, using each group of figures in order. Working out some examples will best explain how this is done.

Example: Find the square root of 2,116.

Step 1. $\sqrt{2,116}$ *Write the number down under the radical sign.*

Step 2. $\sqrt{\overline{21}\ \overline{16.}}$ *Separate the groups of two figures, proceeding from right to left. In dealing with a whole number, a decimal point is assumed to be at the right of the last number composing the group. It is convenient to place the decimal point there, in case it is necessary to work out the answer into a decimal.*

Step 3.

$$\begin{array}{r} 4 \\ \sqrt{\overline{21}\ \overline{16.}} \end{array}$$

4 | 16
        5

We mentally select the largest number that equals or closely approaches 21 when squared. $4^2 = 16$, whereas 5^2 would be 25. 5, therefore, is too high, leaving 4 the largest number that when squared closely approximates 21. We then subtract the square of 4, which is 16, from 21, leaving a remainder of 5, and place the 4, which will be the first figure in our answer, above the radical sign over the 21 group.

Step 4.

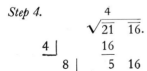

We then bring down the next group, 16, and place it beside the figure 5. Draw a _| to the left of this new figure, 516, and place there a number that is double the square root (4) already found. This is the figure 8.

Step 5.

$$\begin{array}{r} 4 \quad 6 \\ \sqrt{21 \quad 16.} \end{array}$$

$$\begin{array}{r} 4 \mid \qquad 16 \\ \underline{8(x)} \mid \quad 5 \ 16 \\ 5 \ 16 \\ \hline 0 \end{array}$$

Now, by the trial-and-error method, find a number, the first figure of which is 8 and the second figure of which (x) *must be determined, such that when the number is multiplied by the x number, it will equal or nearly equal 516. Suppose we try 6, giving the number 86 to be multiplied by 6. 86 × 6 = 516. We place this number under the 516 already there and subtract, leaving zero. The number 6, therefore, works out perfectly, and we bring it up to the answer line above the radical. The square root of 2,116 is, therefore, 46.*
Proof: 46 × 46 = 2,116.

When a square root of a number does not work out evenly, the answer is carried to a two- or three-decimal figure.

Example: Find the square root of 3,225.

Step. 1. $\sqrt{32 \quad 25.}$

Write the number under the radical sign, dividing it into groups of two figures marked off from right to left of the decimal point. The decimal point is written in automatically.

Step 2.

$$\begin{array}{r} 5 \\ \sqrt{32 \quad 25.} \end{array}$$

$$\begin{array}{r} 5 \mid \quad 25 \\ \hline 7 \end{array}$$

Computing mentally, we select a number the square of which equals or closely approaches the first group of figures. This number is 5 and 5^2 *= 25. Place the 5 to the left of the* ⌐ *and also above the radical over the first group. Subtract 25, placed below the first group, from the group itself, that is, 32 minus 25 equals 7.*

Step 3.

$$\begin{array}{r} 5 \\ \sqrt{32\ \ 25.} \end{array}$$

$$\begin{array}{r|l} 5\ | & 25 \\ \underline{10(x)\ |} & 7\ \ 25 \end{array}$$

Bring down the next group of figures, 25, and place it alongside the remainder 7. Also double the square root 5 already found and place it to the left of the ___|. We must now select the x figure that, placed alongside the double number to the left of the ___|, is also used as the multiplier of this new number to equal or approach 725.

Step 4.

$$\begin{array}{r} 5 \\ \sqrt{32\ \ 25.} \end{array}$$

$$\begin{array}{r|l} 5\ | & 25 \\ \underline{106\ |} & 7\ \ 25 \\ & 6\ \ 36 \end{array}$$

Computed mentally, we find that the x number is 6. We place the 6 alongside the 10, and the new number, 106, is now multiplied by the figure 6:
$$106 \times 6 = 636$$

Step 5.

$$\begin{array}{r} 5\ \ \ 6. \\ \sqrt{32\ \ 25.\ \ \overline{00}\ \ \overline{00}} \end{array}$$

$$\begin{array}{r|l} 5\ | & 25 \\ \underline{106\ |} & 7\ \ 25 \\ & 6\ \ 36 \\ \cline{2-2} & 89\ \ \ 00 \end{array}$$

The figure 636 is subtracted from 725, leaving 89, showing that a fraction is involved. A decimal point is placed above the radical over the decimal point under the radical. Two or more groups of zeros are placed to the right of the decimal point. The first group of 00 is brought down and placed alongside the 89. This will allow us to work out the answer to its first decimal. The procedure is exactly as before.

Step 6.

$$\begin{array}{r} 5 \quad 6. \quad 7 \\ \sqrt{32\ \ 25.\ \ \overline{00}\ \ \overline{00}} \end{array}$$

5 | 25
106 | 7 25
   6 36
1,127 | 89 00
    78 89
    10 11

First we double the square root already found, 56, and bring this figure (2 × 56 = 112) down and place it to the left of the ___. We now find the x number. If we try 7, making the number 1,127, and multiply by 7 we get 7,889, which we place below the 8,900. 7 is therefore satisfactory, and we place it above the radical over the first group of decimal figures.

Step 7.

$$\begin{array}{r} 5 \quad 6. \quad 7 \quad 8 \\ \sqrt{32\ \ 25.\ \ \overline{00}\ \ \overline{00}} \end{array}$$

5 | 25
106 | 7 25
   6 36
1,127 | 89 00
    78 89
1,134(x) | 10 11 00
    9 07 84
    1 03 16

To carry out the answer to two decimal points, we bring down the second group of decimal figures 00 and place it alongside the remainder, 1,011, making this number 101,100. To its left, we bring down double the square root already found, which makes it 2 × 567, or 1,134. We must now select the number (x), which when added to 1,134 to make a five-figure number 11,34x and multiplied by that same number equals or nearly equals 101,100. Computing, we find that the number 8 will serve, making the number 11,348, which when multiplied by 8 equals 90,784. We place the figure 8 above the radical, and unless we want to bring the answer out to three decimals, the square root of 3,225 is 56.78. If a third decimal is desirable, additional groups of 00 are brought down and the process continued.

Skill with square root can only be gained by practice. We will try one additional example, and then the student can try the problems listed thereafter.

Example: What is the square root of 1,579.132?

	3	9.	7	3	8
	$\sqrt{15}$	$\overline{79.}$	$\overline{13}$	$\overline{20}$	$\overline{00}$
3 |	9	xx	xx	xx	xx
	6	79			
69 |	6	21			
		58	13		
787 |		55	09		
		3	04	20	
7,943 |		2	38	29	
			65	91	00
79,468 |			63	57	44

Note: In order to remember which groups of two figures have been brought down, it is sometimes convenient to place an "xx" under the figures as this process occurs. In other words, in the example just given, as the first group 79 was brought down, "xx" was placed under the figures 79. Then when the second group 13 was brought down, the same procedure was followed. This prevents the accidental use of the same group more than once.

Problems for Practice

Find the square roots as shown:

1. $\sqrt{7,7440}$
2. $\sqrt{9,168.7}$
3. $\sqrt{413.8}$
4. $\sqrt{11,923.468}$
5. $\sqrt{0.964}$
6. $\sqrt{8.31728}$

Appendix 2. Quiz Answers

Chapter 1, pages 24–28

1. *c*	9. *b*	17. *b*	25. *d*	33. *d*
2. *d*	10. *a*	18. *a*	26. *a*	34. *a*
3. *b*	11. *d*	19. *c*	27. *c*	35. *c*
4. *d*	12. *c*	20. *c*	28. *c*	36. *b*
5. *c*	13. *b*	21. *d*	29. *b*	37. *a*
6. *c*	14. *d*	22. *a*	30. *d*	38. *d*
7. *d*	15. *b*	23. *c*	31. *c*	39. *c*
8. *d*	16. *a*	24. *b*	32. *a*	40. *d*

Chapter 2, pages 57–61

1. *c*	9. *a*	17. *b*	25. *a*	33. *b*
2. *d*	10. *c*	18. *c*	26. *a*	34. *a*
3. *b*	11. *b*	19. *d*	27. *c*	35. *b*
4. *d*	12. *d*	20. *d*	28. *d*	36. *a*
5. *c*	13. *c*	21. *a*	29. *b*	37. *d*
6. *a*	14. *d*	22. *d*	30. *d*	38. *a*
7. *c*	15. *b*	23. *b*	31. *a*	39. *a*
8. *b*	16. *a*	24. *b*	32. *c*	40. *c*

Chapter 3, pages 93–96

1. *a*	6. *c*	11. *d*	16. *a*	21. *b*
2. *c*	7. *d*	12. *b*	17. *d*	22. *a*
3. *a*	8. *a*	13. *b*	18. *a*	23. *d*
4. *b*	9. *b*	14. *a*	19. *d*	24. *c*
5. *d*	10. *c*	15. *c*	20. *b*	25. *a*

Chapter 4, pages 130–135

1. *c*	9. *a*	17. *c*	25. *a*	33. *c*
2. *a*	10. *d*	18. *a*	26. *d*	34. *a*
3. *b*	11. *b*	19. *b*	27. *c*	35. *d*
4. *d*	12. *c*	20. *a*	28. *a*	36. *d*
5. *c*	13. *d*	21. *c*	29. *d*	37. *a*
6. *d*	14. *d*	22. *b*	30. *b*	38. *b*
7. *b*	15. *b*	23. *d*	31. *b*	39. *c*
8. *c*	16. *d*	24. *b*	32. *a*	40. *a*

Chapter 5, pages 168–173

1. *d*	9. *a*	17. *a*	25. *a*	33. *b*
2. *d*	10. *a*	18. *d*	26. *d*	34. *a*
3. *b*	11. *b*	19. *c*	27. *b*	35. *d*
4. *a*	12. *b*	20. *d*	28. *c*	36. *c*
5. *c*	13. *d*	21. *b*	29. *b*	37. *b*
6. *b*	14. *c*	22. *c*	30. *a*	38. *d*
7. *c*	15. *d*	23. *c*	31. *c*	39. *a*
8. *d*	16. *d*	24. *a*	32. *d*	40. *c*

Chapter 6, pages 192–194

1. *b*	6. *d*	11. *c*	16. *b*	21. *c*
2. *a*	7. *a*	12. *d*	17. *d*	22. *a*
3. *b*	8. *c*	13. *a*	18. *b*	23. *d*
4. *d*	9. *b*	14. *a*	19. *a*	24. *c*
5. *d*	10. *d*	15. *c*	20. *c*	25. *a*

Chapter 7, pages 229–232

1. *a*	6. *b*	11. *c*	16. *c*	21. *b*
2. *b*	7. *c*	12. *d*	17. *a*	22. *a*
3. *a*	8. *a*	13. *b*	18. *d*	23. *c*
4. *b*	9. *a*	14. *c*	19. *c*	24. *d*
5. *d*	10. *c*	15. *b*	20. *c*	25. *b*

Chapter 8, pages 260–262

1. *a*	6. *b*	11. *c*	16. *d*	21. *c*
2. *a*	7. *a*	12. *b*	17. *c*	22. *a*
3. *a*	8. *d*	13. *b*	18. *b*	23. *d*
4. *c*	9. *d*	14. *d*	19. *a*	24. *c*
5. *a*	10. *a*	15. *b*	20. *b*	25. *a*

Chapter 9, pages 293–295

1. *c*	6. *d*	11. *d*	16. *b*	21. *c*
2. *d*	7. *b*	12. *b*	17. *a*	22. *d*
3. *b*	8. *a*	13. *c*	18. *d*	23. *a*
4. *a*	9. *c*	14. *c*	19. *d*	24. *a*
5. *b*	10. *a*	15. *a*	20. *b*	25. *d*

Chapter 10, pages 337–340

1. *b*	6. *b*	11. *c*	16. *d*	21. *c*
2. *a*	7. *c*	12. *d*	17. *b*	22. *c*
3. *d*	8. *b*	13. *b*	18. *a*	23. *d*
4. *c*	9. *b*	14. *a*	19. *a*	24. *c*
5. *c*	10. *d*	15. *c*	20. *b*	25. *d*

Chapter 11, pages 370–373

1. *b*	6. *a*	11. *d*	16. *c*	21. *b*
2. *d*	7. *c*	12. *b*	17. *d*	22. *d*
3. *c*	8. *a*	13. *a*	18. *a*	23. *a*
4. *b*	9. *d*	14. *a*	19. *c*	24. *c*
5. *b*	10. *c*	15. *b*	20. *b*	25. *b*

Chapter 12, pages 402–405

1. *b*	6. *d*	11. *c*	16. *d*	21. *a*
2. *c*	7. *c*	12. *c*	17. *c*	22. *c*
3. *b*	8. *d*	13. *c*	18. *b*	23. *c*
4. *a*	9. *b*	14. *d*	19. *c*	24. *c*
5. *d*	10. *a*	15. *d*	20. *b*	25. *d*

Practice Problems in Appendix 1, page 413

1. 88
2. 95.75+
3. 20.34+
4. 109.15+
5. 0.98+
6. 2.884+

Appendix 3. Summary of Formulas

1. Ohm's Law for Direct Current

$$R = \frac{E}{I}$$

$$I = \frac{E}{R}$$

$$E = IR$$

where E = volts
  R = ohms
  I = amperes

2. Ohm's Law for Alternating Current

$$Z = \frac{E}{I}$$

$$I = \frac{E}{Z}$$

$$E = IZ$$

where E = volts
  Z = impedance in ohms
  I = amperes

3. Power

a. In DC Circuits

$$W = EI$$

$$W = I^2 R$$

$$W = \frac{E^2}{R}$$

where W = watts
  E = volts
  I = amperes

b. In AC Circuits

Apparent power in watts:
$$W = EI$$

Actual or "true" power in watts:
$$W = EI \times \text{P.F.}$$
where P.F. = power factor

4. Computing *R*, *E*, or *I*, Where *W* and either *I* or *E* are Known

$$R = \frac{W}{I^2}$$

$$I = \frac{W}{E}$$

$$E = \frac{W}{I}$$

5. Resistances

a. Of the same ohmic value in series
$$R_{\text{total}} = RN$$
where *R* = resistance in ohms of each similar unit
N = number of similar units

b. Of different ohmic values in series
$$R_{\text{total}} = R_1 + R_2 + R_3 + \text{etc.}$$

c. Of the same ohmic value in parallel
$$R_{\text{total}} = \frac{R}{N}$$

d. Of different ohmic values in parallel
$$R_{\text{total}} = \frac{1}{\dfrac{1}{R_1} + \dfrac{1}{R_2} + \dfrac{1}{R_3} + \text{etc.}}$$

6. Efficiency of a Circuit, Generator, etc.

$$\text{Percentage efficiency} = \frac{\text{watts output}}{\text{watts input}} \times \frac{100}{1}$$

7. Ampere Turns (m.m.f.)

$$\text{M.m.f.} = TI$$

where T = number of turns of wire
I = amperes

8. Frequency of Alternators

a. Inductor alternator only

$$F = \frac{N \times \text{r.p.m.}}{60}$$

where F = frequency in cycles per second
N = number of poles
r.p.m. = revolutions per minute

b. Revolving-field and revolving-armature alternators

$$F = \frac{N \times \text{r.p.m.}}{120}$$

9. Relationship between the Number of Turns, the Current, and the Voltage in Transformers with Unity Coupling

$$\frac{E_p}{E_s} = \frac{T_p}{T_s} = \frac{I_s}{I_p}$$

where E_p = primary voltage
E_s = secondary voltage
T_p = primary turns
T_s = secondary turns
I_p = primary current
I_s = secondary current

10. Inductors

a. In series without mutual coupling

$$L_{\text{total}} = L_1 + L_2 + \text{etc.}$$

b. In a series-aiding circuit

$$L_{\text{total}} = L_1 + L_2 + 2M$$

where M = value of mutual coupling in henrys
L = inductance in henrys

c. In a series-opposing circuit

$$L_{\text{total}} = L_1 + L_2 - 2M$$

d. In a parallel circuit without mutual coupling

$$L_{\text{total}} = \cfrac{1}{\cfrac{1}{L_1} + \cfrac{1}{L_2} + \text{etc.}}$$

e. In a parallel circuit with mutual coupling

$$L_{\text{total}} = \cfrac{1}{\cfrac{1}{L_1 \pm M} + \cfrac{1}{L_2 \pm M}}$$

where $+M$ if an aiding circuit
$\quad\ -M$ if an opposing circuit

11. Capacitors

a. Of the same value in series

$$C_{\text{total}} = \frac{C}{\mathcal{N}}$$

where C = capacitance of each similar unit
$\quad\ \mathcal{N}$ = number of similar units

b. Of different values in series.

$$C_{\text{total}} = \cfrac{1}{\cfrac{1}{C_1} + \cfrac{1}{C_2} + \text{etc.}}$$

c. Of different values in parallel

$$C_{\text{total}} = C_1 + C_2 + \text{etc.}$$

d. Of the same value in parallel

$$C_{\text{total}} = \mathcal{N}C$$

where $\ C$ = capacitance of each similar unit
$\quad\ \mathcal{N}$ = number of similar units

12. Alternating Current*

$$E_{eff.} = 0.707 \times E_{max.} \qquad E_{max.} = E_{avg.}/0.636$$
$$E_{eff.} = 1.11 \times E_{avg.} \qquad E_{max.} = E_{eff.}/0.707$$
$$E_{max.} = 1.575\dagger \times E_{avg.} \qquad E_{avg.} = 0.636 \times E_{max.}$$
$$E_{max.} = 1.414\dagger \times E_{eff.} \qquad E_{avg.} = 0.9 \times E_{eff.}$$

where $E_{eff.}$ = r.m.s. or effective AC voltage
$E_{max.}$ = maximum or peak AC voltage
$E_{avg.}$ = average AC voltage

13. Reactance

a. Inductive

$$X_L = 6.28FL$$

where F = frequency in cycles per second
L = inductance in henrys

b. Capacitive

$$X_C = \frac{1}{6.28FC}$$

where C = capacitance in farads

c. Effective

$X = X_L - X_C$ (where inductive reactance predominates)
$X = X_C - X_L$ (where capacitive reactance predominates)

14. Impedance

a. Inductive circuits

$$Z = \sqrt{R^2 + X_L{}^2}$$

b. Capacitive circuits

$$Z = \sqrt{R^2 + X_C{}^2}$$

c. Where effective reactance is known

$$Z = \sqrt{R^2 + X^2}$$

* All computations are approximate.
† The third decimal figure is often omitted.

15. Resonant Frequency

$$F = \frac{1}{6.28 \sqrt{LC}}$$

where F = frequency in cycles per second
C = capacitance in farads
L = inductance in henrys

16. Regulation of a Generator

$$\text{Percentage regulation} = \frac{V_0 - V_f}{V_f} \times \frac{100}{1}$$

where V_0 = no-load voltage
V_f = full-load voltage

17. Multiplier for DC Voltmeters

$$R_{\text{mult.}} = \left(\frac{V_2}{V_1} - 1\right) \times R_m$$

where R_m = internal resistance of meter
V_1 = original range in volts
V_2 = desired range in volts

18. Shunt for DC Ammeters, Milliammeters, etc.

$$R_{\text{shunt}} = \frac{R_m \times I_m}{I - I_m}$$

where R_m = internal resistance
I_m = full-scale current in amperes
I = required current in amperes

19. Relationship of Wave Length and Frequency

$$\text{Wave length in meters} = \frac{300,000,000}{\text{frequency in cycles}} \quad \text{or} \quad \frac{\text{velocity}}{\text{frequency}}$$

$$\text{Frequency in cycles} = \frac{300,000,000}{\text{wave length in meters}}$$

Appendix 4. Resistor Color Coding and Identification

In order to be able to readily identify the ohmic value of a resistor, it has been found most convenient to use a *color-code* system. Two methods are in common use, the sole difference being in the arrangement of the color markings.

RETMA Color Code for Resistors (Ohms)
Basic Reference Chart

Color	1st figure (A)	2nd figure (B)	Multiplier (C)	Tolerance (D), %
Silver			0.01	10
Gold			0.1	5
Black		0	1.0	
Brown	1	1	10	1
Red	2	2	100	2
Orange	3	3	1000	3
Yellow	4	4	10000	4
Green	5	5	100000	
Blue	6	6	1000000	
Purple	7	7	10000000	
Gray	8	8	100000000	
White	9	9	1000000000	
No color				20

Method 1

The resistor bears colored bands that are read from left to right. There are four bands in all (though the fourth may be omitted). For convenience, they may be termed *A*, *B*, *C*, and *D*.

The first band from the left (*A*) indicates the first significant figure of the resistance value in ohms, and the second band (*B*) refers to the second such figure. The third band (*C*) indicates the *number of ciphers* that appear after the first two significant figures. The fourth band (*D*), when present, indicates the degree of *tolerance*, that is, the accuracy attained by the particular type of resistor.

Examples of Method 1

1. A resistor has three color bands, blue, green, and brown, when read from the left to the right. Referring to the chart, we see that the color blue represents the figure "6," the color green stands for the figure "5," and brown indicates a single cipher. The resistance is therefore 650 ohms. Since there is no fourth band, we know that the resistor is one that is only accurate to a figure plus or minus 20 per cent.

2. A resistor has four color bands which are (from left to right) red, green, yellow, and silver. Red is "2," green is "5," and the third color band, which indicates the number of ciphers after the first two significant figures, is yellow, or four ciphers. Total resistance is therefore 250,000 ohms. The silver band indicates the tolerance is plus or minus 10 per cent.

Method 2

In this method, the color of the body of the resistor is considered as the first band (*A*), while the color on the *left* side with the center dot facing the observer is considered as band *B*. The third band (*C*) is replaced by the center dot; and the fourth portion of the color code (*D*), when present, is represented by the color of the *right* end of the unit. Remember the resistor is being observed with the center dot facing the observer.

Examples of Method 2

1. A resistor has a blue body color, a left-end color that is green, and a center dot that is brown. The resistor is therefore 650 ohms plus or minus 20 per cent.

2. A resistor has a violet body color, a red left-end color, a green center dot, and a gold right end. Violet stands for "7," red for "2," and green is five ciphers. The resistance is therefore 7,200,000 ohms. The tolerance assures accuracy within plus or minus 5 per cent since the right-end color is gold.

Appendix 5. Capacitor Color Coding and Identification

Color coding of capacitors is somewhat more intricate than that used for resistors because of the great variety of types available for specialized purposes. However, the colors themselves, as they affect the significant figures, are identical to those of the resistor color code (see the chart below). The essential variation that must be taken into consideration is the greater number of colored bands or dots, but for practical purposes, the first three portions of the color coding, that is, Color A, Color B, and color C, must be interpreted. It must also be remembered that the capacitance values are read in micromicrofarads ($\mu\mu$f).

RETMA Color Code for Capacitors (MMF)
Basic Reference Chart

Color	1st figure (A)	2nd figure (B)	Multiplier (C)	Tolerance (D), %
Black	0	0	1	20
Brown	1	1	10	1
Red	2	2	100	2
Orange	3	3	1000	$2\frac{1}{2}$ or 3
Yellow	4	4	10000	
Green	5	5		5
Blue	6	6		
Violet	7	7		
Gray	8	8		
White	9	9		10
Gold			0.1	
Silver			0.01	10

New Type of Molded Mica Capacitors

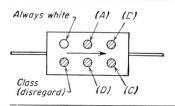

First dot is always white. This indicates a new type of molded mica capacitor. Direction for reading indicated by arrow or equivalent marking.

Old Type of Molded Mica Capacitors

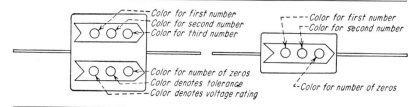

Ceramic Tubular Capacitors

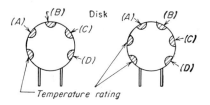

Ceramic tubular capacitors read from the end color to the right. End color identifies inside lead. Leads may be axial or radial.

Ceramic Disk Capacitors

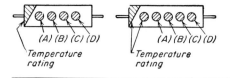

Ceramic disk capacitors are read from left to right with leads held downward.

Examples of Old Type Molded Mica Capacitors

1. The capacitor is a mica unit with two sets of arrows pointing to the right. The upper arrow has dots that are colored

green (5), black (0), and black (0) reading from *left* to *right*. The lower arrow has dots that are colored black (0), silver (10 per cent), and green (500 volts DC working voltage), these colors being read from *right* to *left*. *Wherever there are two rows of colors, the first row is read from left to right and the second row is read from right to left.*

Since the upper left dot is neither black nor white, we know immediately the older method of reading the code is being followed, that is, the first dot actually represents a significant figure. The first and second colors give us the figure of "50." Since the third dot is black, one other cipher is involved, making the full number "500." The black lower right dot signifies there are no further ciphers. We therefore can read the capacitor as being one of 500 $\mu\mu$f (0.0005 μf). Tolerance is 10 per cent (silver dot) and DC working voltage 500 (green).

2. The mica capacitor has a single arrow with dots that are colored red (2), green (5), and brown (a single cipher) reading from left to right. The capacitance is therefore 250 $\mu\mu$f (0.00025 μf).

3. The mica capacitor has two sets of arrows with colored dots reading green, black, and black on top and reading brown, silver, and green from right to left on the bottom. Green is "5," black is "0," and black *for the third dot also* indicates "0," making the first three significant figures "500." The brown dot on the lower left adds one additional zero to the total, making the capacitance 5,000 $\mu\mu$f (0.005 μf). The silver dot describes the capacitor as having an accuracy within 10 per cent, and the green dot indicates a working DC voltage of 500.

In these examples, it will be noted that *three* significant figures appeared on each upper line of the double-lined coding. In the following examples, using the new code, only *two* significant figures appear on the first line. It should also be noted that a blank space may appear instead of a color, and the presence of such a blank space, instead of a color in the third dot, would mean that there is no third significant figure at all.

Example of New Type Molded Mica Capacitors

The mica capacitor has a double set of colored dots reading on top (from left to right) white, red, and orange and reading on the lower part (from right to left) red, red, and white. The white upper left dot indicates that the new color code is being used. Therefore, the first two significant figures are "2" (red) and "3" (orange). The multiplier color (lower right dot) is red (100 on the chart, that is, two ciphers). The capacitance is therefore 2300 $\mu\mu$f, with a DC working voltage of 500 and plus or minus 2 per cent accuracy. [The working voltage of 500 would not be read from the chart in this case, but reference to its classification characteristic (white lower *left* dot) would give this data.]

Example of a Tubular Paper Capacitor

A tubular paper capacitor has six colored bands painted on its body, the first band (A) being red, the second band (B) being green, the third band (C) being brown, the fourth band (D) being yellow, and the fifth and sixth bands (E and F) being brown and green, respectively. Since A (red) equals 2, B (green) equals 5, and C (brown) equals 10 (one cipher), the capacitance is read as 250 $\mu\mu$f. D is yellow and therefore indicates 5 per cent accuracy. E and F are both actually colored, and we therefore know that the capacitor rating is above 1,000 volts DC. Brown equals 1 and green equals 5, or 1,500 volts. (If F were not colored, we would have been dealing with the capacitor rated below 1,000 volts, the brown E then indicating 100 volts. In either case, it should be noted, ciphers were added to allow a reading in hundreds.)

List of Visual Aids

The films listed below and on the following pages can be used to supplement much of the material in this book. While, for the convenience of users, the films have been grouped by chapter subjects, it is recommended that they be reviewed before using in order to determine specific applicability in terms of subject matter and suitability for a particular group. Two special groups of films are included at the end of the bibliography—one showing industrial applications of electrical principles, the other stressing safety practices.

Both motion pictures and filmstrips are included in this list, the character of each being indicated by the self-explanatory abbreviations "MP" and "FS". Immediately following this identification is the name of the producer. If the distributor is different from the producer, the name of the distributor follows the name of the producer. Abbreviations are identified in the list of sources at the end of the bibliography. In most instances, the films can be borrowed or rented from local or state 16mm film libraries. (A nationwide list of these local sources is given in *A Directory of 2660 16mm Film Libraries*, available from the Superintendent of Documents, Washington 25, D.C.) Unless otherwise indicated, the motion pictures are 16mm sound black-and-white films and the filmstrips are 35mm silent black-and-white filmstrips. The length of the motion pictures is given in minutes (min), that of the filmstrips in frames (fr).

This bibliography is suggestive only, and film users should examine the latest annual edition and supplements of *Educational Film Guide* and *Filmstrip Guide* published by the H. W. Wilson Company, New York. The *Guides*, standard reference books, are available in most school, college, and public libraries.

Chapter 1. Introduction to Electricity

Adventure in Electronics (FS   GE   36fr   color). Walt Disney cartoon, featuring Donald Duck, explaining the essential principles of electronics.

Amperes, Volts, and Ohms (MP   USN/UWF   8min). Explains the meaning, relationship, and measurement of amperes, volts, and ohms. (Related filmstrip, 23fr)

Basic Electricity (MP   USAF/UWF   20min   color). An animated cartoon explaining the fundamentals of electricity, including voltage, current, resistance, magnetic fields, induction, primary and secondary coils, series and parallel circuits.

Basic Electronics (MP   USAF/UWF   17min   color). An animated cartoon explaining the meaning of atoms and electrons, vacuum tube, cathode, rectifier tube, amplifier tube, grid, and bridge circuits.

The Electron: An Introduction (MP   USOE/UWF   16min). Nature of electrons, electron flow in solid conductors, electromotive force, types and control of electron flow, electron flow and magnetic fields, and induced electron flow. (Related filmstrip, 40fr)

Electrostatics (MP   EBF   11min). Explains positive and negative electrification, role of insulators and conductors, movement of charges in the electroscope, the Compton electrometer, and lightning as nature's display of static electricity.

Ohm's Law (MP   USA/UWF   19min). Explains the elements of electricity; electrical energy, its source, transmission, and use; composition of matter; use of force and energy; how Ohm's law functions; resistance; and the purpose and use of meters.

Principles of Electricity (MP   GE   20min   color). Explains the actions of electrons within an atom, the principles involved in the flow of current, magnetism and magnetic fields, and the meanings of volt, ampere, and ohm.

What Is Electricity? (MP   EBF   13min). Presents classical electrostatic experiments, including those of Oersted and Faraday, and illustrates industrial achievements made possible by man's electrical knowledge.

Chapter 2. Batteries

Charging Storage Batteries (MP USA/UWF 16min). Explains the charging, care, and preparation of storage batteries. Discusses constant voltage methods and modifications.

Primary Cell (MP EBF 11min). Demonstrates by animation the ionization of an electrolyte, electron flow, action at electrodes, polarization, and function of the depolarizer. Shows the characteristics and uses of a single cell and of cells connected as a battery in series and in parallel.

The Story of a Storage Battery (MP USBM 32min). Explains by animation the principle of a storage battery; shows the operations in the manufacture of storage batteries; gives instructions on the care of batteries; illustrates industrial and domestic uses of batteries.

Voltaic Cell, Dry Cell, and Storage Battery (MP USA/UWF 18min). Explains the principles of a voltaic cell, a dry cell, and a storage battery.

Chapter 3. The Electric Circuit

Elements of Electrical Circuits (MP EBF 11min). Explains the nature of electric currents and circuits, electron motions, conductors, insulators, and factors affecting resistance. Contains animated drawings and photographic demonstrations. (Related filmstrip, 89fr)

Series and Parallel Circuits (MP EBF 11min). Explains the relationship between resistance, current, and voltage in series circuits and in parallel circuits; the advantages of each type of circuit; and a simple series-parallel combination circuit. (Related filmstrip, 86fr)

Series and Parallel Circuits (MP USN/UWF 8 min). Illustrates series and parallel circuits, explaining current flow and voltage drop across each lamp. (Related filmstrip, 26fr)

Chapter 4. Electromagnetism

Coil and Electric Currents (MP Ed Pic 9min). Explains the

nature of fields of force around a current-carrying wire. Gives the theory of solenoids and electromagnets, induction coils, and electric motors.

Current and Electromotive Force (MP USN/UWF 11min). Explains the electron theory, arrangement of molecules, building up of current, conductors, electromotive force, resistance, and chemical and mechanical sources of electromotive force. (Related filmstrip, 38fr)

Electrodynamics (MP EBF 11min). Explains the principles of current electricity and electromagnetism, including magnetic field of a coil, electromagnets, magnetic hypothesis, recalescence, induction by electric currents, and transformers.

Chapter 5. Alternating Current

Alternating Current (FS USAF/UWF 50fr). An elementary introduction to the principles of alternating current. Demonstrates and explains Lenz's Law, simple wave alternator, frequency, effective value, voltage-current-time relationship, and power.

Chapter 6. Inductance

Inductance (MP USN/UWF 35min). Shows how a magnetic force reacts around a coil, the nature of self-inductance, and how to increase the inductance of a coil. (Related filmstrip, 38fr)

Chapter 7. Capacitance

Capacitance (MP USN/UWF 31min). Demonstrates electron flow through a circuit, the charging and discharging of condensers, variations of a charge on a condenser in relation to time, and the behavior of capacitance with alternating current. (Related filmstrip, 22fr)

RCL: Resistance, Capacitance (MP USN/UWF 34min). Explains current and voltage in relation to time, voltage and current curves, the relationship of current and voltage, the measurement of voltage at source, the addition of phase components, and the effect of impedance on resonance. (Related filmstrip, 34fr)

Chapter 9. The Electric Generator

Principle of the Generator (MP   YAF   10min). Uses animation to explain the principles of electromagnetic induction and to relate these principles to the operation of the transformer.

Rotating Magnetic Fields (MP   USOE/UWF   13min). Explains a rotating magnetic field pattern, three-phase winding in a demonstration stator, factors that cause rotation of the magnetic field, and the construction of polyphase motors. (Related filmstrip, 44fr)

Single-phase and Polyphase Circuits (MP   USOE/UWF   17min). Explains a single-phase synchronous generator, the use of sine curves to illustrate flow changes, a two-phase system and three-phase system, and ways to simplify wiring. (Related filmstrip, 51fr)

Squirrel-cage Rotor Principles (MP   USOE/UWF   10min). Laws of magnetism and induced e.m.f.; electron flow in squirrel-cage rotor setting up magnetic poles which create torque; construction of squirrel-cage rotors. (Related filmstrip, 28fr)

Chapter 10. The Electric Motor

Across-the-Line Starters (MP   USOE/UWF   15min). Theory and operation of a manually operated thermal overload switch, a magnetically operated across-the-line starter, a drum reversing switch for a three-phase motor, and a magnetic reversing switch. (Related filmstrip, 37fr)

Commutation of D-C Machines (MP   West   24min). Presents the theory and maintenance of commutation of direct-current motors and generators. Shows how troubles arise from stray oil and grease, moisture, looseness of mounting, etc., and the practical procedures of preventive maintenance and repair.

D.C. Motor. Part 1: Mechanical Overhaul (MP   USOE/UWF   20min). How to test for electrical and mechanical faults, dismantle a direct-current motor, turn the commutator, repair and replace field coils, assemble the motor, and adjust and make final tests. (Related filmstrip, 37fr)

D.C. Motor. Part 2: Rewinding (MP   USOE/UWF   37min). How to dismantle and clean an armature core, determine commutator pitch, reinsulate the core, insert coils, band an armature, shape coil ends, lay in and solder leads, balance and impregnate the armature, and turn a commutator. (Related filmstrip, 43fr)

Direct Current Controllers (MP   USOE/UWF   15min). Shows shunt motors and direct-current controllers in operation, and by animation, a direct-current faceplate controller connected to a shunt motor. (Related filmstrip, 27fr)

Motor Selection and Application (FS series   GE). Ten filmstrips, 30 to 50 frames each with accompanying records averaging 20 to 25 minutes each, comprising a course on motors. Titles are (1) *The Fundamentals of Motors;* (2) *The Types of Motors;* (3) *Fundamentals of Motor Selection;* (4) *The Selection and Application of AC Polyphase Induction Motors;* (5) *The Selection and Application of Single Phase Integral Horsepower Motors;* (6) *The Selection and Application of DC Motors;* (7) *The Selection and Application of Synchronous Motors;* (8) *The Selection and Application of Adjustable Speed Drives;* (9) *The Selection and Application of Gear Motors;* (10) *The Selection and Application of Fractional Horsepower Motors.*

Reduced Voltage Starters (MP   USOE/UWF   23min). Principle of the transformer; operation of a manual starting compensator, thermal overload relay, and automatic starting compensator. (Related filmstrip, 46fr)

Repulsion-induction Motor: General Overhaul (MP   USOE/UWF   25min). How to check a repulsion-induction motor for electrical and mechanical faults, dismantle it, remove a damaged coil, wind and insulate a new coil, and assemble and lubricate the motor. (Related filmstrip, 33fr)

Repulsion Motor Principles (MP   USOE/UWF   18min). Explains construction of repulsion motor; rotor circuits and effect of brush position; short-circuiting and brush-lifting mechanism; applications of repulsion motors. (Related filmstrip, 40fr)

Split-phase Motor: Rewinding (MP   USOE/UWF   28min).

How to test a split-phase motor for electrical and mechanical faults; dismantle and strip the stator; rewind the stator; form and install skein windings; insulate; lace, dip, and bake the stator; and assemble, lubricate, and test the motor. (Related filmstrip, 40fr)

Split-phase Motor Principles (MP USOE/UWF 17min). Construction of stator and rotor; comparison of winding in two-phase stator with split-phase stator; effects of winding resistances and inductive reactances; use of capacitor to produce phase displacement. (Related filmstrip, 48fr)

Three-phase Motor. Part 1: Preparing to Rewind (MP USOE/ UWF 17min). How to interpret and record name-plate data of a three-phase motor, identify the line and finish leads, remove coils and determine coil span, use a coil winding machine, and end-tape machine-wound coils. (Related filmstrip, 35fr)

Three-phase Motor. Part 2: Rewinding (MP USOE/UWF 17min). How to insert mush coils and separators or "willies"; fold, trim, and wedge slot insulation around windings; insert phase insulation; and make a delta connection. (Related filmstrip, 31fr)

Wound-rotor Controllers (MP USOE/UWF 17min). Wound-rotor motor principles; operation of a faceplate controller, drum-type nonreversing controller, drum-type reversing controller, and automatic magnetic starter for a wound-rotor motor. (Related filmstrip, 40fr).

Chapter 11. Rectification of Alternating Current

Principles of Gas-filled Tubes (MP USOE/UWF 15min). Theory of ionization applied to gas-filled tubes; control of current in circuits employing gas-filled tubes; use of the gas diode as a rectifier; action of the grid in a gas triode; application of the gas triode as a grid-controlled rectifier. (Related filmstrip, 36fr)

Vacuum Tubes: Electron Theory and the Diode Tube (MP USAF/ UWF 16min). Explains electron behavior in matter, electron sources in vacuum tubes, symbols of tubes, functioning of tube in a circuit, and effect of plate voltage changes, space charge, and diode and duo-diode as reflectors.

Chapter 12. The Electric Meter

Accent on Accuracy (MP GE 19min color). Explains the need for and the development and manufacture of General Electric's I-50 watthour meter.

Circuit Testing with Meters and Multimeters. Part 1: Theory (MP USA/UWF 30min). Explains the theory and construction of meters and shows various types of meters used for circuit testing and associated external equipment.

Circuit Testing with Meters and Multimeters. Part 2: Practical Application (MP USA/UWF 37min). Demonstrates how to use meters in testing transformers, capacitors, resistors, telephone loop circuits, etc.

Volt Ohmmeter Operation (MP USN/UWF 15min). Shows how to operate a volt ohmmeter (Weston and other types) to measure ohms and volts.

Industrial Applications of Electricity and Electronics

Adventures in Research (MP West 20min). Explains the underlying principles involved in such electronic devices as the X ray, pinhole detector, stroboscope, ignitron, cathode-ray tube, and photoelectric cell. For lay audiences primarily.

Dynamic Measurement (MP MTP 25min color). Tells the story of "electronic yardsticks" which have replaced many time-honored measuring tools and demonstrates the ways in which electromechanical and electronic devices are used in science and industry.

Electronics at Work (MP West 20min). Explains the six basic functions of electronic tubes and how each tube is used in industrial applications.

Electronics at Work Course (FS series West). Ten filmstrips each with a disc recording, $33\frac{1}{3}$ rpm, 10 to 15 minutes each) explaining the basic principles and applications of electronics in industry. Titles are (1) *Electronics and the Electron Theory of Matter;* (2) *Theory of Current Rectification by Vacuum Tubes;* (3) *Neutralization of Space Charge by Gas in a Tube;* (4) *Electronic Amplification;* (5) *Electronic Generation of High-frequency Alternating Currents;* (6) *Electronic Oscillators for Radio and Carrier Current Transmission;* (7) *Basic Circuits for Electronic Control;* (8) *Industrial Applications of Electronic Regulation;* (9) *Industrial Applications of Electronic Control;* (10) *Electronic Conversion of Light into Electricity and of Electricity into Light.*

Motors in Industry (MP   GE   27min   color). Story of progressive mechanization from hand operations through continuous processing with electric motors and controls leading to greater productivity.

Project Tinkertoy (MP   USN/UWF   28min). A report on a joint U.S. Navy–National Bureau of Standards project to develop a new system of electronics design and manufacture using the building-block principle by which resistors, capacitors, tube sockets, and other parts of common design are machine-assembled into functional electronic products.

Transistor (MP   AT&T   10min). Describes the part transistors are likely to play in communications and the entire electronics field.

Safety

Artificial Respiration (MP   USCG/UWF   11min). Explains and demonstrates two new methods of artificial respiration adopted by the U.S. Coast Guard—the Holger-Nielsen, or back-pressure, arm-lift method, and the Emerson, or back-pressure, hip-lift method.

Protecting Electric Equipment from High Impact Shock (MP   USN/UWF   13min). Explains causes of high impact shock; resulting damage to electrical equipment; preventive maintenance.

Safety Precautions for Electronics Personnel (MP   USN/UWF   18min). Shows electrical and mechanical hazards which electronics technicians encounter in their normal work; stresses precautions which should be employed to prevent accidents.

Using Electricity Safely (FS McGraw 33fr). Cautions in using and repairing electrical equipment—making splices, soldering, repairing cords, connecting plugs and sockets, etc.

SOURCES OF FILMS LISTED

AT&T—American Telephone and Telegraph Company, Information Department, 195 Broadway, New York 7, N.Y.

EBF—Encyclopaedia Britannica Films, Inc., 1150 Wilmette Ave., Wilmette, Ill.

Ed Pic—Edited Pictures System, 165 West 46th St., New York 19, N.Y.

GE—General Electric Company, 1 River Rd., Schenectady 5, N.Y.

M Graw—McGraw-Hill Book Company, Inc., Text-Film Department, 330 West 42d St., New York 36, N.Y.

MTP—Modern Talking Picture Service, 30 Rockefeller Plaza, New York, N.Y.

USA—U.S. Department of the Army, Washington 25, D.C.

USAF—U.S. Department of the Air Force, Washington 25, D.C.

USBM—U.S. Bureau of Mines, 4800 Forbes St., Pittsburgh, Pa.

USCG—U.S. Coast Guard, Washington 25, D.C.

USN—U.S. Department of the Navy, Washington 25, D.C.

USOE—U.S. Office of Education, Washington 25, D.C. (Films distributed by United World Films, Inc.)

UWF—United World Films, Inc., 1445 Park Ave., New York 29, N.Y.

West—Westinghouse Electric Corporation, 511 Wood St., Pittsburgh 30, Pa.

YAF—Young America Films, 18 East 41st St., New York 17, N.Y.

Index